THE OLD FARMER'S ALMANAC

CALCULATED ON A NEW AND IMPROVED PLAN FOR THE YEAR OF OUR LORD

Being 3rd after Leap Year and (until July 1) 151st year of Canadian Confederation

FITTED FOR OTTAWA, WITH SPECIAL CORRECTIONS
AND CALCULATIONS TO ANSWER FOR ALL THE CANADIAN PROVINCES.

Containing, besides the large number of Astronomical Calculations and the Farmer's Calendar for every month in the year, a variety of
NEW, USEFUL, & ENTERTAINING MATTER.

ESTABLISHED IN 1792
BY ROBERT B. THOMAS (1766–1846)

The mind is not a vessel to be filled, but a hearth to be lighted.

–Irene Parlby, English-born Canadian activist (1868–1965)

Cover design registered
U.S. Trademark Office

Copyright © 2018 by Yankee Publishing Incorporated
ISSN 0078-4516

Library of Congress
Card No. 56-29681

Cover illustration by Steven Noble • Original wood engraving (above) by Randy Miller

THE OLD FARMER'S ALMANAC • DUBLIN, NH 03444 • 603-563-8111 • ALMANAC.CA

CONTENTS

7

8

13

2019 TRENDS
Forecasts, Facts, and Fascinating Ideas 6

206

84

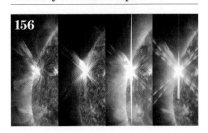

156

GLAD "TIDINGS"

Good news, Patrons! We may be "Old," but every year we also bring you the "new"—and 2019 is no exception.

In the Calendar Page spreads (120–147), you'll find on the left-hand pages our customary "calendar of the heavens," replete with its galaxy of celestial information and sea of tidal data, the latter now back on these pages after a year's hiatus.

On the right-hand pages, as you enjoy discovering each month's special days and Moon phases intermixed with trivia that is trivial even by trivia standards, don't overlook the "doggerel"—longtime writer Tim Clark's amusing, italicized, vertical weather rhyme—which is usually an uncannily accurate forecast!

Please join us in welcoming Vermonter Julia Shipley, award-winning writer and poet, as the first woman in 227 years to pen our Farmer's Calendar essays. A keen observer of nature, Julia is a farmer, too, having raised cows, sheep, chickens, turkeys, and vegetables on her 6-acre homestead.

Speaking of farmers, we're always interested in hearing from hardworking farm families about how they are successfully meeting today's challenges. If you're a farmer or rancher (or you know one), young or old, in the United States or Canada, with a story to share, please let us know at Almanac.ca/Feedback.

Really good news for us is that you continue to send us questions, comments, and observations via snail mail, email (Almanac.ca/Feedback), social media, and telephone. That's right: When the phone rings, we, the editors, actually answer it—or we call you back (if you leave a number). We appreciate that you care enough to let us know how we're doing.

We'd love to meet you. If your travels take you to New Hampshire, do drop in! We'll personally sign your Almanac, show you around our headquarters, and regale you with Almanacky tales. Or visit from home via Almanac.ca/Webcam and view our barn-red office building in Dublin, with the church steeple, Police Department, and Town Hall behind it.

In closing this opening, we send you glad tidings, wish you a new year filled with good news, and thank you for your trust in this Almanac. We're here for you and because of you.

–J. S., JUNE 2018

However, it is by our works and not our words that we would be judged. These, we hope, will sustain us in the humble though proud station we have so long held in the name of

Your obedient servant,

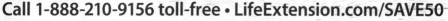

2019 TRENDS

WHAT'S COOKING?

Instead of scheduling our days around mealtimes, we're scheduling our meals around everything else going on in our days.

–Laurie Demeritt, CEO, The Hartman Group, Bellevue, Washington

SMART FOODS

Consumers are seeking potent energy sources to power their brains.

–Kara Nielsen, VP, trends and marketing, CCD Innovation, Emeryville, California

- coffee creamer made with grass-fed butter
- beverages made with reishi mushrooms

PEOPLE ARE TALKING ABOUT . . .

- nutritionists in restaurants to help patrons choose healthy foods

BUZZWORD

Eatertainment: a restaurant that offers board games or arcades

- commuters bringing cutlery and ingredients to work to create gourmet lunches
- exercising at grocery stores
- DNA kits that help us to choose foods based on genetics

MENUS ARE GOING MEATLESS

Top-end restaurants used to serve steak and potatoes, but now they have lentil dishes and other plant-based proteins.

–Mike von Massow, associate professor, University of Guelph, Ontario

- **43%** of Canadians plan to eat more plant-based proteins (soya, lentils, and chia seeds are growing in popularity)

PROOF IS A PRIORITY

People want proof of food sources:

- scannable packages linking to videos of producer animals being well treated
- ice cream made with "traceable" milk (to identify the source farm)

- restaurants certified as "green" that, e.g., use recyclable containers, solar panels, food from local sources; reduce waste and water use; compost

- menus "augmented" with apps that show food prep and/or ingredients used

EATING IS EXTRA

Average time spent preparing, presenting, and cleaning up food each day by generation (in minutes):

- Traditionalists: **101**
- Baby boomers: **136**
- Gen Xers: **143**
- Millennials: **88**

FRESHNESS FIRST

- Produce is being grown indoors at restaurants, then served to diners.

- Mini-farms are appearing in grocery store aisles and on rooftops.

- Greenhouses are being built adjacent to supermarkets.

FROM DISCARDED TO DELICIOUS

- Imperfect fruit is being pressed into juice.

- Fruit pulp is being made into chips.

- Plant leaves and stems are being used in "root-to-stem" cooking.

FLAVORS WE CRAVE

- sugar-free syrups made from dates, sorghum, and yacon root

- banana milk and flour

- fish-free tomato "sushi"

- bacon-flavor seaweed

"GROCERANT" GROWTH

Convenience has more currency than ever, with restaurants and food markets colliding in the ready-to-eat spaces at grocery stores.

–Sylvain Charlebois, professor, Dalhousie University, Halifax, Nova Scotia

(continued)

BY THE NUMBERS

22%
of U.S. vegetable buyers want produce grown on store premises

20%
of Canadians trust health claims on food packages

40%
of Canadians have fallen victim to "food fraud" (e.g., honey, saffron, or olive oil diluted with cheaper ingredients)

70%
of U.S. consumers want to understand an ingredients list

IN THE GARDEN

People want plant-related projects that are easy
and lifestyle-friendly—adaptive to short attention spans,
hectic schedules, and smaller spaces.

–Tom Soulsby, senior horticulturist, Chicago Botanic Garden

GETTING TO GROUND ZERO

Gardeners are composting, gardening, and reducing their footprint, as zero-waste living becomes aspirational.

–Katie Dubow, creative director, Garden Marketing Group

PEOPLE ARE TALKING ABOUT . . .

• DNA testing used on plants displayed at public botanical gardens to prove that certain species still exist, even though they're no longer found in the wild

• the future of growing indoors hydroponically in Internet-connected, refrigerator-size boxes

GROW TO SHOW

• Succulents are fleshy, compact, colorful, and low-maintenance—and fun to have a bowl-full of on a coffee table.

–Dave Forehand, VP of gardens, Dallas Arboretum and Botanical Gardens

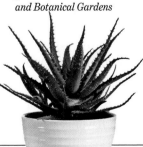

• Edible flowers are everywhere— in salads: pansies and nasturtiums; in water pitchers: roses, lavender, and lilacs; in ice cubes: marigolds and impatiens.

–Jennifer Smock, outdoor supervisor, Kemper Center for Home Gardening, Missouri Botanical Garden

• Gardeners want plants that are social media–shareable: displays of bold tropical foliage with unique colors, shapes, patterns, and variations, indoors and out.

–Soulsby   *(continued)*

HARDINESS IS IN HIGH DEMAND

Gardeners want plants that stand up to extreme weather, e.g.:

- high winds: native grasses, evergreens, yarrow, and sedum
- drought: date palm, euphorbia, fennel, iris, poppy
- flood: black chokeberry, meadowsweet shrubs, bayberry, ferns
- frost: spruce, birch, and maple trees; hellebore and hosta

–Garden Media Group

YARROW

NATURAL IS NORMAL

- We're partnering with "pests," letting rabbits eat dandelions, parasitoid wasps control caterpillar populations, and tachinid flies manage insects.

–Nancy Lawson, author,
The Humane Gardener
(Princeton Architectural Press, 2017)

BY THE NUMBERS

7.2%:
average reduction in home energy use due to trees

52%
of Americans use indoor plants to clean the air

$503
is the average spent on lawn and garden products and services per U.S. household

30 million
households purchased food preservation products in 2016

- We're planting pollinator gardens on "hellstrips"—patches of grass between roads and sidewalks.

THE PROS' PICKS

- Dwarf produce: 'Raspberry Shortcake' raspberry, 'Little Miss Figgy' fig, 'Peach Sorbet' blueberry, 'Patio Pride' pea
- Ornamental hot peppers (to eat and for visual interest):

'Midnight Fire', 'Hot Pops Purple', 'Sedona Sun', 'Paracho', 'Joker', 'Salsa' series
–Smock

'HOT POPS PURPLE'

- Burpee's Space Saver series: 'Patio Baby' eggplant, 'Tangerine Dream' sweet pepper, 'Tidy Treats' small-fruited tomato
–Forehand

- For patio containers and small spaces: 'Atlas' beefsteak tomato, shrublike 'Confetti' pepper with variegated foliage, 'Jungle Parrot' snack-size bell pepper, and 'Fioretto' cauliflower, which produces small florets that stay crunchy when cooked and are sweeter than those from large-head varieties
–Venelin Dimitrov, senior product manager, W. Atlee Burpee and Company

(continued)

photos to owners and providing GPS tracking of routes

- food made with pet-friendly grains and vegetables

- portable systems to wash dogs in any room of the house

- touch screen computer games and TV shows to keep pets mentally sharp

OUR ANIMAL FRIENDS

It's a go-anywhere, mobile world— and that includes our pets.

–David Dorman, publisher, Pets Magazine

PEOPLE ARE TALKING ABOUT . . .

- "yappy hours" at bars for dogs and their owners or for people looking for pets

- pet doors operated with microchips to allow entry only to authorized animals

- paid "pawternity leave" to allow new pet owners time to spend with their animals

- wearing matching pajamas with their pets

COUNTING CATS AND DOGS

Pets in the U.S.:
- Cats: **94.2 million**
- Dogs: **89.7 million**

–American Pet Products Association National Pet Owners Survey

In Canada:
- Cats: **8.8 million**
- Dogs: **7.6 million**

–Canadian Animal Health Institute

PET PERKS FOR GOOD HEALTH
- dog walkers sending postwalk

BY THE NUMBERS

10%
of pets have social media accounts

$1 billion
is the annual revenue of the dog-walking industry

$5.76 billion
is spent annually on pet services (e.g., pet-sitting, boarding, grooming, training)

$2.8 billion
is spent annually on U.S. sales of cat litter

12%
of pet dogs are under 8 pounds

- workouts on in-home treadmills alongside owners

- mouse-shape food containers, hidden around the house, to encourage domestic felines to hunt

PET CONVENIENCES

Products will perform more and more daily pet care tasks for us.
–*David Lummis, market research analyst, Packaged Facts*

- Cats and small litter-trained dogs will use automatic-flush toilets.

- Robots will launch tennis balls for dogs to chase when home alone.

- Balls will track how fast a dog can fetch.

- We'll see home-delivered veterinary care, grooming, oral health care, and training, as well as doggie day care pickup.

- Self-propelled devices will clean aquariums while photographing the fish.

MONEY MATTERS

The lifestyle of minimalism and intentionally owning less will continue to grow.
–*Joshua Becker, author,* The More of Less *(WaterBrook, 2016)*

WE WANT IT OUR WAY

In order to succeed in the new age of commerce, retailers must include profound experiences, product and brand curation, and a frictionless shopping journey.
–*Oliver Chen, senior equity research analyst, Cowen*

SIGNS OF SKEPTICISM

According to Kit Yarrow, author, *Decoding the New Consumer Mind* (Jossey-Bass, 2014) . . .

- We're overloaded with info: "Shoppers are looking for trustworthy partners, whether retailers or vloggers [video bloggers], to help them make good choices by doing the research for them."

- We're wary of company claims: "We're looking for cues that businesses are worthy, that go beyond the products we're considering." *(continued)*

BY THE NUMBERS

14% of Americans carry no cash

52% of U.S. adults say that their current finances are "excellent" or "good"

$17.2 billion: the estimated e-commerce taxes that go uncollected annually

COLLECTIBLES

Attendance at flea markets and online bidding at decor and design auctions have reached all-time highs.

–Kathleen Guzman, appraiser, Heritage Auctions

THE NEXT BIG THING?

A younger generation is seeking iconic original movie props, rare autographs, and unique objects representing key points in mass culture.

–Eric Bradley, editor, Antique Trader Antiques & Collectibles Price Guide

FANDOM FAVES

• Comic book and film fans are dressing up as characters ("cosplay") to search for accessories at antique shops.

• Harry Potter fans fancy vintage brooms, neckties, and eyeglass frames.

SOLD FOR . . .

$4,025:
1930s children's barbershop chair

$8,625:
1950s Roy Rogers "Ride Trigger" coin-operated kiddie ride

$158,600:
original town plan for the city of Pittsburgh, Pa.

$432,500:
telescope owned by Albert Einstein

$708,000:
original map used to secure funding for Disneyland in 1953

• *Star Wars* fans quest for military surplus backpacks, belts, and straps.

• *Totoro* fans love vintage umbrellas and straw hats.

–Gary Piattoni, appraiser, Evanston, Illinois

COMPETING INTERESTS

While older collectors crave nostalgia, younger buyers seek simple technology:

• rotary phones
• film cameras
• manual typewriters
• View-Masters

–Piattoni

(continued)

AROUND THE HOUSE

As baby boomers age and environmentally conscious millennials begin settling into homes, the demand for smaller houses will begin to exceed the demand for larger ones.
–*Joshua Becker, author,* The More of Less *(WaterBrook, 2016)*

WE'RE GREENER WITH . . .
• "breathing rooms" filled with plants to clean the air and clear our minds
• plants as art: "statement" plants in pots and staghorn ferns in driftwood hung like paintings

WALLPAPER POSSIBILITIES
• impregnated with scratch-and-sniff fragrances

• lighting up when you touch it
• made with naturally shed peacock feathers

THE INSIDE STORY
We'll see a rise in minimalism, tiny furniture, and clever storage spaces.
–*Patty Shapiro, Montreal-based trend forecaster*

• televisions mounted on easels, toilets that flush when told, showers programmed for a specific temperature and timed to save water, and glass garage doors used as walls in houses
• homes with "flex space," wired for home offices
• apartment buildings with shared workspaces for communal offices

STYLE NOTES
Decorators are mixing patterns together for a rich and layered look.
–*Eugenia Santiesteban Soto, senior style editor,* Better Homes & Gardens

LIGHT UP YOUR LIFE!
We'll see paintings made from bioluminescent bacteria: The images glow for 2 weeks.

(continued)

BY THE NUMBERS

32: median age of first-time home buyers

33% of Americans would consider living in a haunted house

$16,000: cost of integrating a laundry-folding robot into a home's walls

2019   The Old Farmer's Almanac   17

HEALTH CHECK

Municipal governments are investing in urban nature, spurred by growing evidence of how greenspace affects our social health and physical well-being.

–Holli-Anne Passmore, psychology researcher, University of British Columbia

NATURE IS NURTURE

"Ecotherapy," a process of growth and healing by interacting with nature, is being used to treat a range of conditions such as anxiety, depression, diabetes, and high blood pressure.

–Jennifer Lennox, spokesperson, The Davey Tree Expert Company, Kent, Ohio

PEOPLE ARE TALKING ABOUT . . .

• falling asleep to movies of sheep grazing in a field

• consuming collagen-infused foods for better complexions

• gym workouts based on children's games (e.g., relay races, dodgeball)

COMING SOON . . .

• self-healing cavity fillings: If a crack develops, a little capsule of material opens up to seal it.

• shoes with vibrating insoles to improve balance   *(continued)*

BUZZWORD

Emodiversity: the ability to feel a wide range of healthful, positive emotions (enthusiasm, determination, pride, inspiration, and strength)

If you are using a magnifier to read this...

you don't have a Microsun light.

Say goodbye to eyestrain when you see the difference a Microsun Lamp makes. Put away your readers, magnifying glasses, and enjoy the benefits of true full spectrum light.

MAKE AMERICA BRIGHT AGAIN!

The World's best reading lamp awaits. Try one for 30 days risk-free and see if eyestrain goes away and reading becomes easier. Visit our website to view all our styles, and watch testimonials by people who love and can't live without their Microsun lamps.
Great for crafters, hobbyists and of course, *readers*.

Special offer: FREE SHIPPING use code ALMANAC

888-328-8701

MICROSUN
the light that rises™

www.microsun.com

FARMING TODAY

Young people are cutting their teeth as urban
farmers in the cities, then moving to rural areas into a
more traditional model of small-scale farming.

–Georgia Stanley, manager of membership, British Columbia Association of Farmers' Markets

FARMS GROW HEALTHY KIDS

- Environmental exposures or other elements of the farming lifestyle help kids to be resistant to both allergies and viral respiratory illnesses.
–James Gern, MD, researcher, University of Wisconsin

PEOPLE ARE TALKING ABOUT . . .

- computer games in which players sample an agricultural career

- "renting" a farm animal, beehive, or maple tree; getting photos of its growth cycles; and, eventually, consuming its harvest

CONSUMER CONNECTIONS

- **114,801** U.S. farms sell direct-to-consumer

- **24,510** Canadian farms sell direct-to-consumer

BY THE NUMBERS

69% of new farmers have college degrees

267,500: number of U.S. cows dedicated to producing organic milk in one recent year

39% of U.S. farmland is rented

820 acres: average size of a Canadian farm

GROWERS ARE PRODUCING . . .

- "exotic" vegetables (Asian greens, okra) for culturally diverse customers
–Stanley

- in cities, indoors: "Indoor farming technology will continue to evolve and develop urban agriculture."
–Michael Levenston, executive director, City Farmer Society, Vancouver, British Columbia

- Top 5 veggies surging in sales in Canada:
1. kale
2. yams
3. artichokes
4. okra
5. gingerroot
–Canadian Produce Marketing Association (continued)

CLOTHING UP CLOSE

We will continue to see an expansion of women renting fashion and thinning out their closets.

–Leonard Schlesinger, Baker Foundation Professor, Harvard Business School

INDIVIDUALITY IS US

We want a wardrobe that lets us create more garments, such as jacket linings to wear as blouses.

–Steven Faerm, associate professor of fashion, Parsons School of Design

LADIES' WEAR DAILY

- one-shoulder dresses evoking Grecian statuary
- sheer patterned socks, worn with sneakers or sandals

MEN'S WEAR DAILY

- modern kimonos, in muted blues and grays
- dress pants with athletic stripes

MULTITASKING TOGS INCLUDE . . .

- patch pockets to snap off and wear on other garments
- shirtsleeves to take off and attach to outerwear
- coats to use as backpacks, sleeping bags, or blankets

DISRUPTION IN THE RAG TRADE

If it is not local, online, or off-price, it is not happening.

–Jan Rogers Kniffen, retail consultant, Greenwich, Connecticut

BY THE NUMBERS

15%
of consumers have ordered apparel using subscription boxes

79%
of women own at least one unworn pair of shoes

$323:
average amount spent on clothing annually, by men

$571: average amount spent on clothing annually, by women

RETAILERS ARE REVVED UP BY . . .

- steaming out wrinkles so that items can be immediately worn
- opening early to repair commuters' ripped buttons, torn cuffs, or stains
- turning clothing "stores" into gathering spots, with spa services, juice bars, classes, and tailors

CULTURE CUES

Hundreds of thousands of people are joining citizen science projects which collectively lead to discoveries that would be impossible with conventional science.

–Caren Cooper, assistant head, Biodiversity Research Lab, North Carolina Museum of Natural Sciences

PEOPLE ARE TALKING ABOUT . . .

● movies of laundry being washed

● hobbyhorse rider competitions

● playing shorter rounds of golf and tennis matches because they are time-stressed

● "cargo" bikes with detachable hand trucks for toting up to 50 pounds

● "citizen scientists" counting urban trees

PICK-ME-UPS

● **1,456:** number of times U.S. moms and dads pick up after their children annually

● **71%** of parents have been injured by stepping on a toy

GIVING IS GOOD

● Study participants who were given money and told to buy a gift for someone were happier than those who were instructed to spend it on themselves.

QUIET, PLEASE!

Shhhh! for . . .

● stores with "quiet hours"

● self-imposed smartphone-free time periods

● fold-up, portable pods for privacy in crowded spaces ■

BY THE NUMBERS

16% of Americans celebrate Thanksgiving on a date other than the holiday to save travel costs

94% of the U.S. population has a recycling program available to them

Choose Life
Grow Young with HGH

From the landmark book Grow Young with HGH comes the most powerful, over-the-counter health supplement in the history of man. Human growth hormone was first discovered in 1920 and has long been thought by the medical community to be necessary only to stimulate the body to full adult size and therefore unnecessary past the age of 20. Recent studies, however, have overturned this notion completely, discovering instead that the natural decline of Human Growth Hormone (HGH), from ages 21 to 61 (the average age at which there is only a trace left in the body) and is the main reason why the body ages and fails to regenerate itself to its 25 year-old biological age.

Like a picked flower cut from the source, we gradually wilt physically and mentally and become vulnerable to a host of degenerative diseases, that we simply weren't susceptible to in our early adult years.

Modern medical science now regards aging as a disease that is treatable and preventable and that "aging", the disease, is actually a compilation of various diseases and pathologies, from everything, like a rise in blood glucose and pressure to diabetes, skin wrinkling and so on. All of these aging symptoms can be stopped and rolled back by maintaining Growth Hormone levels in the blood at the same levels HGH existed in the blood when we were 25 years old.

There is a receptor site in almost every

cell in the human body for HGH, so its regenerative and healing effects are very comprehensive.

Growth Hormone, first synthesized in 1985 under the Reagan Orphan drug act, to treat dwarfism, was quickly recognized to stop aging in its tracks and reverse it to a remarkable degree. Since then, only the lucky and the rich have had access to it at the cost of $10,000 US per year.

The next big breakthrough was to come in 1997 when a group of doctors and scientists, developed an all-natural source product which would cause your own natural HGH to be released again and do all the remarkable things it did for you in your 20's. Now available to every adult for about the price of a coffee and donut a day.

GHR now available in America, just in time for the aging Baby Boomers and everyone else from age 30 to 90 who doesn't want to age rapidly but would rather stay young, beautiful and healthy all of the time.

The new HGH releasers are winning converts from the synthetic HGH users as well, since GHR is just as effective, is oral instead of self-injectable and is very affordable.

GHR is a natural releaser, has no known side effects, unlike the synthetic version and has no known drug interactions. Progressive doctors admit that this is the direction medicine is seeking to go, to get the body to heal itself instead of employing drugs. GHR is truly a revolutionary paradigm shift in medicine and, like any modern leap frog advance, many others will be left in the dust holding their limited, or useless drugs and remedies.

It is now thought that HGH is so comprehensive in its healing and regenerative powers that it is today, where the computer industry was twenty years ago, that it will displace so many prescription and non-prescription drugs and health remedies that it is staggering to think of.

The president of BIE Health Products stated in a recent interview, I've been waiting for these products since the 70's. We knew they would come, if only we could stay healthy and live long enough to see them! If you want to stay on top of your game, physically and mentally as you age, this product is a boon, especially for the highly skilled professionals who have made large investments in their education, and experience. Also with the failure of Congress to honor our seniors with pharmaceutical coverage policy, it's more important than ever to take pro-active steps to safeguard your health. Continued use of GHR will make a radical difference in your health, HGH is particularly helpful to the elderly who, given a choice, would rather stay independent in their own home, strong, healthy and alert enough to manage their own affairs, exercise and stay involved in their communities. Frank, age 85, walks two miles a day, plays golf, belongs to a dance club for seniors, had a girl friend again and doesn't need Viagra, passed his drivers test and is hardly ever home when we call - GHR delivers.

HGH is known to relieve symptoms of Asthma, Angina, Chronic Fatigue, Constipation, Lower back pain and Sciatica, Cataracts and Macular Degeneration, Menopause, Fibromyalgia, Regular and Diabetic Neuropathy, Hepatitis, helps Kidney Dialysis and Heart and Stroke recovery.

For more information or to order call
877-849-4777
www.biehealth.ca

These statements have not been evaluated by the FDA. Copyright © 2000. Code OFA.

FOOLPROOF **ADVICE FOR BEGINNERS,**
"BLACK THUMBS," AND ANYONE
TRYING TO GROW FOOD.

JOIN THE

BY SUSAN PEERY

Remember back to last fall or maybe winter. You were thinking, *"I want a garden!"* You scrutinized seed catalogs and ordered beautiful things, some with Latin names that you couldn't pronounce. You strolled down nursery aisles and arrived home with trays of cute, tender seedlings.

When the days got warmer, you marked off a spot, cleared the ground, and turned over the dirt with muscles you didn't know that you had. Dropped seeds into knuckle-deep holes in neat rows. Tamped the earth around the eager seedlings to help them settle into their new digs.

Through the summer, you yanked weeds, beat back bugs, cursed rampaging rabbits or woodchucks, and toted watering cans or hoses (how much is enough?). You got dirty, sweaty, hungry, and tired, watching and waiting for your plot to become . . . picture-perfect. Like those in magazines and on Facebook and Pinterest.

Then, in August—or maybe even earlier, in July—you bought vegetables at a farm stand, thinking: *"Why aren't* my *tomatoes* (beans, carrots, squash—whatever) *like this?"*

Sound familiar? Feeling frustrated just thinking about it?

Take a deep breath. We've all been there. This season will be different. Follow this guidance to go from grief to glory in the garden!

(continued)

You waited for your plot to become picture-perfect, like this one.

GREEN THUMB CLUB

> ### IF YOU GROW IT FOR THE FRUIT OR THE ROOT, YOU NEED FULL SUN. IF YOU GROW IT FOR THE LEAVES, PARTIAL SHADE IS ALL YOU NEED.
> —GARDENING ADAGE

Most vegetables and herbs require about 8 hours of sunlight each day to thrive. Exceptions include shade-tolerant leafy greens and a few herbs. (In the high heat of summer or if a late spring frost threatens, protect tender plants with floating row covers.) Choose a garden site that gets 8 hours of sunlight, ideally with southern exposure unhindered by shade from trees or buildings, a plot into which you can put the tallest plants on the north end so that they do not cast shade on smaller plants to their south.

Soil is slower to warm than air. If you plant seedlings and certain seeds in cold soil, you might as well throw them away. Sure, peas will sprout and thrive when the soil temperature is in the low 40s°F and the days are cool and damp, but melons, most squashes, pumpkins, and tomatoes require soil temperature above 50°F and warm days.

A warm Sun dries out the soil, and plants require frequent watering. This is best done in early morning or evening; water in midday, and much of the moisture may be lost to evaporation. If water is costly, use a hose or watering can at the base of plants instead of broadcasting it with sprinklers.

(continued)

Watering is best done in early morning or evening.

Photo: Westbury/Getty Images

FREEZE DRY AT HOME

Actual Freeze Dried Food

New, Revolutionary Home Freeze Dryers

❧ BE PREPARED
Preserve the food your family loves—fruits, vegetables, and complete meals.

❧ FOOD STAYS FRESH
Lock in the nutrition and taste of any food for up to 25 years.

❧ YEAR-ROUND FLAVORS
Enjoy seasonal harvests like squash, watermelon, and berries all year long.

HAR**V**ESTRIGHT

More Color Options Available!

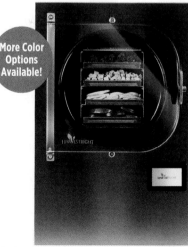

MADE IN AMERICA

1.800.787.7245   HarvestRight.com

F ew of us are naturally blessed with loamy, fertile soil at a pH of 5.5–6.5, the ideal range for most herbs and vegetables. Soil pH (a measure of acidity or alkalinity), together with soil chemistry and structure, will greatly affect the health and vigor of your plants. If your tomatoes are plagued with blossom end rot, this may be due to a calcium deficiency in the soil— something you can easily fix.

Get your soil tested. For most thorough results and specific recommendations, contact your local Cooperative Extension service. Make the advised amendments, adding compost, manure, peat, lime, and other organic material as necessary. *(continued)*

The ideal pH range for growing most herbs and vegetables is 5.5–6.5.

**IN SPRING AT THE END OF THE DAY,
YOU SHOULD SMELL LIKE DIRT.**
–Margaret Atwood, Canadian writer (b. 1939)

I t takes self-control not to overplant a garden—but we've all done it and then struggled to thin seedlings without uprooting their neighbors. Sometimes we've left plants to crowd only to see that none mature to full size. Map out your garden plot, noting the space advised on the seed packet or plant stick. Or try the easy app at Almanac.com/GardenPlanner.

Think again before tucking an extra cherry tomato plant over here, adding another row of green beans there. If a friend gives you two zucchini (cuke, eggplant, pepper—whatever) plants, give them away or plant them in a pot. You'll be glad that you did in July, when your garden is a jungle, with plants competing for sunlight and nutrients.

Develop a spare, minimalist mentality. Leave space: Good air circulation helps to ward off mildew and blight. Plan walkways and spread wood chips or other mulch on the paths. Allow at least 6 feet between indeterminate tomato plants and stake them well. Plant sprawlers like zucchini or pumpkins on the garden's edge and encourage their vines away from the other crops.

Weed as needed and mulch. Well. Mulch helps to minimize weeds and retain moisture. *(continued)*

Good air circulation helps to ward off mildew and blight.

TO NURTURE A GARDEN IS TO FEED NOT JUST THE BODY, BUT THE SOUL.
–Alfred Austin, English poet (1835–1913)

SUCCESS

GARDENING IS LEARNING, LEARNING, LEARNING. THAT'S THE FUN OF THEM. YOU'RE ALWAYS LEARNING.
–HELEN MIRREN, ENGLISH ACTRESS (B. 1945)

Gardening is an experiment. No one (so far) can control the weather, the bugs, or any other force of nature. You can make good choices and educated guesses and adopt best practices and still experience crop failures. But if you follow this guidance, embrace the surprises and uncertainties of each gardening season, and look forward to the next, you are on the road from grief to glory.

SEEDS VS. SEEDLINGS

Which plants should you seed directly into the soil and which should you purchase as seedlings?

Buy seedlings if you do not have a good setup for starting seeds, if you have a short growing season, and/or if you want only two or three plants of a certain crop, such as squashes or tomatoes. Choose stocky, sturdy-looking plants over large, leggy ones. Plant at the depth and spacing recommended on the label.

When sowing seeds directly, follow the directions: If a seed packet says to space seeds 2 inches apart, do it. If a packet says to sow "sparsely," allow at least 1 inch between seeds.　*(continued)*

Buy seedlings if you do not have a good setup for starting seeds.

Most gardeners find these to be the most reliable and rewarding edibles to grow:

1. *Basil, any variety:* Needs warm air and soil; pinch off flowers to encourage leaves. A hint of a frost will finish it.

2. *Beans:* Need 60°F soil; space seeds as directed; choose 'Provider' or 'Blue Lake' (bush varieties) for heavy harvests.

3. *Carrots:* Need light, well-draining soil; sow sparsely to avoid thinning later; tolerate light frost; choose 'Chantenay' and 'Nantes', which keep well.

4. *Cherry tomatoes:* No plot? Put in a large container; especially sweet and productive 'Sun Gold'.

5. *Chives:* Use this hardy perennial herb as a great garnish; eat its flowers; divide in fall.

6. *Garlic:* Plant individual cloves in fall, mulch with hay; rake off mulch in spring; when scapes curl around once, cut off and make pesto; harvest when leaves wither. Save the biggest bulbs for your next crop.

7. *Greens:* Can be planted early; full sun not needed; especially arugula, mesclun, loose-leaf lettuces. Go from seed to salad bowl in 6 weeks!

8. *Parsley:* Seeds are slow to germinate, so buy little plants; especially curly, which is slower to bolt than flatleaf and will last into fall; needs space to put down deep roots.

9. *Peas:* Love cool weather; may need support; especially snap, which outyield shelling peas.

10. *Potatoes:* Plant chunks of sprouted seed potatoes, especially russets, early reds, and yellow-flesh varieties, with eyes upward in a trench; fill in; mulch well. Dig (carefully!) when tops die down. *(continued)*

GARDENING IS JUST ANOTHER DAY AT THE PLANT.

—GARDENING ADAGE

10 EASY EDIBLES

4 TO TRY FOR TRIUMPH

THERE ARE NO GARDENING MISTAKES, ONLY EXPERIMENTS.

–JANET KILBURN PHILLIPS, ENGLISH COTTAGE GARDEN DESIGNER

These plants need specific (perfect) conditions. Proceed with careful attention to the advice below.

1. *Cantaloupes* and *watermelons* need warmth: hot days, warm nights, and a long growing season. A plastic hoop house may help.

2. *Sweet corn* needs rich soil, warm sun, and a lot of moisture.

3. *Tomatillos* need a long growing season; cool August nights stop them. Homegrown are much better than the store-bought specimens.

4. *Asparagus* requires a rich, weed-free, undisturbed bed. Control slugs and asparagus beetles. Harvest in the third year, and, yes, it's worth the wait: Homegrown spears are ambrosial to asparagus lovers.

Get more information on how to grow in pots at Almanac.com.

GOOD, BETTER, BEST

Never let it rest, till your good is better and your better is the best! Get more information on the edibles mentioned here (including how to grow in pots), plus read stories from growers like you at Almanac.com/Gardening. ■

Susan Peery gardens in Nelson, New Hampshire, where she loves to experiment with traditional gardening methods and plants. Like all gardeners, she invokes the mantra "Wait 'til next year!"

Ask the Expert

PLATE YOUR PETALS

Edible flowers are blossoming into an old-is-new-again culinary trend.

BY JODI HELMER

I n garden beds and window boxes, the colorful blossoms of begonias, calendula, nasturtiums, and roses can be dazzling. Did you know that they are also delicious?

Edible flowers have figured in ancient culinary traditions for centuries. Over time, the practice of and interest in using flowers as food fell out of favor. *(continued)*

40

EDIBLE FLOWERS LOOK GREAT BOTH ON THE PLATE AND IN THE GARDEN.

Apple blossoms

Rosalind Creasy, author of *The Edible Flower Garden,* attributes the shift to a misguided (but prevalent) belief that flowers are so beautiful that "only the eyes should feast on them."

Today, the other "ayes" have it: Edible flowers look great both on the plate and in the garden. As you plan your vegetable plots and ornamental beds, add a few of these flowering plants—and double your pleasure.

APPLE BLOSSOMS (*Malus* spp.): Pick from apple trees in late spring; trimming out some flowers helps to maximize fruit production. Use the petals for a mild apple flavor at mealtime: Sprinkle a few in a Waldorf salad or greens dressed with apple cider vinegar. Steep petals in cream to pour on apple pie, crepes, or pastries. (Use in moderation; low levels of cyanide are present in apple wood, bark, and seeds.)

CALENDULA/POT MARIGOLDS *(Calendula officinalis):* These cool-season annuals produce bright orange or yellow flowers. Used in ancient Rome as an inexpensive substitute for saffron, the petals of varieties such as 'Fiesta' and 'Radio' have a tangy taste. Cut the

Calendula

STAY SAFE
IN THE HOME YOU LOVE.

Stairlifts are the perfect solution for **arthritis and COPD sufferers, those with mobility issues, or anyone who struggles with the stairs.**

Receive a **FREE STAIRLIFT BUYING GUIDE** from Acorn Stairlifts which will answer all of your questions on buying a stairlift, such as:

- **When can a stairlift help?**
- **What options are available to me?**
- **How safe are stairlifts?**

YOUR GUIDE TO BUYING A STAIRLIFT
HOW A STAIRLIFT CAN IMPROVE YOUR LIFE IN A FEW EASY STEPS

ACORN STAIRLIFTS

FREE
STAIRLIFT BUYING GUIDE

TO HELP YOU MAKE AN INFORMED DECISION.

CALL TODAY TO RECEIVE YOUR FREE STAIRLIFT BUYING GUIDE & DVD PLUS SAVE $250.

1-866-290-8565
AcornStairlifts.com

Arthritis Foundation
Ease of Use™

A+ BBB ACCREDITED BUSINESS

ACORN STAIRLIFTS

*Not valid on previous purchases. Not valid with any other offers or discounts. Not valid on refurbished models. Only valid towards purchase of a NEW Acorn Stairlift directly from the manufacturer. $250 discount will be applied to new orders. Please mention this ad when calling. AZ ROC 278722, CA 942619, MN LC670698, OK 50110, OR CCB 198506, RI 88, WA ACORNSI8940B, WV WV049654, MA HIC169936, NJ 13VH07752300, PA PA101967, CT ELV 0425003-R5.

Daylilies

petals off the flower and dry them in a warm (100°F) oven. Sprinkle the crushed petals on cheese dishes, omelets, and rice.

Carnations

HANDLE WITH CARE

• Harvest flowers in the morning. Flower petal oils are strongest in cooler temperatures.
• Remove stamens, pistils, and leaflike sepals at the base of blossoms.
• Use and consume flowers on the day of harvest.
• Avoid flowers from plants, gardens, landscapes, roadsides, and florist shops that have been treated with chemicals, pesticides, or other hazardous material.

CARNATIONS (*Dianthus* spp.): The clove-flavor petals of the 300-plus varieties of annual, biennial, and perennial carnations are edible (be sure to remove the bitter white base). Add to cake mixes, candies (especially chocolate), and teas. Sprinkle minced fresh petals over a bowl of berries.

CHRYSANTHEMUMS (*Chrysanthemum* x *morifolium, Dendranthema* x *grandiflora*): Piquant-flavor "mums" make a colorful herb in chowders and egg dishes. Dry the petals in a warm oven (100°F) for several hours until they are crunchy but still colorful.

DAYLILIES (*Hemerocallis* spp.): Use only the *Hemerocallis* genus. Some other lilies contain poisonous alkaloids. Harvest blossoms on the day after they bloom. (Taste as you pick: Pale petals

FOR A LEMONY FLAVOR, HARVEST LILAC FLOWERS JUST AFTER THEY OPEN.

Lilacs

tend to be sweeter, while darker petals tend to have stronger flavor.) Remove petals from the flower base. Add to salads or stir-fried dishes moments before serving. Dried petals are used in Chinese Sweet

Impatiens

and Sour Soup. In the spring, gather 2- to 3-inch-tall shoots to try in pesto.

IMPATIENS *(Impatiens walleriana):* Use the sweet-tasting blossoms of this annual as garnish on plates or in beverages and salads.

GLADIOLUS *(Gladiolus* spp.): Glads taste vaguely like lettuce. Remove the flowers' pistils and stamens and toss a few whole blossoms into green salads for a dash of color. Or, use to hold dip (see "Tulips").

LILACS *(Syringa vulgaris):* For a distinct lemony flavor, harvest these spring flowers immediately after they open. Candied lilac

Gladiolus

46

NASTURTIUMS LOOK LOVELY FLOATING IN A BOWL OF PUNCH.

flowerets make charming cake decorations. Separate individual flowers and use tweezers to dip each one into a beaten egg white, reconstituted egg white powder, or packaged egg whites. Then dip each flower into finely granulated sugar and set it aside to dry before placing on a cake.

NASTURTIUMS
(Tropaeolum majus): This plant is a member of the Brassica family, and dozens of varieties can be grown from seed. Try 'Empress of India' for its deep red-orange flowers and dark blue-green leaves, which impart a peppery or sweet mustard flavor to salad

Nasturtiums

dressings or vinegars and look lovely floating in a tureen of soup or bowl of punch. Be sure to remove the spur

behind the bloom as it may shelter insects.

ROSES (*Rosa* spp.): Roses are famously edible flowers. Note that lighter flowers have a mild flavor; the darker a rose's color, the more likely that it will have a strong metallic taste. Remove the white base.

THYME (*Thymus* spp.): The tiny pink or lavender flowers on this Mediterranean herb are often overlooked in favor of its aromatic leaves. The lavender flowers of French thyme (*T. vulgaris*) embody the earthiness of the herb (sprinkle them on top of baked mushroom caps), while the pink flowers on lemon thyme

Roses

Oleander

LOVELY TO LOOK UPON, FATAL AS FOOD

Caladium *(Caladium bicolor)*, clematis, foxglove *(Digitalis purpurea)*, oleander *(Nerium oleander)*, sweet pea *(Lathyrus odoratus)*, and larkspur *(Delphinium)* are poisonous. To be safe, before planning to eat flowers, identify the plant—using its Latin name—and research it to make sure that it is safe for consumption.

(T. citriodorus) add a citrusy zing.

TUBEROUS BEGONIAS *(Begonia* x *tuberhybrida)*: Brilliant orange, white, pink, red, and yellow tuberous begonia flowers bring light lemon flavor to salads and tea sandwiches. (Avoid if you have kidney stones, gout, or rheumatism: The flowers contain oxalic acid.)

TULIPS *(Tulipa* spp.): Spring's darlings taste a little like fresh baby peas and make a stunning presentation: Remove the pistils and stamens and fill the empty cups with luncheon salad or dip.

ZUCCHINI *(Cucurbita pepo* var. *cylindrica)*: This vegetable's yellow blossoms, when stuffed with cheese, bacon, and mushrooms, make for flavorful and fun appetizers. The flowers have a mild squash flavor that also pairs well with salads and omelets. (If a squash harvest is desired, harvest only male flowers to eat.) ■

Jodi Helmer is a North Carolina–based garden writer.

Tulips

Photos, from top: leoaleks/Getty Images; kanonsky/Getty Images

The ABCs of Pickling

ASPARAGUS, BEETS, CORN–AND CUKES!

by Mare-Anne Jarvela

Pickling is an age-old method of preserving food, sure, but it's also a technique to alter the flavor of familiar vegetables and fruit with herbs and spices and enjoy them in new and delicious ways.

Conveniently, these A–B–C vegetables are harvested at different times, so pick a peck and pickle!

BEFORE YOU BEGIN . . .

Wash and sterilize all jars and lids: Set the empty jars right-side up on the rack in a boiling-water canner. Fill the canner and jars with hot water to 1 inch above the tops of the jars. Bring the water to a boil for 15 minutes. Sterilize the lids by boiling in water for 5 minutes.

(continued)

FOR PERFECT PICKLES

- Use the most uniform and unspoiled produce.
- Pickle fresh produce as soon as possible after it is harvested.
- Use pickling salt. Iodized salt makes the brine cloudy and may change the color and texture of the produce.
- Use distilled white or cider vinegar with 5 percent acidity. Use distilled white vinegar when a light color is desirable.
- For best flavor and nutritional value, eat processed pickled produce within a year, unless otherwise directed.
- Glass canning jars can be reused and will last many years if washed and stored properly.
- Never reuse canning jar lids. After the first use, a lid will no longer seal effectively.

THE ACID INFLUENCE

Pickles are made by immersing fresh vegetables and fruit into an acidic liquid—for example, vinegar. Vinegar keeps pickles crisp and prevents the growth of unwanted bacteria. Unprocessed pickles made with vinegar can be refrigerated and should be eaten within a couple of weeks.

For longer storage, process jars in a boiling-water bath. Start by placing sterilized, filled, and sealed jars into the canner. Cover with boiling water and follow instructions in the recipe for how long to process the jars in the boiling water. This method is used for "high acid" foods. Vinegar makes pickled foods "high acid."

Pressure canning, during which trapped steam increases the pressure and temperature inside the canner, is the safe way to preserve "low-acid" foods. You do not need to pressure-can pickles. ■

Mare-Anne Jarvela's favorite pickles are crunchy cucumber pickles made from her garden's bounty in Munsonville, New Hampshire.

PLEASE TURN TO PAGE 200 FOR PICKLING RECIPES.

2018 ORANGE RECIPE CONTEST WINNERS

Many thanks to the hundreds of you who submitted recipes!

PHOTOS BY LORI PEDRICK · STYLING BY CATRINE KELLY

FIRST PRIZE: $300
CRAN-ORANGE COUSCOUS SALAD

SALAD:
3 cups pearl couscous, cooked
   according to package directions
1 cup goat cheese
¾ cup dried cranberries
½ cup chopped pecans
2 cans (15.5 ounces each) chickpeas,
   drained and rinsed
5 basil leaves, chopped
2 large oranges, peeled and chopped
1 small red onion, chopped

VINAIGRETTE:
½ cup olive oil
¼ cup balsamic vinegar
4 tablespoons orange juice
1 tablespoon orange zest
2 teaspoons honey
salt and freshly ground black pepper,
   to taste

1. *For salad:* Place couscous in a
bowl. Add goat cheese, cranberries,
pecans, chickpeas, basil, oranges,
and onions. Mix well.

2. *For vinaigrette:* In a small
bowl, whisk together oil, vinegar,
orange juice, orange zest,
honey, and salt and pepper.

3. Pour vinaigrette over salad
and stir to coat.

Makes 8 servings.

–*Kristen Heigl, Staten Island, New York*

(continued)

ENTER THE 2019 RECIPE CONTEST: PASTA

Got a great recipe using pasta that's loved by family and
friends? It could win! See contest rules on page 251.

SECOND PRIZE: $200
SPICED ORANGE SALMON WITH CARAMEL EDAMAME CORN SAUCE

2 navel oranges
1 tablespoon soy sauce
1 tablespoon mirin
1 tablespoon white wine
½ teaspoon ground cumin
¼ teaspoon garlic powder
⅛ teaspoon ground thyme
2 fresh salmon fillets (4 ounces each)
salt and freshly ground black pepper, to taste
1 tablespoon olive oil
1 tablespoon brown sugar
½ cup frozen shelled edamame, thawed
3 tablespoons frozen corn, thawed
1 scallion, thinly sliced, for garnish

1. Remove zest and juice from oranges (measure out ½ cup of orange juice). Set zest aside for garnish.

2. In a zip-top bag, combine orange juice, soy sauce, mirin, wine, cumin, garlic powder, and thyme.

3. Pat salmon dry with paper towels and season with salt and pepper. Put salmon into marinade bag and place in refrigerator for 30 minutes.

4. About 10 minutes before cook time, remove bag from refrigerator.

5. In a cast iron skillet, heat oil over medium-high. Remove salmon from bag and reserve marinade. Put salmon, skin side down, into skillet. Cook until skins are crisp and brown, about 3 minutes. Flip salmon, reduce heat to medium, and cook until flesh is firm and flakes easily, about 4 minutes.

6. In a separate skillet over medium heat, combine brown sugar and 1 teaspoon of water. After 1 minute, add reserved marinade. Reduce heat to medium-low and add edamame and corn. Cook, stirring occasionally, until slightly thickened, about 5 minutes. Season with salt and pepper.

7. To serve, spread edamame and corn on two plates. Place salmon on top and sprinkle with orange zest and scallions.

Makes 2 servings.

–Hidemi Walsh, Greenfield, Indiana

(continued)

THIRD PRIZE: $100
ORANGE AND BACON BRUSSELS SPROUTS

6 tablespoons extra-virgin olive oil, divided

2 small oranges, cut in half, then into ½-inch slices

kosher salt, to taste

3 or 4 strips thick-cut bacon, cut into ¼-inch pieces

1½ pounds brussels sprouts, trimmed and halved

1. Preheat oven to 425°F. Brush a rimmed baking sheet with 1 tablespoon of oil.

2. Place oranges in a single layer on prepared baking sheet, turning to coat. Season with salt and drizzle with 1 tablespoon of oil. Roast for 15 minutes, remove from oven, and stir in bacon. Roast until crisp, about 12 minutes.

3. Toss brussels sprouts with remaining 4 tablespoons of oil and season with salt. Add to baking sheet and toss to combine. Roast, stirring once, for 20 to 25 minutes, or until sprouts are tender and browning at edges and oranges are caramelized.

Makes 6 servings.

–Jennifer Miessau, East Haven, Connecticut

HONORABLE MENTION
ORANGE-GLAZED GRILLED CHICKEN WITH CHUNKY ORANGE SALSA

1 cup orange juice

½ cup light brown sugar

2 tablespoons Worcestershire sauce

1 container (6 ounces) orange cream yogurt

4 cooked chicken breast halves

2 cups cooked brown rice

1 lime, quartered, for garnish

1. In a skillet over medium heat, combine orange juice, brown sugar, Worcestershire sauce, and yogurt. Whisk together until smooth and creamy.

2. Place chicken in orange sauce and reduce heat to low. Simmer, turning chicken occasionally until warmed and coated with sauce. Remove chicken from skillet and let sauce continue to simmer until thick.

3. To serve, place a piece of chicken on a bed of brown rice, pour orange sauce over chicken, and top with salsa. Garnish with a slice of lime.

For Chunky Orange Salsa recipe, please turn to page 201.

DUCK STAMP
DYNASTY

by Benjamin Kilbride

This 2017 entry by wildlife
artist Bob Hautman was his third
federal duck stamp win.

Eighty-five years ago, the first federal duck stamp was issued, beginning an era of conservation, collaboration, and—in at least one family—fraternal competition.

Every migratory waterfowl hunter age 16 and older in the United States must purchase a $25, 1¾×1½-inch duck stamp to be properly licensed. The stamp also serves as a free admission pass to National Wildlife Refuges. Over 1 million stamps are sold every year, most of them slipped into waterproof bags and unceremoniously shoved into pockets and glove compartments. However, a rising number of stamps are purchased by nonhunters who stick them on cars and laptops; some even frame them.

Why do people buy these stamps if they don't hunt? It's for the birds, of course.

In 1934, during the Great Depression, conservationists and naturalists became concerned about the increasing destruction of wetlands vital to the survival of waterfowl. At the considerable encouragement of Jay "Ding" Darling, a cartoonist, artist, and conservationist, Congress passed and President Franklin D. Roosevelt signed the Migratory Bird Hunting Stamp Act, aka the "Duck Stamp Act."

This act made the possession of a stamp mandatory for hunters of migratory waterfowl and created a fund for the proceeds of those stamps. Ninety-eight cents of every dollar raised from the sale of duck stamps is used to purchase and conserve waterfowl habitat. The program has raised over $800 million and protected over 6.5 million acres of wetlands since the passing of the Duck Stamp Act.

Today's duck stamp program has a component that Darling and

Stamp © U.S. Fish and Wildlife Service

When it's built by *hand,*

It's connected to the *Heart.*

For three generations, the builders, blacksmiths and craftsmen at Country Carpenters have put their hands and their hearts into designing and building the finest New England Style buildings available. Hand-selected materials, hand-forged hardware, all hand-built and hand-finished by real people. You can feel the difference in your heart.

NEW ENGLAND STYLE
Country Carpenters INC.
POST & BEAM BUILDINGS

COUNTRY BARNS, CARRIAGE HOUSES, POOL & GARDEN SHEDS, CABINS

Visit our models on display!

326 Gilead Street, Hebron, CT 06248 • **860.228.2276** • **countrycarpenters.com**

Roosevelt may not have envisioned: It has become an art competition. Until 1949, the image was drawn or painted by an artist chosen by the U.S. Department of the Interior. Today, a panel of judges chooses the winning design.

The duck stamp program remains the only federally funded art contest still in existence. The competition has captured the attention of collectors far and wide, made and broken friendships, and spawned family legacies.

Unlike some art competitions, the duck stamp contest offers no cash prize. Instead, the winning artist receives publicity, recognition by the media, and fame in the wildlife and conservation community.

The artist can also sell reproductions of the winning image and other work with the prestigious title "by the Federal Duck Stamp artist." For example, Jim Hautman sells prints of his 2017 winning image for from $189 (10,500

printed) to $1,295 each (300 printed). There is a huge market for art from the stamp contest among supporters of national parks and wildlife refuges, the National Audubon Society, and stamp collectors, so there is a good chance that fortune will follow in the wake of fame.

Over a 50-year span, renowned stamp collector Jeanette Cantrell Rudy assembled the world's largest collection of federal duck stamps, which includes rare misprints and early

One day prior to the competition, the judges review all entries (above). The actual judging consists of three rounds, the first being a simple "In" or "Out" vote (below), while the last two rounds are judged numerically.

Photos © U.S. Fish and Wildlife Service

Thanks to BetterWOMAN, I'm winning the battle for
Bladder Control.

All Natural
Clinically-Tested Herbal Supplement

- Reduces Bladder Leaks
- Reduces Bathroom Trips
- Sleep Better All Night
- Safe and Effective – No Known Side Effects
- Costs Less than Traditional Bladder Control Options
- **Live Free of Worry, Embarrassment, and Inconvenience**

You don't have to let bladder control problems control you.
<u>**Call now**</u>**!**

Frequent nighttime trips to the bathroom, embarrassing leaks and the inconvenience of constantly searching for rest rooms in public – for years, I struggled with bladder control problems. After trying expensive medications with horrible side effects, ineffective exercises and uncomfortable liners and pads, I was ready to resign myself to a life of bladder leaks, isolation and depression. But then I tried **BetterWOMAN**.

When I first saw the ad for BetterWOMAN, I was skeptical. So many products claim they can set you free from leaks, frequency and worry, only to deliver disappointment. When I finally tried BetterWOMAN, I found that it actually works! It changed my life. Even my friends have noticed that I'm a new person. And because it's all natural, I can enjoy the results without the worry of dangerous side effects. Thanks to BetterWOMAN, I finally fought bladder control problems and I won!

Also Available: **BetterMAN**®
The 3-in-1 Formula Every Man Needs –
Better **BLADDER**, Better **PROSTATE**, and Better **STAMINA!**
Order online at <u>www.BetterMANnow.com</u>.

Limited Time Offer

Call Now & Ask How To Get A
FREE BONUS BOTTLE
CALL TOLL-FREE 1-888-256-5507
or order online: www.BetterWOMANnow.com

In 1985, Robert Bateman's painting *Mallard Pair–Early Winter* appeared on the WHC Duck Stamp (top left). In 2018, artist Pierre Girard took the top prize with his painting *Autumn Colours–Wood Duck* (bottom left).

sketches. The collection also features the very first duck stamp ever sold, which had originally been bought for $1 by its artist, Ding Darling, who then had co-signed it along with William Mooney, the Washington, D.C., postmaster. Today, that first issue is among the rarest stamps in the series, with an estimated value of $450,000. Rudy's collection is on display at the Smithsonian National Postal Museum in Washington, D.C.

To enter the 2019 duck stamp competition (for the 2020–2021 stamp), you need to be a citizen or resident of the United States and at least 18 years old. Submit your work to the U.S. Fish and Wildlife Service headquarters in Virginia by June 1, 2019. For more information, visit www.fws.gov/birds.

The Canadian Wildlife Habitat Conservation Stamp program is run by Wildlife Habitat Canada [WHC]. While each Migratory Game Bird Hunting Permit must carry a stamp, the stamps and prints are also sold to stamp collectors and wildlife art lovers and for gifts, presentations, and fund-raisers.

Since 1985, $50 million has been generated for habitat conservation and stewardship projects across Canada under WHC's grant program.

From 1985 to 1989, the stamps featured commissioned works from renowned artists such as Robert Bateman. Since 1990, WHC has held an annual competition to depict a chosen bird species. The 2018 winner was Pierre Girard's *Autumn Colours–Wood Duck*. WHC's choice for the 2019 stamp is the canvasback *(Aythya valisineria)*. These beautiful artworks are available at whc.org.

(continued)

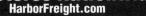

A Family With Its Ducks in a Row

One family in particular has risen to prominence in the duck stamp community—the Hautman brothers. As of 2017, Jim, Joe, and Bob Hautman of Minnesota had won a combined 13 duck stamp contests since 1990, including the last three in a row. In 2015, Joe's migrating trumpeter swans painting (top right) was his fifth win; in 2016, Jim's Canada geese in flight entry (right) was also his fifth win; and in 2017, Bob's pair of mallard ducks artwork (pages 62–63) was his third win. ∎

Benjamin Kilbride is an editorial assistant at *The Old Farmer's Almanac.*

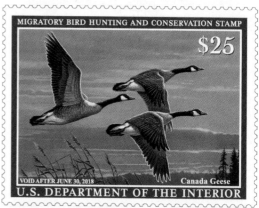

From left, brothers Jim, Joe, and Bob Hautman dominate the federal competition.

Longlight Beeswax Candles

Think *GREEN* - Think *BEESWAX*

- *Environmentally friendly*
- *No Toxins or Carcinogens*
- *Produces Negative Ions to help Purify the Air*
- *Smokeless & Dripless*

100 Hour Coiled Beeswax Candle
- Beautiful Unique Brass Base
- Self-Extinguishing Holder
- 100+ Hour Burn Time
- Refills available

100 Hour Candle — $89
30, 60 & 75 hour available

Our candles make great gifts...

place your order today!

50 Hour Decorator Candle
- Unique Cast Brass Base
- Self-Extinguishing Holder
- 50+ Hour Burn Time
- Refills Available

50 Hour Candle — $55
30, 60 & 75 hour available

Made in USA. All orders plus shipping & handling.

Longlight Candles
1-866-583-3400
longlightcandles.com

Droll Yankees®
buy it once, enjoy it for life™

Yankee Flipper®
Squirrel Proof Bird Feeder

DROLL YANKEES®
Lifetime Warranty
Against Squirrel Damage

Squirrel Activated Motor Driven Rotating Perch
www.drollyankees.com

Photo: Karen Davidson

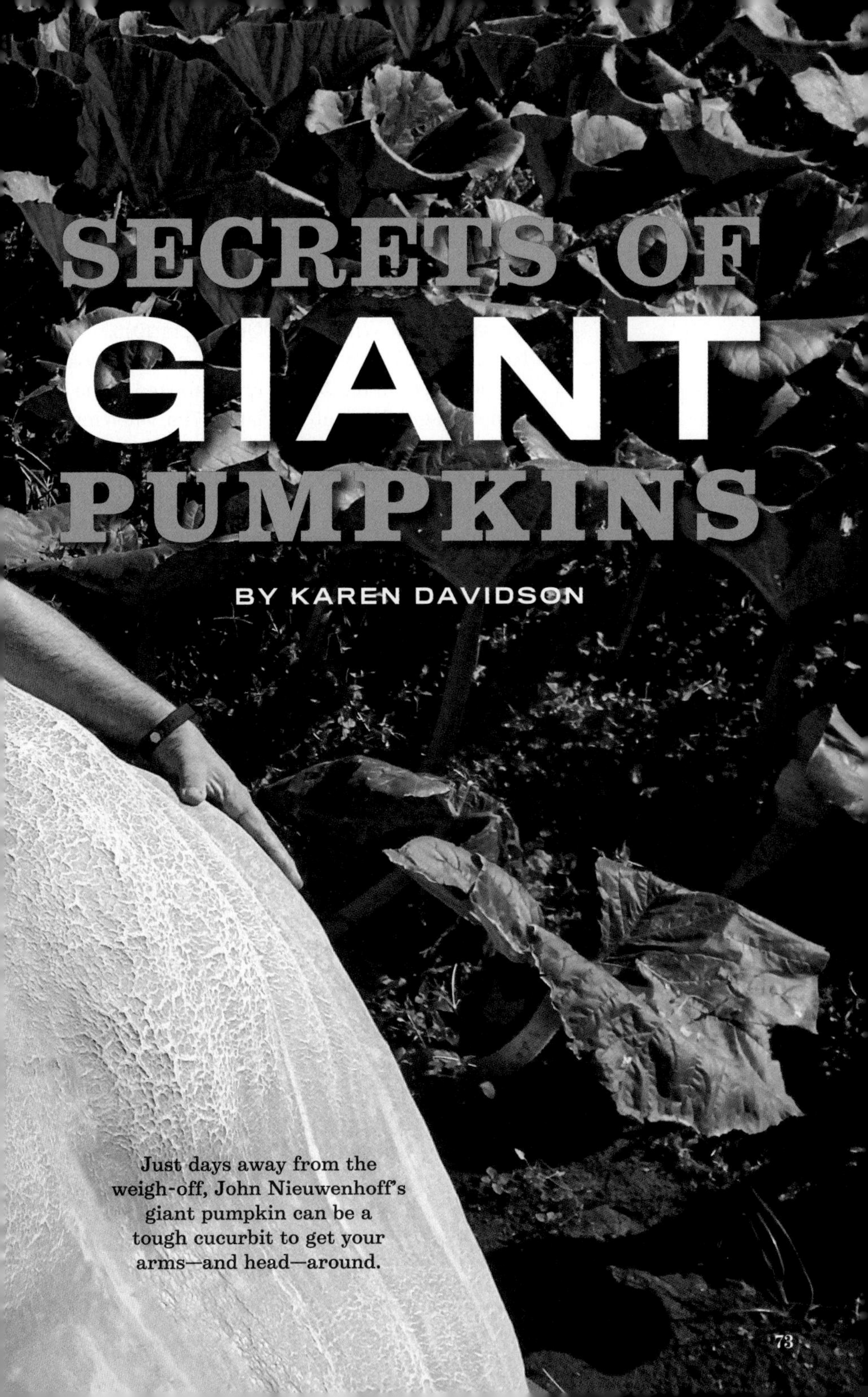

SECRETS OF
GIANT
PUMPKINS

BY KAREN DAVIDSON

Just days away from the
weigh-off, John Nieuwenhoff's
giant pumpkin can be a
tough cucurbit to get your
arms—and head—around.

The English fable about Jack and his sky-high beanstalk dates from 1734. Centuries later, oversize produce still amuses us. There

one envelope was a single seed of 'Atlantic Giant', bred by the grandfather of giant vegetables, "Pumpkin King" and four-time world champion grower Howard Dill of Windsor, Nova Scotia. Today, the pedigrees of most Canadian-grown giant pumpkins originate in Dill's plant breeding. Windsor has become synonymous with giant vegetables, hosting a regatta on the waters of the Minas Basin with

his father's passion for pumpkins. Without pause, he can name the Canadian record for a giant pumpkin: 1,877 pounds, grown by Todd Kline of Shawville, Quebec, in 2016.

"The giant pumpkin craze started in the late 1970s, when my dad started to grow pumpkins in the 400-pound range," Dill says. "He would drive to competitions in Ohio and Pennsylvania and come home with a $100

IT'S PUMPKINS, ESPECIALLY THOSE PLUMP ENOUGH FOR A CINDERELLA CARRIAGE, THAT HOLD MAGICAL APPEAL.

is something fantastical about bulbous beets, gourds long enough to test an Olympic jumper, and colossal cabbage. But it's pumpkins, especially those plump enough for a Cinderella carriage, that hold magical appeal.

Phil Joynson of Enniskillen, Ontario, fell hard for pumpkins two decades ago, when he spied seed packets at a local garden center. Sleeping between the paper covers of

personal vegetable crafts (PVCs) and a pumpkin weigh-off that attracts thousands of people every year.

Danny Dill inherited

THE #1 TIP FOR GROWING GIANT PUMPKINS
Advises one experienced grower: "Plant giant pumpkin seeds in a place accessible by pickup truck. Otherwise, it's like building an ark in the basement."

prize and blue ribbon."

At that time, the driving adventures seemed extreme for such a paltry payoff, but the personal bests were addictive and a backyard hobby—and international business— was born. Danny sells seeds around the world at HowardDill.com.

Phil Joynson also succumbed to Howard Dill's addiction: In addition to looking after his 1-acre pumpkin patch, he oversees the

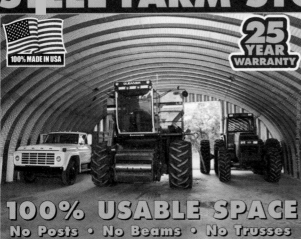

300-member Giant Vegetable Growers of Ontario (GVGO) as its president and is one of the keenest enthusiasts of this nearly year-round activity.

at local weigh-offs, with an eye toward buying the best-bred seeds. "It truly starts with genetics," says Joynson. Plus, the locale in which a prizewinning pumpkin

John Nieuwenhoff and his wife, Sue, split open their pumpkins, scoop out the seeds, and then spread them on window screens to dry for about 2 weeks. In the

A giant pumpkin weighing 930 lbs. on display outside a village in Canada

WINTER IN THE LAND OF GIANTS

In the off-season, growers and wanna-be's learn as much as they can about *Cucurbita maxima*. For novices everywhere, this means perusing Web sites such as www.bigpumpkins .com to see which giant vegetable seeds did well

is grown signals well-suited climate and soils.

Enthusiasts of all levels are advised to join a growers' group, if possible. Membership can provide access to seeds with known parentage. In the case of the GVGO, at the end of the growing season, seed pack coordinator

meantime, he carefully labels resealable plastic bags with the seeds' vital statistics: the pumpkin's end-of-season weight, his name as grower, and the growing season year. When the seeds are suitably dry, the couple puts 1 or 2 seeds in each bag and stores them in a cool, dry location at their

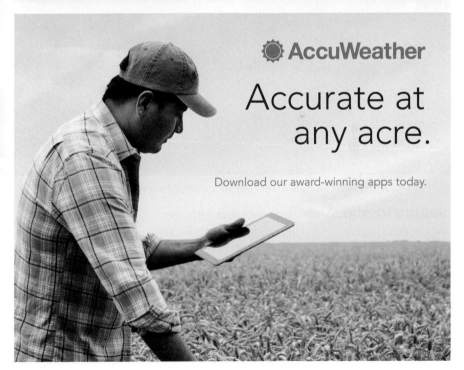

Georgetown, Ontario, home. These seeds and those of GVGO members (already dried, packaged, and labeled) are used in a seed exchange that Nieuwenhoff organizes.

of the seed with a nail file so that the seed will absorb water," she says. "Combine water with hydrogen peroxide [3 percent solution] in the ratio of 10 parts

reptile egg incubator, which, he claims, has an accurate thermostat: "Set the thermostat at 82°F. If your seeds are older than a year, germination might take

A massive pumpkin entered in a pumpkin-growing contest

SPRING RITUALS

As the days begin to grow longer, giant-vegetable growers prepare to start seeds indoors. Sue Nieuwenhoff recommends her annual ritual: "Sand the edges

water to 1 part hydrogen peroxide. Then soak the seeds in the water for 4 to 6 hours." This solution, she explains, prevents fungus growth.

Phil Joynson has other ideas: He germinates seeds in a

longer than 24 hours and as much as another day or two, depending on the age of the seed."

In April, growers prepare their outdoor patches. Nieuwenhoff grows in a 500- to 600-square-foot bed of well-tilled soil liberally sprinkled with 2 inches of mushroom compost. Worm compost is an alternative, he says, but it is expensive. Other growers warn against using animal manure because the risk of accompanying weed seeds is high. Municipal compost is also shunned because it may contain salts.

Nieuwenhoff does not

growing giant vegetables that can swell up to 40 pounds a day. It also helps to prevent blossom end splitting.

SHADE TENTS AND FAKE SNAKES

As the plants grow, the most tedious task for the grower is to prune secondary vines when they reach 10 feet on all sides. Tertiary vines are

removed entirely as they appear. The objective is to focus all of the energy on the solo pumpkin.

Unlike with garden vegetables, mammoth veggie growers do not want the flowers to be open-pollinated by insects or wind. "That's not a good thing," says Joynson. "We do hand pollinations so that we know who the daddy is

WHEN A PUMPKIN IS GROWING 20 TO 40 POUNDS PER DAY, THE PLANT CAN REQUIRE 100 GALLONS OF WATER IN THE SAME TIME PERIOD.

rotate other plants into his patch; he grows only pumpkins and other giant vegetables in it. He stakes his success on a soil test, taken every fall, to adjust micronutrients. "It's not all about the fertility," he says, cautioning against excessive fertilizer. "Your soil needs to be well balanced and high in calcium. I recommend adding a few tablespoons of borax for every 1,000 square feet of soil to boost the boron level." Boron is known to strengthen cell walls, a vital consideration in

DID YOU KNOW?
• Giant vegetables are not eaten—they are grown merely for sport.
• Members of the GVGO get one giant pumpkin seed per breeder.
• Seed companies sell Dill's 'Giant Atlantic', with as many as 15 seeds in a packet.
• Growers' "next" season begins right after a weigh-off, when competitive pumpkins are smashed and seeds are harvested and saved. Pumpkin remains are tossed into compost piles.

and protect the female flower with cups or meshing so that no other pollen gets in."

Every effort is made to protect the fruit from the stresses of sun and wind. A shade tent over a pumpkin is common, as is a mat underneath the fruit to keep it dry. Because mice are known to chew into pumpkins, the Nieuwenhoffs place a fake snake beside their giant—and it seems to work!

Watering is a constant chore. When a pumpkin is growing

With the canopy removed, the Sun can shine on Nieuwenhoff's giant. Note the fake snake at front left.

20 to 40 pounds per day, the plant can require 100 gallons of water in the same time period. Nieuwenhoff's pump puts out 25 gallons per minute, so he calculates 4 minutes per plant. Some growers have a meter on their water supply, while others collect water in totes to have a ready reservoir. No single water prescription works for every grower, because local weather conditions and soil types vary. If soil is too wet or too dry, growth can slow—or stop. Growers take notes through the season in preparation for the following year.

In summer, pumpkins as well as other cousins in the Cucurbitaceae family are prone to powdery mildew and squash vine borers. Hand-spraying with phosphite, a liquid biostimulator, strengthens the plant's constitution to ward off disease. (Do not confuse phosphites with fertilizers. Phosphites have fungicidal properties. Nieuwenhoff uses a product called "TKO" made by a U.S. company called Growth Products.)

WAITING FOR THE WEIGH-OFF

Throughout the season, giant pumpkin growers engage in friendly banter about who's going to win the weigh-off. Many put their faith in the Over the Top

IF SOIL IS TOO WET OR TOO DRY, GROWTH CAN SLOW—OR STOP.

Photo: Karen Davidson

'Porterhouse' Hybrid Tomato

(OTT) chart—accurate to within 5 percent, according to Joynson—which can estimate an 'Atlantic Giant' pumpkin's weight based on three measurements: circumference at the widest part level to the ground, front-to-back length over the top, and side-to-side length over the top.

Prior to the 2017 Erin [Ontario] Fall Fair Pumpkin Weigh-off, Nieuwenhoff used the OTT chart to estimate his giant pumpkin's weight. The result was 1,320 pounds. From appearances, the pumpkins of other competitors were much bigger. But the scale proved that looks can be deceiving: Nieuwenhoff's pumpkin weighed in at 1,401 pounds—earning him a personal best and first prize in the local competition.

In this case, Nieuwenhoff's OTT estimate was low. In giant pumpkin parlance, this is called "going heavy" to the chart, and the data becomes part of the seed vitals. "My pumpkin weighed 6 percent heavy to the chart," says Nieuwenhoff. "We keep track of this information to help make decisions on what to grow in the future as certain genetic lines tend to 'go heavy' to the chart."

It was a fabled ending to a fairy tale that is played out year after year. ∎

Karen Davidson is editor of *The Grower,* a leading Canadian horticultural publication. Learn more at TheGrower.org.

Visitors to the Erin Fall Fair view the array of giant pumpkins before the official weigh-off. Nieuwenhoff's prizewinning entry is in the foreground.

Photo: Karen Davidson

Take me out to the
GARDEN

PARK'S NEW & EXCLUSIVE WHOPPER BELL PEPPER

15%OFF YOUR NEXT ORDER

WITH CODE: WHOPPER18   USE BEFORE: 6/01/2019

*NOT VALID WITH ANY OTHER OFFER. TO REDEEM ENTER THE CODE ABOVE IN YOUR CHECKOUT CART.

1-800-845-3369   www.ParkSeed.com

SITVS
CIRCVLIS
CIRCVN:

Vintage astronomical chart circa 1792 © Getty Images

TERRÆ
COELESTIBVS
DATÆ
Prostant Amstelaedami apud
PETRVM SCHENK,
et GERARDVM VALK.
C. Priv.

ADVENTURES
IN THE
ZODIAC ZONE

WHAT'S BEHIND
THE SUN
AND MOON?

BY BOB BERMAN

Throughout millennia, civilizations have paid great attention to the Moon, Sun, and planets, yes, but also to the stars and constellations behind them—in particular, the zodiac. Those background bodies and patterns matter, but in different ways for astronomers and astrologers. Here's how and why.

THE STELLAR ZOO

As Earth performs its yearly orbit, we view the Sun from a slightly different direction each day. As a result, a stream of background stars parades behind the Sun. Ancient astronomers figured out what lurked behind the Sun on each day of the year. They realized that the Sun's annual circuit never varied and called this solar path the *ecliptic,* because whenever eclipses appeared, they occurred along this imaginary line in the sky. The ecliptic passed through, or in front of, 13 constellations, although most ancient civilizations recognized only 12.

Since the Moon orbits Earth in almost the same flat plane in which we circle the Sun, the Moon also roughly travels along this same celestial road (the deviation is a paltry 5 degrees). All of the planets in our solar system

tably Scorpius, Taurus, and Leo—really do resemble these animals. Others, like Aries, the Ram, require a vivid imagination to envisage.

There are 12 traditional members of the zodiac, but the Sun also spends 18 days every year in front of the stars of Ophiuchus (ah-fee-YOU-kuss), sometimes called the 13th zodiacal constellation. Since the Moon and planets have those slight inclinations in their orbits, they occasionally skirt the edges of a few other star patterns like Ce-

---

THERE ARE 12 TRADITIONAL MEMBERS OF THE ZODIAC, BUT THE SUN ALSO SPENDS 18 DAYS EVERY YEAR IN FRONT OF THE STARS OF OPHIUCHUS, SOMETIMES CALLED THE 13TH ZODIACAL CONSTELLATION.

---

also orbit in pretty much the same flat ring, so they, too, appear against these same stars.

Because the orbits of the Moon and planets are slightly tilted, the ancients conceived of an 18-degree-wide ribbon centered on the ecliptic, wide enough to embrace the paths of all of these bodies. They called this roadway across the sky the *zodiac,* derived from the Greek word for "circle of animals," because more than half of the constellations behind the Sun, Moon, and planets were perceived as animals (e.g., Cancer, the Crab; Taurus, the Bull). Some of these figures—no-

tus, the Whale, and Orion, the Hunter. (This Almanac often gives the positions occupied by the Sun, Moon, and planets. See "Visible Planets" on page 108, as well as "Sky Watch" and "Moon's Astron. Place" on the Left-Hand Calendar Pages, 120–146.)

The zodiacal constellations are different sizes. (The exact boundaries between one constellation and another were not precisely defined until 1930.) Some are huge, some small, and each planet traverses the zodiac path at its own speed. Thus, the amount of time that a celestial body spends in each constellation varies. The Sun lingers for 45 days each year in Virgo but spends only 20 days in

Not Your Grandma's Pain Relief

✓ Smells Better ✓ Works Faster
✓ Lasts Longer ✓ Not Greasy

REAL TIME
Pain Relief®

HEMP Oil Plus

amomile **Arnica** Menth
St. John's Wort **Calendula**
Nutmeg Oil
ch Haze **Wasabi Extra**
riander **MSM** Aloe Ver
Turmeric
permint **Willow Bar**
Emu Oil

Topical Lotion
Net Wt. 4 Fl. Oz. / 120 mL

Real Time Pain Relief is Family Owned and Operated at our core. For 20 years, we have focused on delivering fast acting, Ingredient Based topical pain relief to our valued customers.

HEMP Oil Plus is Real Time Pain Relief's newest pain relieving lotion, and it's made with 19 of Nature's Ingredients including Arnica, Menthol, Turmeric, and of course, Hemp Oil!

HEMP Oil Plus is NOT your Grandma's Pain Relief. It smells great, it isn't greasy, and it doesn't burn. Plus, **HEMP Oil Plus** delivers fast pain relief without the use of harsh chemicals.

"It's so nice to now have a safe way to use hemp oil without worry."
Mabel S. - Jacksonville, FL

Worry-Free Way to Use Hemp Oil: The hemp oil used in **HEMP Oil Plus** is a 100% Pure and Organic extract of Industrial Hemp Seeds, which is legal Nationwide and THC free.

Real Time Pain Relief Products are also available on Amazon.com!

Available at
amazon

Limited Offer!

For a Limited Time,
Old Farmer's Almanac readers can receive a special offer. Just go to the following link for details!

Visit: RTPR.com/OFA

To Order Go To RTPR.com or Call 877-787-7180

FA-HOP-18

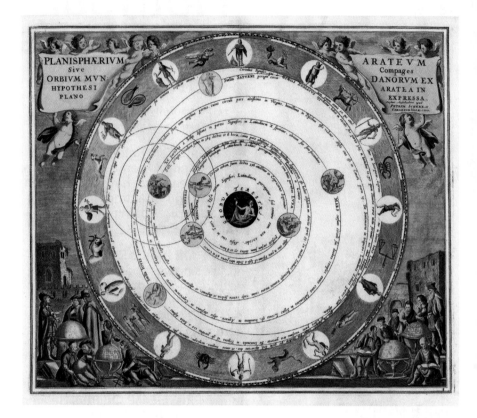

ASTROLOGY'S "SIGNS" EACH OCCUPY 30-DEGREE-WIDE "SLICES" OF SPACE.

Cancer. Mercury changes position rapidly, while Saturn requires almost 30 years to make one full circuit.

THE ASTRONOMER'S VIEW

Today, every serious backyard astronomer can trace out the zodiac, the imaginary ribbon that circles the sky. Watching the sky nightly, modern astronomers can see that the Moon moves rapidly along this path, one Moon diameter per hour. (Remember, the Moon completes a full circuit in just a month.)

On many nights, observers see the zodiac aglow, with the Moon lurking in one part of the sky and planets lighting up other parts. This year, for example, on July 4, we should easily observe the Moon, Mars, and Mercury gathered together in Cancer, Jupiter against the stars of Ophiuchus, and Saturn in Sagittarius.

(continued)

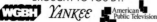

THE ASTROLOGER'S VIEW

Astrologers, too, use the terms "zodiac," "ecliptic," "retrograde motion," and all of the constellation names, except for Scorpius, which astrologers call Scorpio.

Astrologers in India follow the actual constellations of the night sky, but European and American astrology instead uses imaginary signs that do not correspond with the visible star patterns. Moreover, astrology's "signs" each occupy 30-degree-wide "slices" of space, whereas, as noted, the actual star patterns' sizes vary greatly. Thus, any night's *astrological* location of Jupiter will not match Jupiter's actual *(astronomical)* location in the night sky—the area at which you might aim a telescope.

Consider this: On June 21, the day of the summer solstice, astrology places the Sun in the zodiac sign of Cancer, which explains why all places on Earth where the Sun is directly overhead on that day are said to lie on the Tropic of Cancer. A few thousand years ago, the actual constellations and the astrological signs more or less coincided, although never exactly. Today, due to Earth's axis having a 26,000-year-long wobble, the star pattern behind the Sun on the solstice is at the Gemini–Taurus boundary. It is nowhere near Cancer.

So it is that the Moon's Place given in the Almanac's Left-Hand Calendar Pages (120–146) does not coincide with its place in the "Secrets of the Zodiac" pages (228–229). The Calendar Pages are astronomical; the "Secrets of the Zodiac" are astrological. This seeming discrepancy is never a mistake. It's the ancient legacy of very different ways of perceiving the heavens. ∎

Bob Berman, the *Old Farmer's Almanac* astronomy editor, is the director of Overlook Observatory in Woodstock and Storm King Observatory in Cornwall, both in New York.

RETROGRADE REVISITED

The Sun and planets move rather slowly against the background stars. A totally separate and much faster sky-motion is the daily whooshing of stars and planets alike, as they rise, cross the sky toward the west, and then set—the effect of being viewed from rapidly spinning (rotating) Earth.

Because everything in the solar system orbits in the same direction, the Sun, Moon, and planets are all usually observed to move eastward along the zodiac. The only exceptions are when the speedy innermost planets Mercury and Venus are on the side of their orbits nearest to Earth; they then appear to move backward—in what is called "retrograde motion"—for a short time. (Think of a truck seemingly moving backward as we pass it on the highway.) Similarly, whenever Earth passes the slower outer planets, they too temporarily appear to travel in retrograde.

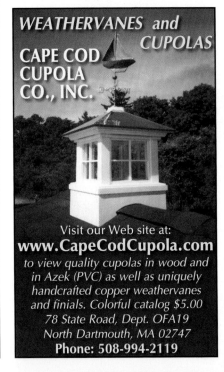

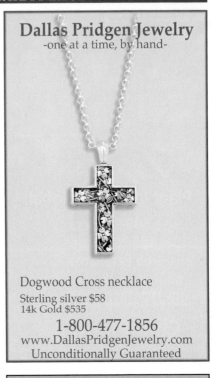

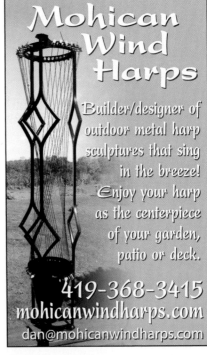

WINTER 2018–19

These weather maps show the winter (November through March) and summer (June through August) predictions for Canada, including regions 1 to 5 (pages 215–220) and the General Weather Forecast (opposite). Forecast terms here represent deviations from the normals; see page 212.

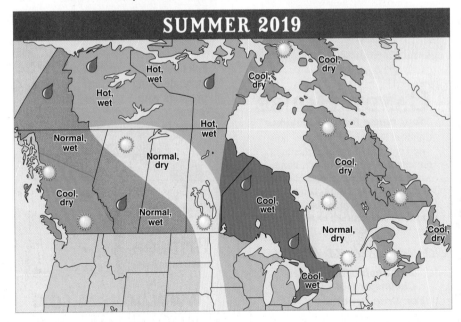

SUMMER 2019

THE GENERAL WEATHER REPORT AND FORECAST

FOR REGIONAL FORECASTS, SEE PAGES 215-220.

W hat's shaping the weather? Solar Cycle 24, the smallest in more than 100 years, is well into its declining phase after reaching double peaks in late 2011 and early 2014. As solar activity continues to decline from these low peaks toward the minima in 2019, we expect below-normal winter temperatures in most of the nation, except for Pacific Canada and the southern two-thirds of Ontario, where temperatures will be normal, and Atlantic Canada, where temperatures will be above normal, on average. Snowfall generally will be above normal everywhere.

Important factors in the coming weather patterns include a weak El Niño, the Atlantic Multidecadal Oscillation (AMO) in a continued warm phase, the North Atlantic Oscillation (NAO) in a neutral phase, and the Pacific Decadal Oscillation (PDO) in the early stages of its warm cycle. Oscillations are linked ocean–atmosphere patterns that influence the weather over periods of weeks to years.

WINTER 2018-19 Temperatures will be normal in Pacific Canada and the southern two-thirds of Ontario and above normal, on average, in Atlantic Canada, but colder than normal elsewhere. Nearly all of Canada will have above-normal snowfall. much of Nunavut and near or below normal elsewhere. Rainfall will be below normal in Atlantic Canada, southern Quebec, a swath from southern Manitoba up through northern Alberta, and southern British Columbia and above normal elsewhere.

SPRING temperatures will be near or below normal across the entire Commonwealth. Precipitation will be below normal in Atlantic Canada and above normal elsewhere.

SUMMER temperatures will be warmer than normal in the Northwest Territories and

AUTUMN temperatures will be above normal in the Prairies, British Columbia, and the Yukon, and below normal elsewhere. Precipitation will be below normal in the Prairies, British Columbia, and western Quebec and above normal elsewhere.

How Accurate Was Our Forecast Last Winter?

O ur forecasts were 79% accurate in their predictions of the change in temperature and precipitation from the previous winter, nearly matching our 80% historical accuracy rate. Our temperature forecasts were 71% accurate, missing only in the Prairies and Yukon, while our precipitation forecasts were 86% accurate, missing only in Southern Ontario. Our snowfall forecasts were correct in most of Canada, with less snow than we forecast in the northern parts of the Prairies and British Columbia and more snow in the Northwest Territories.

As shown on the table below using one representative city from each region, the average difference between our winter-season temperature forecasts and the actual temperatures was 1.2 degrees C.

REGION/ CITY	Nov.–Mar. Temp Departure From Normal (degrees)		REGION/ CITY	Nov.–Mar. Temp Departure From Normal (degrees)	
	PREDICTED	ACTUAL		PREDICTED	ACTUAL
1. Saint John's, NL	0.2	1.0	5. Vancouver, BC	0.2	0.7
2. Montreal, QC	0.2	1.8	6. Watson Lake, YT	1.6	–1.4
3. Toronto, ON	1.0	0.5	7. Yellowknife, NT	1.8	0.8
4. Regina, SK	0.6	–0.4			

THE OLD
FARMER'S ALMANAC

Established in 1792 and published every year thereafter
ROBERT B. THOMAS, *founder* (1766–1846)

YANKEE PUBLISHING INC.

EDITORIAL AND PUBLISHING OFFICES
P.O. Box 520, 1121 Main Street, Dublin, NH 03444
Phone: 603-563-8111 • Fax: 603-563-8252

EDITOR *(13th since 1792):* Janice Stillman
ART DIRECTOR: Colleen Quinnell
MANAGING EDITOR: Jack Burnett
SENIOR EDITORS: Sarah Perreault, Heidi Stonehill
EDITORIAL ASSISTANTS: Tim Clark,
Benjamin Kilbride
WEATHER GRAPHICS AND CONSULTATION:
AccuWeather, Inc.

V.P., NEW MEDIA AND PRODUCTION:
Paul Belliveau
PRODUCTION DIRECTORS:
Susan Gross, David Ziarnowski
SENIOR PRODUCTION ARTISTS:
Rachel Kipka, Jennifer Freeman, Janet Selle

WEB SITE: ALMANAC.CA

DIGITAL EDITOR: Catherine Boeckmann
DIGITAL ASSISTANT EDITOR: Christopher Burnett
NEW MEDIA DESIGNERS: Lou S. Eastman, Amy O'Brien
E-COMMERCE DIRECTOR: Alan Henning
PROGRAMMING: Peter Rukavina

CONTACT US

We welcome your questions and comments about articles in and topics for this Almanac. Mail all editorial correspondence to Editor, The Old Farmer's Almanac, P.O. Box 520, Dublin, NH 03444-0520; fax us at 603-563-8252; or contact us through Almanac.ca/Feedback. *The Old Farmer's Almanac* can not accept responsibility for unsolicited manuscripts and will not acknowledge any hard-copy queries or manuscripts that do not include a stamped and addressed return envelope.

All printing inks used in this edition of *The Old Farmer's Almanac* are soy-based. This product is recyclable. Consult local recycling regulations for the right way to do it.

Thank you for buying this Almanac! We hope that you find it "useful, with a pleasant degree of humor." Thanks, too, to everyone who had a hand in it, including advertisers, distributors, printers, and sales and delivery people.

OUR CONTRIBUTORS

Bob Berman, our astronomy editor, is the director of Overlook Observatory in Woodstock and Storm King Observatory in Cornwall, both in New York. In 1976, he founded the Catskill Astronomical Society. Bob has led many aurora and eclipse expeditions, venturing as far as the Arctic and Antarctic.

Julia Shipley, a journalist and poet, wrote the Farmer's Calendar essays that appear in this edition. She raises animals and vegetables on a small farm in Northern Vermont. Her recordings of the essays are available free at Almanac.ca/Podcast.

Tim Clark, a retired English teacher from New Hampshire, has composed the weather doggerel on the Calendar Pages since 1980.

Bethany E. Cobb, our astronomer, is an Associate Professor of Honors and Physics at George Washington University. She conducts research on gamma-ray bursts and specializes in teaching astronomy and physics to non–science majoring students. When she is not scanning the sky, she enjoys rock climbing, figure skating, and reading science fiction.

Celeste Longacre, our astrologer, often refers to astrology as "a study of timing, and timing is everything." A New Hampshire native, she has been a practicing astrologer for more than 25 years. Her book, *Celeste's Garden Delights* (2015), is available for sale on her Web site, www.celestelongacre.com.

Michael Steinberg, our meteorologist, has been forecasting weather for the Almanac since 1996. In addition to college degrees in atmospheric science and meteorology, he brings a lifetime of experience to the task: He began predicting weather when he attended the only high school in the world with weather Teletypes and radar.

THE OLD
FARMER'S ALMANAC

Established in 1792 and published every year thereafter

ROBERT B. THOMAS, *founder* (1766–1846)

YANKEE PUBLISHING INC.
P.O. Box 520, 1121 Main Street, Dublin, NH 03444
Phone: 603-563-8111 • Fax: 603-563-8252

PUBLISHER *(23rd since 1792):* Sherin Pierce
EDITOR IN CHIEF: Judson D. Hale Sr.

FOR DISPLAY ADVERTISING RATES
Go to Almanac.ca/AdvertisingInfo or
call 800-895-9265, ext. 109

Stephanie Bernbach-Crowe • 914-827-0015
Steve Hall • 800-736-1100, ext. 320

FOR CLASSIFIED ADVERTISING
Cindy Levine, RJ Media • 212-986-0016

AD PRODUCTION COORDINATOR:
Janet Selle • 800-895-9265, ext. 168

PUBLIC RELATIONS
Quinn/Brein • 206-842-8922
Ginger Vaughan
ginger@quinnbrein.com

CONSUMER MAIL ORDERS
Call 800-ALMANAC (800-256-2622)
or go to Almanac.ca/Shop

RETAIL SALES
Stacey Korpi • 800-895-9265, ext. 160
Janice Edson, ext. 126

DISTRIBUTORS
NATIONAL: Curtis Circulation Company
New Milford, NJ
BOOKSTORE: Thomas Allen & Son Ltd.
Markham, ON

Old Farmer's Almanac publications are available for sales promotions or premiums. Contact Beacon Promotions, info@beaconpromotions.com.

YANKEE PUBLISHING INCORPORATED

Jamie Trowbridge, *President;* Judson D. Hale Sr., *Senior Vice President;* Paul Belliveau, Jody Bugbee, Judson D. Hale Jr., Brook Holmberg, Sherin Pierce, *Vice Presidents.*

The Old Farmer's Almanac/Yankee Publishing Inc. assumes no responsibility for claims made by advertisers or failure by its advertisers to deliver any goods or services advertised herein. Publication of any advertisement by The Old Farmer's Almanac/Yankee Publishing Inc. is not an endorsement of the product or service advertised therein.
PRINTED IN U.S.A.

"To you, it's the perfect lift chair. To me, it's the best sleep chair I've ever had."

— J. Fitzgerald, VA

Sit up, lie down — and anywhere in between!

Easy-to-use remote for massage, heat, recline and lift

Our Perfect Sleep Chair® is just the chair to do it all. It's a chair, true – the finest of lift chairs – but this chair is so much more! It's designed to provide total comfort and relaxation not found in other chairs. It can't be beat for comfortable, long-term sitting, TV viewing, relaxed reclining and – yes! – peaceful sleep. Our chair's recline technology allows you to pause the chair in an infinite number of positions, including the Trendelenburg position and the zero gravity position where your body experiences a minimum of internal and external stresses. You'll love the other benefits, too: It helps with correct spinal alignment, promotes back pressure relief, and encourages better posture to prevent back and muscle pain.

And there's more! The overstuffed, oversized biscuit style back and unique seat design will cradle you in comfort. Generously filled, wide armrests provide enhanced arm support when sitting or reclining. The high and low heat settings along with the multiple massage settings, can provide a soothing relaxation you might get at a spa – just imagine getting all that in a lift chair! It even has a battery backup in case of a power outage. Shipping charge includes white glove delivery. Professionals will deliver the chair to the exact spot in your home where you want it, unpack it, inspect it, test it, position it, and even carry the packaging away! You get your choice of fabrics and colors – **Call now!**

This lift chair puts you safely on your feet!

The Perfect Sleep Chair®
1-888-602-3060

Please mention code 109424 when ordering.

© 2018 *first*STREET for Boomers and Beyond, Inc.

46471

ECLIPSES

There will be five eclipses in 2019, three of the Sun and two of the Moon. Solar eclipses are visible only in certain areas and require eye protection to be viewed safely. Lunar eclipses are technically visible from the entire night side of Earth, but during a penumbral eclipse, the dimming of the Moon's illumination is slight. See the **Astronomical Glossary, page 110,** for explanations of the different types of eclipses.

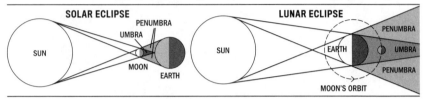

JANUARY 5: PARTIAL ECLIPSE OF THE SUN. This eclipse is visible from North America only in westernmost Alaska. (It is also visible from northeastern China, Mongolia, Japan, eastern Russia, and northern Micronesia.) In Bethel, Alaska, for example, the eclipse will begin at 3:25 P.M. AKST, reach a maximum (obscuring about 60% of the Sun) at 4:51 P.M. AKST, and end at 6:16 P.M. AKST, with the Sun being very low on the horizon for the entire duration of the partial eclipse.

JANUARY 20-21: TOTAL ECLIPSE OF THE MOON. This eclipse is visible from North America. The Moon will enter the penumbra at 9:35 P.M. EST on January 20 (6:25 P.M. PST on January 20) and leave the penumbra at 2:50 A.M. EST on January 21 (11:50 P.M. PST on January 20).

JULY 2: TOTAL ECLIPSE OF THE SUN. This eclipse is not visible from North America. (It is visible only from eastern Oceania and most of South America.)

JULY 16-17: PARTIAL ECLIPSE OF THE MOON. This eclipse is not visible from North America. (It is visible only from Australasia, most of Asia, Africa, all of Europe except for northernmost Scandinavia, and most of South America.)

DECEMBER 26: ANNULAR ECLIPSE OF THE SUN. This eclipse is not visible from North America. (It is visible only from the Middle East, northeastern Africa, Asia except for northern and eastern Russia, northern and western Australia,

Micronesia, and the Solomon Islands.)

TRANSIT OF MERCURY. Mercury will pass directly between Earth and the Sun on November 11. Because Mercury is so small relative to the observed disk of the Sun, the transit is not visible with just a filter over the naked eye—appropriately filtered telescopes or binoculars are necessary for viewing. The transit will be visible from most of North America from 7:35 A.M. EST to 1:04 P.M. EST (4:35 A.M. PST to 10:04 A.M. PST; it will be in progress at sunrise in mid– to western North America).

THE MOON'S PATH

The Moon's path across the sky changes with the seasons. Full Moons are very high in the sky (at midnight) between November and February and very low in the sky between May and July.

FULL-MOON DATES (ET)

	2019	2020	2021	2022	2023
JAN.	21	10	28	17	6
FEB.	19	9	27	16	5
MAR.	20	9	28	18	7
APR.	19	7	26	16	6
MAY	18	7	26	16	5
JUNE	17	5	24	14	3
JULY	16	5	23	13	3
AUG.	15	3	22	11	1 & 30
SEPT.	14	2	20	10	29
OCT.	13	1 & 31	20	9	28
NOV.	12	30	19	8	27
DEC.	12	29	18	7	26

Leading Acid Reflux Pill Becomes an Anti-Aging Phenomenon

Clinical studies show breakthrough acid reflux treatment also helps maintain vital health and helps protect users from the serious conditions that accompany aging such as fatigue and poor cardiovascular health

"ACCIDENTAL" ANTI-AGING BREAKTHROUGH: Originally developed for digestive issues, AloeCure not only ends digestion nightmares... it revitalizes the entire body. Some are calling it the greatest accidental discovery in decades.

Stewart Blum
Health Correspondent

Seattle, WA – A clinical study on a leading acid reflux pill shows that its key ingredient relieves digestive symptoms while suppressing the inflammation that contributes to premature aging in men and women.

And, if consumer sales are any indication of a product's effectiveness, this 'acid reflux pill turned anti-aging phenomenon' is nothing short of a miracle.

Sold under the brand name AloeCure, it was already backed by clinical data documenting its ability to provide all day and night relief from heartburn, acid reflux, constipation, irritable bowel, gas, bloating, and more.

But soon doctors started reporting some incredible results…

"With AloeCure, my patients started reporting less joint pain, more energy, better sleep, and even less stress and better skin, hair, and nails" explains Dr. Liza Leal; a leading integrative health specialist and company spokesperson.

AloeCure contains an active ingredient that helps improve digestion by acting as a natural acid-buffer that improves the pH balance of your stomach.

Scientists now believe that this acid imbalance is what contributes to painful inflammation throughout the rest of the body.

The daily allowance of AloeCure has shown to calm this inflammation which is why AloeCure is so effective.

Relieving other stressful symptoms related to GI health like pain, bloating, fatigue, cramping, constipation, diarrhea, heartburn, and nausea.

Now, backed with new clinical studies, AloeCure is being recommended by doctors everywhere to help improve digestion, calm painful inflammation, soothe joint pain, and even reduce the appearance of wrinkles – helping patients to look and feel decades younger.

FIX YOUR GUT & FIGHT INFLAMMATION

Since hitting the market, sales for AloeCure have taken off and there are some very good reasons why.

To start, the clinical studies have been impressive. Participants taking the active ingredient in AloeCure saw a stunning 100% improvement in digestive symptoms, which includes fast and lasting relief from reflux.

Users also experienced higher energy levels and endurance, relief from chronic discomfort and better sleep. Some even reported healthier looking skin, hair, and nails.

Doctors are calling AloeCure the greatest accidental health discovery in decades!

EXCITING RESULTS FROM PATIENTS

To date over 5 million bottles of AloeCure have been sold, and the community seeking non-pharma therapy for their GI health continues to grow.

According to Dr. Leal, her patients are absolutely thrilled with their results and are often shocked by how fast it works.

"For the first time in years, they are free from concerns about their digestion and almost every other aspect of their health," says Dr. Leal, "and I recommend it to everyone who wants to improve GI health

without resorting to drugs, surgery, or OTC medications."

With so much positive feedback, it's easy to see why the community of believers is growing and sales for the new pill are soaring.

THE SCIENCE BEHIND ALOECURE

AloeCure is a pill that's taken just once daily. The pill is small. Easy to swallow. There are no harmful side effects and it does not require a prescription.

The active ingredient is a rare Aloe Vera component known as acemannan.

Made from of 100% organic Aloe Vera, AloeCure uses a proprietary process that results in the highest quality, most bio-available levels of acemannan known to exist.

According to Dr. Leal and several of her colleagues, improving the pH balance of your stomach and restoring gut health is the key to revitalizing your entire body.

When your digestive system isn't healthy, it causes unwanted stress on your immune system, which results in inflammation in the rest of the body.

The recommended daily allowance of acemannan in AloeCure has been proven to support digestive health, and calm painful inflammation without side effects or drugs.

This would explain why so many users are experiencing impressive results so quickly.

HOW TO GET ALOECURE

In order to get the word out about AloeCure, the company is offering special introductory discounts to all who call. Discounts will automatically be applied to all callers, but don't wait. This offer may not last forever. Call toll-free: 1-800-547-0173

THESE STATEMENTS HAVE NOT BEEN EVALUATED BY THE FDA. THESE PRODUCTS ARE NOT INTENDED TO DIAGNOSE, TREAT, CURE OR PREVENT ANY DISEASE. RESULTS MAY VARY. OFFER NOT AVAILABLE TO RESIDENTS OF IOWA

BRIGHT STARS

TRANSIT TIMES

This table shows the time (ET) and altitude of a star as it transits the meridian (i.e., reaches its highest elevation while passing over the horizon's south point) at Ottawa on the dates shown. The transit time on any other date differs from that of the nearest date listed by approximately 4 minutes per day. To find the time of a star's transit for your location, convert its time at Ottawa using Key Letter C **(see Time Corrections, page 238).**

STAR	CONSTELLATION	MAGNITUDE	JAN. 1	MAR. 1	MAY 1	JULY 1	SEPT. 1	NOV. 1	ALTITUDE (DEGREES)
Altair	Aquila	0.8	**1:10**	9:18	6:18	2:18	**10:11**	**6:11**	53.3
Deneb	Cygnus	1.3	**2:00**	10:08	7:09	3:09	**11:01**	**7:01**	89.8
Fomalhaut	Psc. Aus.	1.2	**4:17**	**12:25**	9:25	5:25	1:21	**9:17**	14.8
Algol	Perseus	2.2	**8:27**	**4:35**	**1:35**	9:35	5:31	1:31	85.5
Aldebaran	Taurus	0.9	**9:54**	**6:02**	**3:02**	11:02	6:59	2:59	61.1
Rigel	Orion	0.1	**10:32**	**6:40**	**3:40**	11:41	7:37	3:37	36.4
Capella	Auriga	0.1	**10:35**	**6:43**	**3:43**	11:43	7:40	3:40	90.6
Bellatrix	Orion	1.6	**10:43**	**6:51**	**3:51**	11:51	7:48	3:48	51.0
Betelgeuse	Orion	var. 0.4	**11:13**	**7:21**	**4:21**	**12:21**	8:18	4:18	52.0
Sirius	Can. Maj.	−1.4	12:07	**8:11**	**5:11**	**1:11**	9:07	5:07	28.0
Procyon	Can. Min.	0.4	1:01	**9:05**	**6:05**	**2:05**	10:01	6:02	50.0
Pollux	Gemini	1.2	1:07	**9:11**	**6:11**	**2:11**	10:08	6:08	72.7
Regulus	Leo	1.4	3:29	**11:33**	**8:34**	**4:34**	**12:30**	8:30	56.7
Spica	Virgo	var. 1.0	6:46	2:54	**11:50**	**7:50**	**3:46**	11:46	33.8
Arcturus	Boötes	−0.1	7:36	3:44	12:44	**8:40**	**4:37**	**12:37**	64.1
Antares	Scorpius	var. 0.9	9:49	5:58	2:58	**10:54**	**6:50**	**2:50**	18.3
Vega	Lyra	0	11:56	8:04	5:04	1:05	**8:57**	**4:57**	83.4

Table header: **TIME OF TRANSIT (ET)** — **BOLD = P.M.** LIGHT = A.M.

RISE AND SET TIMES

To find the time of a star's rising at Ottawa on any date, subtract the interval shown at right from the star's transit time on that date; add the interval to find the star's setting time. To find the rising and setting times for your city, convert the Ottawa transit times above using the Key Letter shown at right before applying the interval **(see Time Corrections, page 238).** Deneb, Algol, Capella, and Vega are circumpolar stars—they never set but appear to circle the celestial north pole.

STAR	INTERVAL (H. M.)	RISING KEY	DIR.*	SETTING KEY	DIR.*
Altair	6 39	B	EbN	D	WbN
Fomalhaut	3 43	E	SE	A	SW
Aldebaran	7 13	B	ENE	D	WNW
Rigel	5 29	D	EbS	B	WbS
Bellatrix	6 29	B	EbN	D	WbN
Betelgeuse	6 33	B	EbN	D	WbN
Sirius	4 53	D	ESE	B	WSW
Procyon	6 24	B	EbN	D	WbN
Pollux	8 15	A	NE	E	NW
Regulus	6 53	B	EbN	D	WbN
Spica	5 17	D	EbS	B	WbS
Arcturus	7 26	A	ENE	E	WNW
Antares	4 03	E	SEbE	A	SWbW

*b = "by"

New Arthritis Painkiller Works on Contact and Numbs the Pain in Minutes

New cream works faster and is more targeted than oral medications. Key ingredients penetrate the skin within minutes to relieve joint arthritis pain. Users report significant immediate relief.

Apeaz™: Quick Acting Pain and Arthritis Cream is Now Available Without a Prescription

By Robert Ward
Associated Health Press

BOSTON – Innovus Pharmaceuticals has introduced a new arthritis pain relief treatment that works in minutes.

Sold under the brand name Apeaz™, the new pain relief cream numbs the nerves right below the skin.

When applied to an arthritic joint, or a painful area on the body, it delivers immediate relief that lasts for hours and hours.

The powerful painkilling effect is created by the creams active ingredients, three special medical compounds.

Anesthetics are used in hospitals during surgery. They block nerve signals from the brain so that patients don't feel pain and they work fast.

The anesthetic found in Apeaz™ is the strongest available without a prescription.

The cream form allows users to directly target their area of pain. It works where it is applied. The company says this is why the product is so effective and fast acting.

"Users can expect to start feeling relief immediately after applying," explains Dr. Bassam Damaj, President of Innovus Pharmaceuticals.

"There will be a pleasant warming sensation that is followed by a cool, soothing one. This is how you know that the active ingredients have reached the affected joint and tissue."

Works In Minutes

For arthritis suffers, Apeaz™ offers impressive advantages over traditional medications. The most obvious is how quickly it relieves pain discomfort.

The cream contains the maximum approved OTC dose of a top anesthetic, which penetrates the skin in a matter of minutes to numb the area that's in pain. This relief lasts for several hours.

Published pre-clinical animal studies have shown that the ingredients in Apeaz™ can also prevent further bone and cartilage destruction.

There are also no negative side effects like from oral medication. Apeaz™ delivers its ingredients through the skin. Oral medications are absorbed in the digestive tract. Overtime, the chemicals in pills can tear the delicate lining of the stomach, causing ulcers and bleeding.

When compared to other arthritis medications, Apeaz™ is a fraction of the cost. At less than $2 a day, the cream quickly is becoming a household name.

Those with terrible arthritis in their hands and fingers, love how easy Apeaz™ is to open. The jar fits in the palm of the hand, which makes it much easier to use.

Instant Pain Relief Without a Prescription

Many Apeaz™ users report significant improvements in daily aches and pain. Many more report increased flexibility and less stiffness. They are moving with less pain for the first time in years, like Henry Esber, an early user of Apeaz™.

"I've tried more pills than I can count. I've also had a handful of cortisone shots. Nothing is as effective as this product. With Apeaz™, I get relief right away. I rub a little on my hands. It keeps the pain away. It also prevents the pain from getting really bad. It's completely changed my life."

How It Works

Apeaz™ contains the highest, non-prescription OTC dose of a medical compound that fights pain on contact. When applied to the skin it goes to work within minutes by penetrating right to the source of your pain, numbing the nerve endings.

"This is why Apeaz™ is so effective for people with arthritis pain. It reduces pain while adding an additional potential layer of joint support," explains Damaj.

How to Get Apeaz™

In order to get the word out about Apeaz™, the company is offering special introductory discounts to all who call. Discounts will automatically be applied to all callers, but don't wait. This offer may not last forever. Call toll-free: 1-800-411-8480.

THE TWILIGHT ZONE/METEOR SHOWERS

Twilight is the time when the sky is partially illuminated preceding sunrise and again following sunset. The ranges of twilight are defined according to the Sun's position below the horizon. **Civil twilight** occurs when the Sun's center is between the horizon and 6 degrees below the horizon (visually, the horizon is clearly defined). **Nautical twilight** occurs when the center is between 6 and 12 degrees below the horizon (the horizon is distinct). **Astronomical twilight** occurs when the center is between 12 and 18 degrees below the horizon (sky illumination is imperceptible). When the center is at 18 degrees (**dawn** or **dark**) or below, there is no illumination.

LENGTH OF ASTRONOMICAL TWILIGHT (HOURS AND MINUTES)									
LATITUDE	JAN. 1- APR. 10	APR. 11- MAY 2	MAY 3- MAY 14	MAY 15- MAY 25	MAY 26- JULY 22	JULY 23- AUG. 3	AUG. 4- AUG. 14	AUG. 15- SEPT. 5	SEPT. 6- DEC. 31
37°N to 42°N	1 33	1 39	1 47	1 52	1 59	1 52	1 47	1 39	1 33
43°N to 47°N	1 42	1 51	2 02	2 13	2 27	2 13	2 02	1 51	1 42
48°N to 49°N	1 50	2 04	2 22	2 42	–	2 42	2 22	2 04	1 33
50°N to 55°N	1 54	2 15	2 52	3 25	–	3 11	2 37	2 10	1 53
56°N to 60°N	2 12	3 04	–	–	–	–	–	2 46	2 11

TO DETERMINE THE LENGTH OF TWILIGHT: The length of twilight changes with latitude and the time of year. See the **Time Corrections, page 238,** to find the latitude of your city or the city nearest you. Use that figure in the chart above with the appropriate date to calculate the length of twilight in your area.

TO DETERMINE ARRIVAL OF DAWN OR DARK: Calculate the sunrise/sunset times for your locality using the instructions in **How to Use This Almanac, page 116.**

Subtract the length of twilight from the time of sunrise to determine when dawn breaks. Add the length of twilight to the time of sunset to determine when dark descends.

EXAMPLE:
OTTAWA, ONT. (LATITUDE 45°25')

Sunrise, August 1	5:47 A.M. ET
Length of twilight	– 2 13
Dawn breaks	3:34 A.M.
Sunset, August 1	8:31 P.M. ET
Length of twilight	+2 13
Dark descends	10:44 P.M.

PRINCIPAL METEOR SHOWERS

SHOWER	BEST VIEWING	POINT OF ORIGIN	DATE OF MAXIMUM*	NO. PER HOUR**	ASSOCIATED COMET
Quadrantid	Predawn	N	Jan. 4	25	–
Lyrid	Predawn	S	Apr. 22	10	Thatcher
Eta Aquarid	Predawn	SE	May 4	10	Halley
Delta Aquarid	Predawn	S	July 30	10	–
Perseid	Predawn	NE	Aug. 11-13	50	Swift-Tuttle
Draconid	Late evening	NW	Oct. 9	6	Giacobini–Zinner
Orionid	Predawn	S	Oct. 21-22	15	Halley
Taurid	Late evening	S	Nov. 9	3	Encke
Leonid	Predawn	S	Nov. 17-18	10	Tempel-Tuttle
Andromedid	Late evening	S	Nov. 25-27	5	Biela
Geminid	All night	NE	Dec. 13-14	75	–
Ursid	Predawn	N	Dec. 22	5	Tuttle

*May vary by 1 or 2 days   **In a moonless, rural sky   **Bold** = most prominent

New Pill Can Relieve the Need for Adult Diapers and Padded Underwear

According to Dr. Seipel, Leaking, Squirming, Squeezing, and Night Time Bathroom Trips... Even Accidents Can Now be a Thing of the Past!

NEW YORK, NEW YORK — If life isn't hard enough, now you have to worry about making it to the bathroom in time. The feeling of your bladder bursting and the down right panic of "not making it" in time can be absolutely overwhelming.

Don't even dare to laugh, cough or sneeze at the "wrong" time and when did you start to become scared to take a big sip of tea, coffee or water? You're not alone in your battle to control your bladder. According to The National Institute of Health, as many as 33 million Americans are affected by bladder control issues described above.

The Family Secret Even the Family Doesn't Know

"Most people who have overactive bladders choose to keep their problem a secret," says Dr. Tracey Seipel, a longtime clinician who is one of the world's leading experts in natural urological healthcare.

"They don't even tell their spouse or families about it. It affects their lives in every way, influencing where they go, and even what they will wear in case they have an accident."

A 100% natural, drug-free aid developed by Dr. Seipel is now available in a remarkable, fast-acting natural formula called UriVarx™ featuring urox. This sophisticated patented herbal compound has been shown in clinical studies to help improve UriVarx™ with reductions in bladder frequency, nocturia (having to urinate at night), urgency, and bladder discomfort, sometimes in as little as two weeks.

Dr. Seipel's formula has made a believer out of 45-year-old, mother of three, Brandy W., from Brisbane, Australia. A friend told her about Dr. Seipel's formula. "I was finding that although I felt I needed to urinate, I wasn't as desperate to run to

the toilet. Now, when I get up in the morning," she adds, "I'm able to make the coffee and even have a cup before needing to go, which is a great improvement!"

How Does It Work?

"UriVarx™ helps support bladder health by revitalizing bladder tone and function, and by helping support the kidney. UriVarx™ promotes normal urinary frequency, and reduces urgency, nocturia and those embarrassing, away-from-home bladder accidents," says Dr. Seipel. "The compound invigorates the tone of the bladder wall, assisting a healthy level of firmness by enhancing the bladder's muscular elasticity. This reduces the frequent urge to urinate."

Positive Clinical Trial

This natural, drug-free UriVarx™ formula has performed well in a clinical study. Thirty days later 77% of participants were experiencing benefits. Results like these are not surprising to Dr. Seipel who single-handedly pioneered the bladder care category in the early 2000's, receiving an award from the prestigious US Nutrition Business Journal for her work.

Her patented formula consisting of select, synergistically paired botanicals like Crateva nurvala, Equisetum arvense and Lindera aggregata, was 15 years in the making.

No More Diapers

Insiders in the adult diaper industry are keeping a close eye on Dr. Seipel's bladder support breakthrough because of people like 78-year-old retired teacher, Glenda B. from Gold Coast, Australia.

Glenda wore adult diapers every day to guard against accidents. "My bladder

Finally a clinically proven pill solution to ease all your bladder problems, without a prescription

capacity was good but the leakage and accidents would occur without warning." Since Glenda discovered Dr. Seipel's UriVarx™ formula, you won't find her shopping in the adult diaper section of the store anymore.

Prostate or Bladder? Hard to Tell

Many men confuse the symptoms of overactive bladder syndrome with prostate woes. Dr. Seipel explains, "Prostate enlargement restricts urine flow. The bladder compensates for this by trying harder and harder to push the urine out." As bladder pressure increases, so does instances of urinary frequency and urgency. Long after a man's prostate woes are relieved, he may still experience the same symptoms thanks to his now-overactive bladder.

"It's a his-and-her formula," she smiles. David M., age 46, can attest to this. "I was having to go to the toilet every hour or so and I had to go to the toilet at least four times per night."

How to Get UriVarx™

If you're ready to alleviate your go-now urination urges, and if you are looking for the confidence and security that a healthy bladder can bring to your life, here's your risk-free opportunity.

Experience the life-changing effect UriVarx™ can have, and get a special introductory discount – **Call Toll-Free: 1-800-736-4601.**

THE VISIBLE PLANETS

Listed here for Ottawa are viewing suggestions for and the rise and set times (ET) of Venus, Mars, Jupiter, and Saturn on specific days each month, as well as when it is best to view Mercury. Approximate rise and set times for other days can be found by interpolation. Use the Key Letters at the right of each listing to convert the times for other localities (see pages 116 and 238).

FOR ALL PLANET RISE AND SET TIMES BY POSTAL CODE, VISIT ALMANAC.CA/ASTRONOMY.

VENUS

The cloud-covered planet starts 2019 at its brightest of the entire year, dominating the predawn east. It gets lower and less luminous thereafter, yet remains visible throughout winter and most of spring. It's low starting in May, but can be glimpsed before dawn in July. Its superior conjunction behind the Sun occurs on August 14, after which it can be seen low in the west 40 minutes after sunset in late September. A month later, Venus is an easier viewing target, and in November and December it becomes even more striking as it gets higher and brighter. It's near the Moon on April 2, June 1, and December 28; meets Jupiter from November 23 to 25; and joins Saturn on December 10 and 11.

Jan. 1	rise	3:51	D	Apr. 1	rise	5:38	D	July 1	rise	4:27	A	Oct. 1	set	7:15	B
Jan. 11	rise	4:03	E	Apr. 11	rise	5:26	C	July 11	rise	4:40	A	Oct. 11	set	7:02	B
Jan. 21	rise	4:17	E	Apr. 21	rise	5:13	C	July 21	rise	5:00	A	Oct. 21	set	6:52	B
Feb. 1	rise	4:32	E	May 1	rise	4:59	C	Aug. 1	rise	5:26	A	Nov. 1	set	6:45	A
Feb. 11	rise	4:44	E	May 11	rise	4:46	B	Aug. 11	rise	5:52	B	Nov. 11	set	5:45	A
Feb. 21	rise	4:51	E	May 21	rise	4:34	B	Aug. 21	set	8:11	D	Nov. 21	set	5:52	A
Mar. 1	rise	4:54	E	June 1	rise	4:24	B	Sept. 1	set	7:58	D	Dec. 1	set	6:06	A
Mar. 11	rise	5:53	D	June 11	rise	4:20	A	Sept. 11	set	7:44	C	Dec. 11	set	6:26	A
Mar. 21	rise	5:48	D	June 21	rise	4:20	A	Sept. 21	set	7:29	C	Dec. 21	set	6:51	A
												Dec. 31	set	7:17	B

MARS

Mars has an off-year in 2019, with no opposition. The Red Planet is highest and brightest on the year's first day as a zero-magnitude "star" in Pisces, high in the south at nightfall with a tiny 7-arcsecond disk for telescope users. Sinking lower in the west, Mars enters Aries in mid-February, Taurus in late March, and Gemini in mid-May. It's lost in solar glare for most of the summer, in conjunction with the Sun on September 2, and low in the October morning sky. Mars is above the Moon on January 12, February 9 and 10, April 8, and May 7. It meets Mercury from June 12 to 22 and is near Virgo's blue star Spica from November 1 to 17. Mars is just to the right of Uranus from February 10 to 12 and above it from February 13 to 16.

Jan. 1	set	11:23	C	Apr. 1	set	11:55	E	July 1	set	10:10	E	Oct. 1	rise	6:09	C
Jan. 11	set	11:20	C	Apr. 11	set	11:50	E	July 11	set	9:50	E	Oct. 11	rise	6:03	C
Jan. 21	set	11:17	D	Apr. 21	set	11:44	E	July 21	set	9:28	E	Oct. 21	rise	5:58	C
Feb. 1	set	11:13	D	May 1	set	11:36	E	Aug. 1	set	9:03	D	Nov. 1	rise	5:53	D
Feb. 11	set	11:11	D	May 11	set	11:27	E	Aug. 11	set	8:39	D	Nov. 11	rise	4:48	D
Feb. 21	set	11:08	D	May 21	set	11:16	E	Aug. 21	set	8:14	D	Nov. 21	rise	4:44	D
Mar. 1	set	11:05	D	June 1	set	11:02	E	Sept. 1	set	7:45	D	Dec. 1	rise	4:40	D
Mar. 11	set	12:03	E	June 11	set	10:47	E	Sept. 11	rise	6:19	B	Dec. 11	rise	4:36	D
Mar. 21	set	11:59	E	June 21	set	10:29	E	Sept. 21	rise	6:14	C	Dec. 21	rise	4:32	E
												Dec. 31	rise	4:28	E

BOLD = P.M. LIGHT = A.M.

JUPITER

The largest planet spends 2019 in the "13th zodiac constellation," Ophiuchus, the Serpent Bearer. It starts the year low in the east before dawn, forming a line with the Moon, Venus, and Mercury. Jupiter is a bit higher and brighter each morning as it rises 2 hours earlier each month. Jove rises before midnight in late March and reaches its opposition on June 10, when it rises at sunset. All summer, Jupiter remains well placed, although it never ascends more than one-third of the way up the sky. It's seen only during the first half of the night in autumn and becomes low in the west in November at nightfall. Lost in solar glare, it passes behind the Sun in conjunction on December 27.

Jan. 1	rise	5:32	E	Apr. 1	rise	1:37	E	July 1	set	3:56	A	Oct. 1	set	9:54	A
Jan. 11	rise	5:03	E	Apr. 11	rise	1:02	E	July 11	set	3:12	A	Oct. 11	set	9:20	A
Jan. 21	rise	4:33	E	Apr. 21	rise	12:18	E	July 21	set	2:30	A	Oct. 21	set	8:47	A
Feb. 1	rise	3:59	E	May 1	rise	11:33	E	Aug. 1	set	1:45	A	Nov. 1	set	8:12	A
Feb. 11	rise	3:28	E	May 11	rise	10:50	E	Aug. 11	set	1:05	A	Nov. 11	set	6:41	A
Feb. 21	rise	2:55	E	May 21	rise	10:06	E	Aug. 21	set	12:26	A	Nov. 21	set	6:10	A
Mar. 1	rise	2:28	E	June 1	rise	9:17	E	Sept. 1	set	11:40	A	Dec. 1	set	5:40	A
Mar. 11	rise	2:54	E	June 11	rise	8:31	E	Sept. 11	set	11:04	A	Dec. 11	set	5:11	A
Mar. 21	rise	2:18	E	June 21	set	4:40	A	Sept. 21	set	10:28	A	Dec. 21	set	4:42	A
												Dec. 31	set	7:32	E

SATURN

The Ringed Planet is parked in Sagittarius all year, which keeps it from getting very high up in 2019. Saturn first appears as a low morning star before sunrise in February. It rises at 1:00 A.M. in May and at sunset on July 9, when it reaches opposition. It's out all night throughout the summer, bright at magnitude +0.1. Its rings, slightly less "open" than during the past few years but still far from edgewise, are gorgeous through any telescope using more than 30×. Saturn is the "star" near the Moon on July 15, August 11 and 12, and September 7.

Jan. 1	set	4:32	A	Apr. 1	rise	3:22	E	July 1	rise	9:13	E	Oct. 1	set	11:46	A
Jan. 11	rise	7:09	E	Apr. 11	rise	2:44	E	July 11	rise	8:31	E	Oct. 11	set	11:08	A
Jan. 21	rise	6:35	E	Apr. 21	rise	2:05	E	July 21	set	4:45	A	Oct. 21	set	10:31	A
Feb. 1	rise	5:56	E	May 1	rise	1:26	E	Aug. 1	set	3:58	A	Nov. 1	set	9:51	A
Feb. 11	rise	5:21	E	May 11	rise	12:47	E	Aug. 11	set	3:15	A	Nov. 11	set	8:15	A
Feb. 21	rise	4:45	E	May 21	rise	12:06	E	Aug. 21	set	2:34	A	Nov. 21	set	7:40	A
Mar. 1	rise	4:16	E	June 1	rise	11:18	E	Sept. 1	set	1:48	A	Dec. 1	set	7:05	A
Mar. 11	rise	4:40	E	June 11	rise	10:36	E	Sept. 11	set	1:08	A	Dec. 11	set	6:31	A
Mar. 21	rise	4:03	E	June 21	rise	9:55	E	Sept. 21	set	12:28	A	Dec. 21	set	5:57	A
												Dec. 31	set	5:24	A

MERCURY

The innermost planet whirls so closely around the Sun that we see it only in twilight. As an evening star low in fading western twilight in 2019, Mercury is marginally visible in the last half of February and October but well seen throughout June. As a morning star, Mercury can be glimpsed during the first halves of January and April but is best seen in August, except for at the very end of that month, and from mid-November through mid-December. Mercury hovers below the Moon and Mars on November 24 and between them the next evening.

DO NOT CONFUSE: *Mercury and Mars on June 18, low in evening twilight: Mercury is brighter.* • *Jupiter and Saturn low in the south throughout summer: Jupiter is more brilliant.* • *Mercury with a sunspot during its Nov. 11 transit, through a solar telescope: Mercury is uniformly round and black.* • *Venus and Jupiter on Nov. 23 and 24, low in western twilight: Venus is brighter.*

APHELION (APH.): The point in a planet's orbit that is farthest from the Sun.

APOGEE (APO.): The point in the Moon's orbit that is farthest from Earth.

CELESTIAL EQUATOR (EQ.): The imaginary circle around the celestial sphere that can be thought of as the plane of Earth's equator projected out onto the sphere.

CELESTIAL SPHERE: An imaginary sphere projected into space that represents the entire sky, with an observer on Earth at its center. All celestial bodies other than Earth are imagined as being on its inside surface.

CIRCUMPOLAR: Always visible above the horizon, such as a circumpolar star.

CONJUNCTION: The time at which two or more celestial bodies appear closest in the sky. **Inferior (Inf.):** Mercury or Venus is between the Sun and Earth. **Superior (Sup.):** The Sun is between a planet and Earth. Actual dates for conjunctions are given on the **Right-Hand Calendar Pages, 121–147;** the best times for viewing the closely aligned bodies are given in **Sky Watch** on the **Left-Hand Calendar Pages, 120–146.**

DECLINATION: The celestial latitude of an object in the sky, measured in degrees north or south of the celestial equator; comparable to latitude on Earth. This Almanac gives the Sun's declination at noon.

ECLIPSE, LUNAR: The full Moon enters the shadow of Earth, which cuts off all or part of the sunlight reflected off the Moon. **Total:** The Moon passes completely through the umbra (central dark part) of Earth's shadow. **Partial:** Only part of the Moon passes through the umbra. **Penumbral:** The Moon passes through only the penumbra (area of partial darkness surrounding the umbra). **See page 102** for more information about eclipses.

ECLIPSE, SOLAR: Earth enters the shadow of the new Moon, which cuts off all or part of the Sun's light. **Total:** Earth passes through the umbra (central dark part) of the Moon's shadow, resulting in totality for observers within a narrow band on Earth. **Annular:** The Moon appears silhouetted against the Sun, with a ring of sunlight showing around it. **Partial:** The Moon blocks only part of the Sun.

ECLIPTIC: The apparent annual path of the Sun around the celestial sphere. The plane of the ecliptic is tipped 23½° from the celestial equator.

ELONGATION: The difference in degrees between the celestial longitudes of a planet and the Sun. **Greatest Elongation (Gr. Elong.):** The greatest apparent distance of a planet from the Sun, as seen from Earth.

EPACT: A number from 1 to 30 that indicates the Moon's age on January 1 at Greenwich, England; used in determining the date of Easter.

EQUINOX: When the Sun crosses the celestial equator. This event occurs two times each year: **Vernal** is around March 20 and **Autumnal** is around September 22.

EVENING STAR: A planet that is above the western horizon at sunset and less than 180° east of the Sun in right ascension.

GOLDEN NUMBER: A number in the 19-year Metonic cycle of the Moon, used in determining the date of Easter. See **page 150** for this year's Golden Number.

MAGNITUDE: A measure of a celestial object's brightness. **Apparent magnitude** measures the brightness of an object as seen from Earth. Objects with an apparent magnitude of 6 or less are observable to the naked eye. The lower the magnitude, the greater the brightness; an object with a magnitude of –1, e.g., is

Break Free from Neuropathy with a New Supportive Care Cream

A patented relief cream stands to help millions of Americans crippled from the side effects of neuropathy by increasing sensation and blood flow wherever it's applied

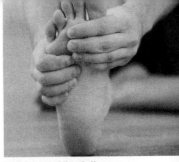

Raymond Wilson
The Associated Heath Press

AHP — A recent breakthrough stands to help millions of Americans plagued by burning, tingling and numb legs and feet.

But this time it comes in the form of a cream, not a pill, suggesting the medical community may have been going about the problem all wrong.

The breakthrough, called *Diabasens*, is a new relief cream developed for managing the relentless discomfort caused by neuropathy.

When applied directly to the legs and feet, it causes arteries and blood vessels to expand, increasing the flow of warm, nutrient rich blood to damaged tissue.

However, what's most remarkable about the cream...and what makes it so brilliant...is that it contains one of the only natural substances known to activate a special sensory pathway right below the surface of the skin.

This pathway is called TRPA1 and it controls the sensitivity of nerves. In laymen terms, it determines whether you feel pins and needles or soothing relief.

Studies show that symptoms of neuropathy arise when the nerves in your legs deteriorate and blood flow is lost to the areas which surround them.

As the nerves begins to die, sensation is lost. This lack of sensation is what causes the feelings of burning, tingling and numbness.

This is why the makers of *Diabasens* say their cream has performed so well in a recent clinical use survey trial: it increases sensation and blood flow where ever its applied.

No Pills or Prescriptions

Until now, many doctors have failed to consider a topical cream as an effective way to manage neuropathy. *Diabasens* is proving it may be the only way going forward.

"Most of today's treatment methods have focused on minimizing discomfort instead of attacking its underlining cause. That's why millions of adults are still in excruciating pain every single day, and are constantly dealing with side effects" explains Dr. Esber, the creator of *Diabasens*.

"*Diabasens* is different. Since the most commonly reported symptoms — burning, tingling and numb legs and feet — are caused by lack of sensation of the nerves, we've designed the formula increase their sensitivity.

And since these nerves are located right below the skin, we've chosen to formulate it as a cream. This allows for the ingredients to get to them faster and without any drug like side effects" he adds.

Study Finds Restoring Sensation the Key To Relief

With the conclusion of their latest human clinical use survey trial, Dr. Esber and his team are now offering *Diabasens* nationwide. And regardless of the market, its sales are exploding.

Men and women from all over the country are eager to get their hands on the new cream and, according to the results initial users reported, they should be.

Diabasens is shown to provide relief from:

- Burning
- Swelling
- Tingling
- Heaviness
- Numbness
- Cold extremities

In the trial above, as compared to baseline, participants taking *Diabasens* saw a staggering 51% increase sensitivity in just one week. This resulted in significant relief from burning, tingling and nubmness throughout their legs.

Many participants taking *Diabasens*

Topical Cream Offers Sufferers a Safer, More Effective Avenue of Relief: Diabasens increases sensation and blood flow wherever its applied. It's now being used to relieve painful legs and feet.

described feeling much more balanced and comfortable throughout the day. They also noticed that after applying, there was a pleasant warming sensation that was remarkably soothing.

Targets Nerve Damage Right Below the Skins Surface

Diabasens is a topical cream that is to be applied to your legs and feet twice a day for the first two weeks then once a day after. It does not require a prescription.

Studies show that neuropathy is caused when the peripheral nerves break down and blood is unable to circulate into your legs and feet.

As these nerves deteriorate, sensation is lost. This is why you may not feel hot or cold and your legs and feet may burn, tingle and go numb.

Additionally, without proper blood flow, tissues and cells in these areas start to die, causing unbearable pain.

An ingredient called cinnamaldehyde in *Diabasens* is one of the only compounds in existence that can activate TRPA1, a special sensory pathway that runs through your entire body.

According to research, activating this pathway (which can only be done with a cream) increases the sensitivity of nerves, relieving feelings of tingling and numbness in your legs and feet.

Supporting ingredients boost blood flow, supplying the nerves with the nutrients they need for increased sensation.

How to Get *Diabasens*

In order to get the word out about *Diabasens*, the company is offering special introductory discounts to all who call. Discounts will automatically be applied to all callers, but don't wait. This offer may not last forever. **Call toll-free: 1-800-516-6923.**

brighter than one with a magnitude of +1.

MIDNIGHT: Astronomically, the time when the Sun is opposite its highest point in the sky. Both 12 hours before and after noon (so, technically, both A.M. and P.M.), midnight in civil time is usually treated as the beginning of the day. It is displayed as 12:00 A.M. on 12-hour digital clocks. On a 24-hour cycle, 00:00, not 24:00, usually indicates midnight.

MOON ON EQUATOR: The Moon is on the celestial equator.

MOON RIDES HIGH/RUNS LOW: The Moon is highest above or farthest below the celestial equator.

MOONRISE/MOONSET: When the Moon rises above or sets below the horizon.

MOON'S PHASES: The changing appearance of the Moon, caused by the different angles at which it is illuminated by the Sun. **First Quarter:** Right half of the Moon is illuminated. **Full:** The Sun and the Moon are in opposition; the entire disk of the Moon is illuminated. **Last Quarter:** Left half of the Moon is illuminated. **New:** The Sun and the Moon are in conjunction; the Moon is darkened because it lines up between Earth and the Sun.

MOON'S PLACE, Astronomical: The position of the Moon within the constellations on the celestial sphere at midnight. **Astrological:** The position of the Moon within the tropical zodiac, whose twelve 30° segments (signs) along the ecliptic were named more than 2,000 years ago after constellations within each area. Because of precession and other factors, the zodiac signs no longer match actual constellation positions.

MORNING STAR: A planet that is above the eastern horizon at sunrise and less than 180° west of the Sun in right ascension.

NODE: Either of the two points where a celestial body's orbit intersects the ecliptic. **Ascending:** When the body is moving from south to north of the ecliptic. **Descending:** When the body is moving from north to south of the ecliptic.

OPPOSITION: The Moon or a planet appears on the opposite side of the sky from the Sun (elongation 180°).

PERIGEE (PERIG.): The point in the Moon's orbit that is closest to Earth.

PERIHELION (PERIH.): The point in a planet's orbit that is closest to the Sun.

PRECESSION: The slowly changing position of the stars and equinoxes in the sky caused by a slight wobble as Earth rotates around its axis.

RIGHT ASCENSION (R.A.): The celestial longitude of an object in the sky, measured eastward along the celestial equator in hours of time from the vernal equinox; comparable to longitude on Earth.

SOLSTICE, Summer: When the Sun reaches its greatest declination (23½°) north of the celestial equator, around June 21. **Winter:** When the Sun reaches its greatest declination (23½°) south of the celestial equator, around December 21.

STATIONARY (STAT.): The brief period of apparent halted movement of a planet against the background of the stars shortly before it appears to move backward/westward (retrograde motion) or forward/eastward (direct motion).

SUN FAST/SLOW: When a sundial is ahead of (fast) or behind (slow) clock time.

SUNRISE/SUNSET: The visible rising/setting of the upper edge of the Sun's disk across the unobstructed horizon of an observer whose eyes are 15 feet above ground level.

TWILIGHT: See page 106. ∎

2018

JANUARY
S	M	T	W	T	F	S
	1	2	3	4	5	6
7	8	9	10	11	12	13
14	15	16	17	18	19	20
21	22	23	24	25	26	27
28	29	30	31			

FEBRUARY
S	M	T	W	T	F	S
				1	2	3
4	5	6	7	8	9	10
11	12	13	14	15	16	17
18	19	20	21	22	23	24
25	26	27	28			

MARCH
S	M	T	W	T	F	S
				1	2	3
4	5	6	7	8	9	10
11	12	13	14	15	16	17
18	19	20	21	22	23	24
25	26	27	28	29	30	31

APRIL
S	M	T	W	T	F	S
1	2	3	4	5	6	7
8	9	10	11	12	13	14
15	16	17	18	19	20	21
22	23	24	25	26	27	28
29	30					

MAY
S	M	T	W	T	F	S
		1	2	3	4	5
6	7	8	9	10	11	12
13	14	15	16	17	18	19
20	21	22	23	24	25	26
27	28	29	30	31		

JUNE
S	M	T	W	T	F	S
					1	2
3	4	5	6	7	8	9
10	11	12	13	14	15	16
17	18	19	20	21	22	23
24	25	26	27	28	29	30

JULY
S	M	T	W	T	F	S
1	2	3	4	5	6	7
8	9	10	11	12	13	14
15	16	17	18	19	20	21
22	23	24	25	26	27	28
29	30	31				

AUGUST
S	M	T	W	T	F	S
			1	2	3	4
5	6	7	8	9	10	11
12	13	14	15	16	17	18
19	20	21	22	23	24	25
26	27	28	29	30	31	

SEPTEMBER
S	M	T	W	T	F	S
						1
2	3	4	5	6	7	8
9	10	11	12	13	14	15
16	17	18	19	20	21	22
23	24	25	26	27	28	29
30						

OCTOBER
S	M	T	W	T	F	S
	1	2	3	4	5	6
7	8	9	10	11	12	13
14	15	16	17	18	19	20
21	22	23	24	25	26	27
28	29	30	31			

NOVEMBER
S	M	T	W	T	F	S
				1	2	3
4	5	6	7	8	9	10
11	12	13	14	15	16	17
18	19	20	21	22	23	24
25	26	27	28	29	30	

DECEMBER
S	M	T	W	T	F	S
						1
2	3	4	5	6	7	8
9	10	11	12	13	14	15
16	17	18	19	20	21	22
23	24	25	26	27	28	29
30	31					

2019

JANUARY
S	M	T	W	T	F	S
		1	2	3	4	5
6	7	8	9	10	11	12
13	14	15	16	17	18	19
20	21	22	23	24	25	26
27	28	29	30	31		

FEBRUARY
S	M	T	W	T	F	S
					1	2
3	4	5	6	7	8	9
10	11	12	13	14	15	16
17	18	19	20	21	22	23
24	25	26	27	28		

MARCH
S	M	T	W	T	F	S
					1	2
3	4	5	6	7	8	9
10	11	12	13	14	15	16
17	18	19	20	21	22	23
24	25	26	27	28	29	30
31						

APRIL
S	M	T	W	T	F	S
	1	2	3	4	5	6
7	8	9	10	11	12	13
14	15	16	17	18	19	20
21	22	23	24	25	26	27
28	29	30				

MAY
S	M	T	W	T	F	S
			1	2	3	4
5	6	7	8	9	10	11
12	13	14	15	16	17	18
19	20	21	22	23	24	25
26	27	28	29	30	31	

JUNE
S	M	T	W	T	F	S
						1
2	3	4	5	6	7	8
9	10	11	12	13	14	15
16	17	18	19	20	21	22
23	24	25	26	27	28	29
30						

JULY
S	M	T	W	T	F	S
	1	2	3	4	5	6
7	8	9	10	11	12	13
14	15	16	17	18	19	20
21	22	23	24	25	26	27
28	29	30	31			

AUGUST
S	M	T	W	T	F	S
				1	2	3
4	5	6	7	8	9	10
11	12	13	14	15	16	17
18	19	20	21	22	23	24
25	26	27	28	29	30	31

SEPTEMBER
S	M	T	W	T	F	S
1	2	3	4	5	6	7
8	9	10	11	12	13	14
15	16	17	18	19	20	21
22	23	24	25	26	27	28
29	30					

OCTOBER
S	M	T	W	T	F	S
		1	2	3	4	5
6	7	8	9	10	11	12
13	14	15	16	17	18	19
20	21	22	23	24	25	26
27	28	29	30	31		

NOVEMBER
S	M	T	W	T	F	S
					1	2
3	4	5	6	7	8	9
10	11	12	13	14	15	16
17	18	19	20	21	22	23
24	25	26	27	28	29	30

DECEMBER
S	M	T	W	T	F	S
1	2	3	4	5	6	7
8	9	10	11	12	13	14
15	16	17	18	19	20	21
22	23	24	25	26	27	28
29	30	31				

2020

JANUARY
S	M	T	W	T	F	S
			1	2	3	4
5	6	7	8	9	10	11
12	13	14	15	16	17	18
19	20	21	22	23	24	25
26	27	28	29	30	31	

FEBRUARY
S	M	T	W	T	F	S
						1
2	3	4	5	6	7	8
9	10	11	12	13	14	15
16	17	18	19	20	21	22
23	24	25	26	27	28	29

MARCH
S	M	T	W	T	F	S
1	2	3	4	5	6	7
8	9	10	11	12	13	14
15	16	17	18	19	20	21
22	23	24	25	26	27	28
29	30	31				

APRIL
S	M	T	W	T	F	S
			1	2	3	4
5	6	7	8	9	10	11
12	13	14	15	16	17	18
19	20	21	22	23	24	25
26	27	28	29	30		

MAY
S	M	T	W	T	F	S
					1	2
3	4	5	6	7	8	9
10	11	12	13	14	15	16
17	18	19	20	21	22	23
24	25	26	27	28	29	30
31						

JUNE
S	M	T	W	T	F	S
	1	2	3	4	5	6
7	8	9	10	11	12	13
14	15	16	17	18	19	20
21	22	23	24	25	26	27
28	29	30				

JULY
S	M	T	W	T	F	S
			1	2	3	4
5	6	7	8	9	10	11
12	13	14	15	16	17	18
19	20	21	22	23	24	25
26	27	28	29	30	31	

AUGUST
S	M	T	W	T	F	S
						1
2	3	4	5	6	7	8
9	10	11	12	13	14	15
16	17	18	19	20	21	22
23	24	25	26	27	28	29
30	31					

SEPTEMBER
S	M	T	W	T	F	S
		1	2	3	4	5
6	7	8	9	10	11	12
13	14	15	16	17	18	19
20	21	22	23	24	25	26
27	28	29	30			

OCTOBER
S	M	T	W	T	F	S
				1	2	3
4	5	6	7	8	9	10
11	12	13	14	15	16	17
18	19	20	21	22	23	24
25	26	27	28	29	30	31

NOVEMBER
S	M	T	W	T	F	S
1	2	3	4	5	6	7
8	9	10	11	12	13	14
15	16	17	18	19	20	21
22	23	24	25	26	27	28
29	30					

DECEMBER
S	M	T	W	T	F	S
		1	2	3	4	5
6	7	8	9	10	11	12
13	14	15	16	17	18	19
20	21	22	23	24	25	26
27	28	29	30	31		

A CALENDAR OF THE HEAVENS FOR 2019

–Beth Krommes

The Calendar Pages (120–147) are the heart of *The Old Farmer's Almanac*. They present sky sightings and astronomical data for the entire year and are what make this book a true almanac, a "calendar of the heavens." In essence, these pages are unchanged since 1792, when Robert B. Thomas published his first edition. The long columns of numbers and symbols reveal all of nature's precision, rhythm, and glory, providing an astronomical look at the year 2019.

HOW TO USE THE CALENDAR PAGES

The astronomical data on the **Calendar Pages (120–147)** are calculated for Ottawa, Ontario. Guidance for calculating the times of these events for your locale appears on **pages 116–117.** Note that the results will be *approximate.* For the *exact* time of any astronomical event at your locale, go to **Almanac.ca/Astronomy** and enter your postal code. While you're there, print the month's "Sky Map," useful for viewing with "Sky Watch" in the Calendar Pages.

For a list of 2019 holidays and observances, see **pages 148 and 150.** Also check out the **Glossary of Almanac Oddities** on **pages 152 and 154,** which describes some of the more obscure entries traditionally found on the **Right-Hand Calendar Pages (121–147).**

ABOUT THE TIMES: All times are given in ET (Eastern Time), except where otherwise noted as NT (Newfoundland Time, +1½ hours), AT (Atlantic Time, +1 hour), CT (Central Time, –1), MT (Mountain Time, –2), or PT (Pacific Time, –3). Between 2:00 A.M., March 10, and 2:00 A.M., November 3, Daylight Saving Time is assumed in those locales where it is observed.

ABOUT THE TIDES: For tidal information, see **pages 120–147, 236–237,** and **241.** Tide times and heights also are available at **Almanac.ca/Tides.**

The Left-Hand Calendar Pages, 120 to 146

On these pages are the year's astronomical predictions for Ottawa, Ontario. Learn how to calculate the times of these events for your locale here or go to **Almanac.ca/Rise** and enter your postal code.

A SAMPLE MONTH

SKY WATCH: The paragraph at the top of each Left-Hand Calendar Page describes the best times to view conjunctions, meteor showers, planets, and more. (Also see **How to Use the Right-Hand Calendar Pages, p. 118.**)

1   2   3 4 5   6   7 8

DAY OF YEAR	DAY OF MONTH	DAY OF WEEK	☼ RISES H. M.	RISE KEY	☼ SETS H. M.	SET KEY	LENGTH OF DAY H. M.	SUN FAST M.	SUN DECLINATION ° '	HIGH TIDE TIMES HALIFAX	☾ RISES H. M.	RISE KEY	☾ SETS H. M.	SET KEY	☾ ASTRON. PLACE	☾ AGE
60	1	Fr.	6:41	D	5:50	B	11 09	*15	7 s. 30	4 5	3:59	E	1:07	A	SAG	25
61	2	Sa.	6:40	D	5:51	B	11 11	*15	7 s. 07	5 6	4:45	E	2:01	A	SAG	26
62	3	**F**	6:38	D	5:52	C	11 14	*15	6 s. 44	6 6¾	5:24	E	2:58	A	CAP	27
63	4	M.	6:36	D	5:54	C	11 18	*14	6 s. 21	6¾ 7½	5:58	D	3:57	B	CAP	28

1. To calculate the sunrise time in your locale: Choose a day. Note its Sun Rise Key Letter. Find your (nearest) city on **page 238**. Add or subtract the minutes that correspond to the Sun Rise Key Letter to/from the sunrise time for Ottawa.

EXAMPLE:

To calculate the sunrise time in Vancouver, British Columbia, on day 1:

Sunrise, Ottawa, with Key Letter D (above)	6:41 A.M. ET
Value of Key Letter D for Vancouver (p. 238)	+ 17 minutes
Sunrise, Vancouver	6:58 A.M. PT

To calculate your sunset time, repeat, using Ottawa's sunset time and its Sun Set Key Letter value.

2. To calculate the length of day: Choose a day. Note the Sun Rise and Sun Set Key Letters. Find your (nearest) city on **page 238**. Add or subtract the minutes that correspond to the Sun Set Key Letter to/from Ottawa's length of day. *Reverse* the sign (e.g., minus to plus) of the

Sun Rise Key Letter minutes. Add or subtract it to/from the first result.

EXAMPLE:

To calculate the length of day in Brandon, Manitoba, on day 1:

Length of day, Ottawa (above)	11h. 09m.
Sunset Key Letter B for Brandon (p. 238)	+ 28m.
	11h. 37m.
Reverse sunrise Key Letter D for Brandon (p. 238, +46 to -46)	- 46m.
Length of day, Brandon	10h. 51m.

3. Use Sun Fast to change sundial time to clock time. A sundial reads natural (Sun) time, which is neither Standard nor Daylight time. To calculate clock time on a sundial in Ottawa, subtract the minutes given in this column; add the minutes when preceded by an asterisk [*]. To

–Beth Krommes

convert the time to your (nearest) city, use Key Letter C on **page 238.**

EXAMPLE:

To change sundial to clock time in Ottawa or Thunder Bay, Ont., on day 1:

Sundial reading (Ottawa or Thunder Bay)	12:00 noon
Add Sun Fast (p. 116)	+ 15 minutes
Clock time, Ottawa	12:15 P.M. ET
Use Key Letter C for Thunder Bay (p. 239)	+ 53 minutes
Clock time, Thunder Bay	1:08 P.M. ET

4. This column gives the degrees and minutes of the Sun from the celestial equator at noon ET.

5. This column gives the approximate times of high tides in Halifax. For example, the first high tide occurs at 4:00 A.M. and the second occurs at 5:00 P.M. the same day. (A dash indicates that high tide occurs on or after midnight and is recorded on the next day.) Because of the great variations in tide times and heights on both the east and west coasts, no one locality can be used as a mean. Twice-weekly times and heights of high tides at Churchill, Manitoba, and Vancouver, British Columbia, are provided on **page 236.**

6. To calculate the moonrise time in your locale: Choose a day. Note the Moon Rise Key Letter. Find your (nearest) city on **page 238.** Add or subtract the minutes that correspond to the Moon Rise Key Letter to/from the moonrise time given for Ottawa. (A dash indicates that the

LONGITUDE OF CITY	CORRECTION MINUTES	LONGITUDE OF CITY	CORRECTION MINUTES
58°–76°	0	116°–127°	+4
77°–89°	+1	128°–141°	+5
90°–102°	+2	142°–155°	+6
103°–115°	+3		

moonrise occurs on/after midnight and is recorded on the next day.) Find the longitude of your (nearest) city on **page 238.** Add a correction in minutes for your city's longitude (see table, bottom left). Use the same procedure with Ottawa's moonset time and the Moon Set Key Letter value to calculate the time of moonset in your locale.

EXAMPLE:

To calculate the time of moonset in Toronto, Ontario, on day 1:

Moonset, Ottawa, with Key Letter A (p. 116)	1:07 P.M. ET
Value of Key Letter A for Toronto (p. 239)	+ 21 minutes
Correction for Toronto longitude, 79°23'	+ 1 minute
Moonset, Toronto	1:29 P.M. ET

7. This column gives the Moon's *astronomical* position among the constellations (not zodiac) at midnight. For *astrological* data, see **pages 228–231.**

Constellations have irregular borders; on successive nights, the midnight Moon may enter one, cross into another, and then move to a new area of the previous. It visits the 12 zodiacal constellations, as well as Auriga **(AUR),** a northern constellation between Perseus and Gemini; Cetus **(CET),** which lies south of the zodiac, just south of Pisces and Aries; Ophiuchus **(OPH),** primarily north of the zodiac but with a small corner between Scorpius and Sagittarius; Orion **(ORI),** whose northern limit first reaches the zodiac between Taurus and Gemini; and Sextans **(SEX),** which lies south of the zodiac except for a corner that just touches it near Leo.

8. This column gives the Moon's age: the number of days since the previous new Moon. (The average length of the lunar month is 29.53 days.) *(continued)*

The Right-Hand Calendar Pages, 121 to 147

The Right-Hand Calendar Pages contain celestial events; religious observances; proverbs and poems; civil holidays; historical events; folklore; tide heights; weather prediction rhymes; Farmer's Calendar essays; and more.

A SAMPLE MONTH

1 2 3 4 5 6 7 8 9 10

1	Fr.	ALL FOOLS' • *If you want to make a fool of yourself, you'll find a lot of people ready to help you.*	*Flakes*	an inch long, who v
2	Sa.	Tap dancer Charles "Honi" Coles born, 1911 • Tides {5.1 5.0	*alive!*	in fresh water, pro pond across the r
3	**B**	2nd S. of Easter • Writer F. Scott Fitzgerald married Zelda Sayre, 1920	*Spring's*	emerged a month c
4	M.	Annunciation[T] • ☌♆☾ • *Ben Hur* won 11 Academy Awards, 1960	*arrived!*	to spend the next 3
5	Tu.	☾ AT ☋ • Blizzard left 27.2" snow, St. John's, Nfld., 1999 • Tides {5.8 6.2	*Or is this*	on land before ret their wet world.
6	W.	☾ ON EQ. • ☌♀☾ • Twin mongoose lemurs born, Busch Gardens, Tampa, Fla., 2012	*warmth*	You can't mis

1. The bold letter is the Dominical Letter (from A to G), a traditional ecclesiastical designation for Sunday determined by the date on which the year's first Sunday falls. For 2019, the Dominical Letter is **F.**

2. Civil holidays and astronomical events.

3. Religious feasts: A [T] indicates a major feast that the church has this year temporarily transferred to a date other than its usual one.

4. Sundays and special holy days.

5. Symbols for notable celestial events. For example, ☌♆☾ on the 4th day means that a conjunction (☌) of Neptune (♆) and the Moon (☾) occurs: They are aligned along the same celestial longitude and appear to be closest together in the sky. See "Celestial Symbols" below.

6. Proverbs, poems, and adages.

7. Noteworthy historical events, folklore, and legends.

8. High tide heights, in feet, at Halifax, Nova Scotia.

9. Weather prediction rhyme.

10. Farmer's Calendar essay.

Celestial Symbols

⊙ Sun	⊕ Earth	⛢ Uranus	☌ Conjunction (on the same celestial longitude)	☋ Descending node
○●☾ Moon	♂ Mars	♆ Neptune	☊ Ascending node	☍ Opposition (180 degrees from Sun)
☿ Mercury	♃ Jupiter	♇ Pluto		
♀ Venus	♄ Saturn			

PREDICTING EARTHQUAKES

Note the dates in the Right-Hand Calendar Pages when the Moon rides high or runs low. The date of the high begins the most likely 5-day period of earthquakes in the Northern Hemisphere; the date of the low indicates a similar 5-day period in the Southern Hemisphere. Also noted are the 2 days each month when the Moon is on the celestial equator, indicating the most likely time for earthquakes in either hemisphere.

EARTH AT PERIHELION AND APHELION

Perihelion: January 3, 2019 (ET). Earth will be 91,403,554 miles from the Sun. **Aphelion:** July 4, 2019 (ET). Earth will be 94,513,221 miles from the Sun.

 Find more heavenly details at Almanac.ca/Astronomy.

Why We Have Seasons

In the Northern Hemisphere, the summer solstice marks the beginning of summer and occurs when the North Pole is tilted toward the Sun. The winter solstice marks the beginning of winter and occurs when the North Pole is tilted away from the Sun.

The equinoxes occur when the hemispheres equally face the Sun. At this time, the Sun rises due east and sets due west. The vernal equinox marks the beginning of spring; the autumnal equinox marks the beginning of autumn.

The seasons occur because as Earth revolves around the Sun, its axis remains tilted at 23.5 degrees from the perpendicular. This tilt causes different latitudes on Earth to receive varying amounts of sunlight throughout the year.

In the Southern Hemisphere, the seasons are the reverse of those in the Northern Hemisphere.

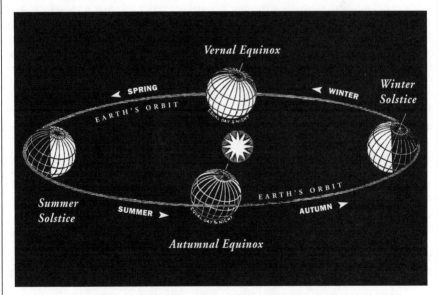

THE FIRST DAYS OF THE 2019 SEASONS

VERNAL (SPRING) EQUINOX: March 20, 5:58 P.M. EDT

SUMMER SOLSTICE: June 21, 11:54 A.M. EDT

AUTUMNAL (FALL) EQUINOX: Sept. 23, 3:50 A.M. EDT

WINTER SOLSTICE: Dec. 21, 11:19 P.M. EST

NOVEMBER

SKY WATCH: Mars, having resumed its normal eastward motion against the stars, speeds from Capricornus into Aquarius, gaining elevation to stand about a third of the way up the southern sky at nightfall. Just 12 arcseconds wide and at magnitude zero, it's lost half its width and is now too small to show useful detail in telescopes. On the 1st, Jupiter meets Mercury low in the west; both soon vanish. The Moon floats left of ever-lower Saturn on the 11th, close below Mars on the 15th, and to the left of Taurus's main star, Aldebaran, on the 23rd. The action switches to the predawn sky, where the Moon meets returning Venus on the 6th. Venus hovers near Virgo's Spica from the 6th to the 12th and stands 25 degrees high by month's end.

● **NEW MOON**	7th day	11:02 A.M.
○ **FULL MOON**	23rd day	12:39 A.M.
☽ **FIRST QUARTER**	15th day	9:54 A.M.
☾ **LAST QUARTER**	29th day	7:19 P.M.

After 2:00 A.M. on November 4, Eastern Standard Time is given.

GET THESE PAGES WITH TIMES SET TO YOUR POSTAL CODE AT ALMANAC.CA/ACCESS.

DAY OF YEAR	DAY OF MONTH	DAY OF WEEK	☀ RISES H.M.	RISE KEY	☀ SETS H.M.	SET KEY	LENGTH OF DAY H.M.	SUN FAST M.	SUN DECLINATION ° '	HIGH TIDE TIMES HALIFAX		☽ RISES H.M.	RISE KEY	☽ SETS H.M.	SET KEY	☽ ASTRON. PLACE	☽ AGE
305	1	Th.	7:42	D	5:50	B	10 08	14	14 s. 33	2¾	3	12:19	A	3:10	D	CAN	24
306	2	Fr.	7:43	D	5:49	B	10 06	14	14 s. 52	4	4¼	1:31	B	3:45	D	LEO	25
307	3	Sa.	7:45	D	5:47	B	10 02	14	15 s. 11	5¼	5½	2:44	B	4:16	C	LEO	26
308	4	**G**	6:46	D	4:46	B	10 00	14	15 s. 30	5¼	5½	2:57	C	3:44	C	VIR	27
309	5	M.	6:48	D	4:45	B	9 57	14	15 s. 48	6	6¼	4:09	C	4:12	C	VIR	28
310	6	Tu.	6:49	D	4:43	B	9 54	14	16 s. 06	6¾	7	5:20	C	4:40	B	VIR	29
311	7	W.	6:50	D	4:42	B	9 52	14	16 s. 24	7½	7¾	6:29	D	5:11	B	LIB	0
312	8	Th.	6:52	D	4:41	B	9 49	13	16 s. 41	8	8½	7:37	D	5:44	B	LIB	1
313	9	Fr.	6:53	D	4:39	B	9 46	13	16 s. 58	8¾	9¼	8:43	E	6:21	A	SCO	2
314	10	Sa.	6:55	D	4:38	B	9 43	13	17 s. 15	9½	10	9:44	E	7:03	A	OPH	3
315	11	**G**	6:56	D	4:37	B	9 41	13	17 s. 32	10¼	10¾	10:39	E	7:50	A	SAG	4
316	12	M.	6:57	E	4:36	B	9 39	13	17 s. 48	11	11½	11:29	E	8:41	A	SAG	5
317	13	Tu.	6:59	E	4:35	B	9 36	13	18 s. 04	11½	—	12:11	E	9:37	A	SAG	6
318	14	W.	7:00	E	4:34	B	9 34	13	18 s. 20	12¼	12¼	12:48	E	10:35	A	CAP	7
319	15	Th.	7:02	E	4:33	B	9 31	13	18 s. 35	1	1¼	1:20	D	11:35	B	CAP	8
320	16	Fr.	7:03	E	4:32	B	9 29	12	18 s. 50	2	2¼	1:49	D	—	-	AQU	9
321	17	Sa.	7:04	E	4:31	B	9 27	12	19 s. 05	3¼	3¼	2:15	D	12:36	B	AQU	10
322	18	**G**	7:06	E	4:30	A	9 24	12	19 s. 19	4¼	4½	2:40	C	1:39	B	AQU	11
323	19	M.	7:07	E	4:29	A	9 22	12	19 s. 33	5	5¼	3:05	C	2:43	C	CET	12
324	20	Tu.	7:08	E	4:28	A	9 20	12	19 s. 46	5¾	6	3:32	B	3:48	C	PSC	13
325	21	W.	7:10	E	4:27	A	9 17	11	20 s. 00	6¼	6¾	4:00	B	4:57	D	CET	14
326	22	Th.	7:11	E	4:27	A	9 16	11	20 s. 13	7	7½	4:33	B	6:07	D	ARI	15
327	23	Fr.	7:12	E	4:26	A	9 14	11	20 s. 25	7¾	8¼	5:12	A	7:19	D	TAU	16
328	24	Sa.	7:14	E	4:25	A	9 11	10	20 s. 37	8¼	9	5:59	A	8:31	E	TAU	17
329	25	**G**	7:15	E	4:24	A	9 09	10	20 s. 49	9	9¾	6:55	A	9:38	E	ORI	18
330	26	M.	7:16	E	4:24	A	9 08	10	21 s. 00	10	10½	7:59	A	10:38	E	GEM	19
331	27	Tu.	7:17	E	4:23	A	9 06	9	21 s. 11	10¾	11½	9:09	A	11:30	E	CAN	20
332	28	W.	7:19	E	4:23	A	9 04	9	21 s. 22	11½	—	10:22	B	12:13	D	CAN	21
333	29	Th.	7:20	E	4:22	A	9 02	9	21 s. 32	12½	12½	11:35	B	12:49	D	LEO	22
334	30	Fr.	7:21	E	4:22	A	9 01	8	21 s. 42	1½	1½	—	-	1:21	D	LEO	23

To use this page, see p. 116; for Key Letters, see p. 238. LIGHT = A.M. **BOLD** = P.M.   **2019**

Shorter and shorter now the twilight clips
The days, as through the sunset gate they crowd . . .
–Alice Cary

DAY OF MONTH	DAY OF WEEK	DATES, FEASTS, FASTS, ASPECTS, TIDE HEIGHTS, AND WEATHER	
1	Th.	All Saints' • Architect James Renwick Jr. born, 1818 • First direct flight from Canada to USSR, 1966	Dank
2	Fr.	All Souls' • Storm blocked Ben Franklin's view of lunar eclipse, Philadelphia, 1743 • {5.4 5.4}	and
3	Sa.	Sadie Hawkins Day • *Mariner 10* spacecraft launched, Cape Canaveral, Fla., 1973 • {5.7 5.6}	dismal,
4	**G**	24th ☋. af. ℙ. • **DAYLIGHT SAVING TIME ENDS, 2:00 A.M.** • ☾ ON EQ.	dearie.
5	M.	☌♀☾ • *In the evening, one may praise the day.* • {6.2 5.9}	Just
6	Tu.	**ELECTION DAY (U.S.)** • ☿ GR. ELONG. (23° EAST) • Composer Pyotr Ilyich Tchaikovsky died, 1893	short
7	W.	**NEW** ● • Evangelist Billy Graham born, 1918 • Tides {6.5 6.1}	of
8	Th.	☌♃☾ • Black bears head to winter dens now. • Tides {6.5 6.0}	abysmal;
9	Fr.	☌♀☾ • Worst day of storm that caused 12 major shipwrecks on Great Lakes, U.S. and Canada, 1913	
10	Sa.	Statue of Our Lady of Prompt Succor first in U.S. to be canonically crowned, New Orleans, La., 1895	hardly what
11	**G**	25th ☋. af. ℙ. • **REMEMBRANCE DAY** • ☾ RUNS LOW • ☌♄☾	we'd
12	M.	Indian Summer • ☌♇☾ • 208-mile-long, 60-mile-wide iceberg discovered, 1956 • {5.7 5.4}	call
13	Tu.	☾ AT ☋ • ♀ STAT. • Lobsters move to offshore waters.	cheery.
14	W.	☾ AT APO. • Yale U. announced will admit women following fall, 1968 • {5.2 5.2}	Rain
15	Th.	☌♂☾ • First gas-turbine electric locomotive in U.S. track-tested, Erie, Pa., 1948 • {5.1 5.0}	comes
16	Fr.	Louis Riel, Métis leader and founder of Man., died, 1885 • Tides {5.1 4.9}	and
17	Sa.	St. Hugh of Lincoln • ☌♅☾ • ☿ STAT. • Tides {5.1 4.9}	goes:
18	**G**	26th ☋. af. ℙ. • Crab apples are ripe now. • {5.3 5.1}	dreary!
19	M.	☾ ON EQ. • Columbus first saw what is now Puerto Rico, 1493 • Tides {5.6 5.3}	At
20	Tu.	☌♄☾ • *One sesame seed won't make oil.* • Tides {5.8 5.5}	least
21	W.	Actress Marlo Thomas born, 1937 • Actor Bill Bixby died, 1993 • Tides {6.1 5.7}	our
22	Th.	**THANKSGIVING DAY (U.S.)** • Explorer La Salle born, 1643 • Pirate Blackbeard died, 1718	turkey
23	Fr.	St. Clement • **FULL BEAVER** ○ • Lake Merced water level dropped 30', Calif., 1852	isn't
24	Sa.	Artist Henri de Toulouse-Lautrec born, 1864 • Pianist Scott Joplin born, 1868	jerky.
25	**G**	27th ☋. af. ℙ. • ☾ RIDES HIGH • ♆ STAT. • {6.7 6.1}	Quirky:
26	M.	☾ AT PERIG. • ☌♃☉ • First major football game played indoors, Chicago Coliseum, Ill., 1896	mild,
27	Tu.	☾ AT ☋ • ☌♀♃ • ☿ IN INF. ☌ • Blizzard with lightning struck parts of S.Dak., 1983	wild,
28	W.	North Pacific Canning Co. formed, B.C., 1888 • {6.1 ___}	wet,
29	Th.	Maj. Henry Hitchcock, Sherman's March, Ga., 1864: *Weather so warm I could not wear any cape after 10 A.M.*	and
30	Fr.	St. Andrew • *A heavy November snow will last until April.*	murky.

Farmer's Calendar

In late autumn, after most of the leaves have fallen, the forest suddenly becomes transparent. The contours of the land leap out in 3-D, exposing all kinds of subtleties. Many of them are small, bashful, the kind of sights that require us to look down instead of up.

For example, just before Thanksgiving, I noticed for the first time some spectacular maple leaves in colors—rose, bright yellow, hunter's orange—that had long since left the canopy above me. They were big leaves, 6 inches or more across, but they were growing on stems less than 18 inches tall.

Why do these tiny trees put forth such unusually large and brilliant leaves? Perhaps it's because now the sunlight streams down to the forest floor unhindered, so these "mini-maples" can suck up energy with their outsized solar collectors.

Once I noticed the first, the second, the third, I saw them everywhere. They fluttered, but there was no breeze. They looked like cops doing that palm-down hand-waggle that means, "You're not going fast enough for me to stop you, but you're going too fast."

The semaphore of the leaves has a similar message: "Slow down. You're going too fast to see me."

DECEMBER

SKY WATCH: Venus excels as a morning star, now at greatest brilliancy at a gorgeous, shadow-casting magnitude –4.9. High at predawn twilight, it's below the Moon on the 3rd. Mercury also begins a good morning apparition, below the Moon on the 5th. On the 6th, Jupiter takes its turn dangling below the crescent Moon. The Geminid meteors should be excellent on the 13th, after the Moon sets at around 10:00 P.M. Zero-magnitude Mars stands above the Moon on the 14th, with both about halfway up the southern sky at nightfall. Jupiter and Mercury hang out together most of the month and are quite close on the 21st, some 10 degrees high, 40 minutes before sunrise. Winter begins with the solstice on the 21st at 5:23 P.M.

● NEW MOON	7th day	2:20 A.M.	○ FULL MOON	22nd day	12:49 P.M.
☽ FIRST QUARTER	15th day	6:49 A.M.	☾ LAST QUARTER	29th day	4:34 A.M.

All times are given in Eastern Standard Time.

GET THESE PAGES WITH TIMES SET TO YOUR POSTAL CODE AT ALMANAC.CA/ACCESS.

DAY OF YEAR	DAY OF MONTH	DAY OF WEEK	☀ RISES H. M.	RISE KEY	☀ SETS H. M.	SET KEY	LENGTH OF DAY H. M.	SUN FAST M.	SUN DECLINATION ° ′	HIGH TIDE TIMES HALIFAX		☾ RISES H. M.	RISE KEY	☾ SETS H. M.	SET KEY	☾ ASTRON. PLACE	☾ AGE
335	1	Sa.	7:22	E	4:21	A	8 59	8	21 s. 51	2½	2¾	12:47	B	1:49	C	VIR	24
336	2	**G**	7:23	E	4:21	A	8 58	8	22 s. 00	3¾	4	1:57	C	2:16	C	VIR	25
337	3	M.	7:24	E	4:21	A	8 57	7	22 s. 09	4¾	5¼	3:07	C	2:43	B	VIR	26
338	4	Tu.	7:25	E	4:20	A	8 55	7	22 s. 17	5½	6	4:16	D	3:12	B	VIR	27
339	5	W.	7:27	E	4:20	A	8 53	6	22 s. 24	6¼	6¾	5:23	D	3:42	B	LIB	28
340	6	Th.	7:28	E	4:20	A	8 52	6	22 s. 32	7	7½	6:29	D	4:17	A	SCO	29
341	7	Fr.	7:29	E	4:20	A	8 51	6	22 s. 38	7¾	8¼	7:32	E	4:57	A	OPH	0
342	8	Sa.	7:30	E	4:20	A	8 50	5	22 s. 45	8½	9	8:30	E	5:41	A	SAG	1
343	9	**G**	7:31	E	4:20	A	8 49	5	22 s. 51	9	9¾	9:22	E	6:31	A	SAG	2
344	10	M.	7:31	E	4:20	A	8 49	4	22 s. 56	9¾	10½	10:08	E	7:26	A	SAG	3
345	11	Tu.	7:32	E	4:20	A	8 48	4	23 s. 01	10½	11	10:48	E	8:23	A	CAP	4
346	12	W.	7:33	E	4:20	A	8 47	3	23 s. 06	11	11¾	11:21	D	9:22	B	CAP	5
347	13	Th.	7:34	E	4:20	A	8 46	3	23 s. 10	11¾	—	11:51	D	10:23	B	AQU	6
348	14	Fr.	7:35	E	4:20	A	8 45	2	23 s. 13	12½	12½	12:18	D	11:24	B	AQU	7
349	15	Sa.	7:36	E	4:21	A	8 45	2	23 s. 17	1¼	1¼	12:43	C	—	-	AQU	8
350	16	**G**	7:36	E	4:21	A	8 45	1	23 s. 19	2¼	2¼	1:07	C	12:26	C	PSC	9
351	17	M.	7:37	E	4:21	A	8 44	1	23 s. 21	3¼	3½	1:32	C	1:29	C	CET	10
352	18	Tu.	7:38	E	4:22	A	8 44	1	23 s. 23	4	4½	1:58	B	2:35	C	PSC	11
353	19	W.	7:38	E	4:22	A	8 44	0	23 s. 24	4¾	5½	2:28	B	3:43	D	CET	12
354	20	Th.	7:39	E	4:22	A	8 43	0	23 s. 25	5½	6¼	3:04	B	4:54	D	TAU	13
355	21	Fr.	7:39	E	4:22	A	8 43	*1	23 s. 26	6½	7	3:47	A	6:07	E	TAU	14
356	22	Sa.	7:40	E	4:23	A	8 43	*1	23 s. 25	7¼	8	4:39	A	7:18	E	TAU	15
357	23	**G**	7:40	E	4:24	A	8 44	*2	23 s. 25	8	8¾	5:41	A	8:24	E	GEM	16
358	24	M.	7:41	E	4:25	A	8 44	*2	23 s. 24	8¾	9½	6:51	A	9:21	E	GEM	17
359	25	Tu.	7:41	E	4:25	A	8 44	*3	23 s. 22	9¾	10¼	8:06	A	10:10	E	CAN	18
360	26	W.	7:41	E	4:25	A	8 44	*3	23 s. 20	10½	11¼	9:22	B	10:50	D	LEO	19
361	27	Th.	7:42	E	4:26	A	8 44	*4	23 s. 18	11¼	—	10:36	B	11:24	D	LEO	20
362	28	Fr.	7:42	E	4:27	A	8 45	*4	23 s. 15	12¼	12¼	11:48	C	11:54	C	LEO	21
363	29	Sa.	7:42	E	4:28	A	8 46	*5	23 s. 11	1	1¼	—	-	12:22	C	VIR	22
364	30	**G**	7:42	E	4:29	A	8 47	*5	23 s. 08	2	2½	12:59	C	12:48	B	VIR	23
365	31	M.	7:42	E	4:29	A	8 47	*6	23 s. 03	3	3¾	2:07	D	1:16	B	VIR	24

To use this page, see p. 116; for Key Letters, see p. 238. LIGHT = A.M. BOLD = P.M.   **2019**

Come give the holly a song;
For it helps to drive stern winter away.
–**Eliza Cook**

DAY OF MONTH	DAY OF WEEK	DATES, FEASTS, FASTS, ASPECTS, TIDE HEIGHTS, AND WEATHER	
1	Sa.	♀ AT GR. ILLUM. EXTENT • –25.6°F, Fort Saskatchewan, Alta., 1990	*Shopping*
2	**G**	**1st S. of Advent** • Chanukah begins at sundown • ☾ ON EQ.	*rush*
3	M.	☌♀☾ • Ill. admitted to Union as 21st state, 1818 • Tides { 6.0 / 5.5	*slowed*
4	Tu.	Naturalist Stuart Criddle died, 1877 • Tides { 6.1 / 5.6	*by*
5	W.	☌☿☾ • Canada's first electric car debuted, Toronto, Ont., 1893 • Tides { 6.2 / 5.7	*slush;*
6	Th.	St. Nicholas • ☌♃☾ • ☿ STAT. • 5" snow, Savannah, Ga., 1740	*we'll*
7	Fr.	St. Ambrose • **Nat'l Pearl Harbor Remembrance Day (U.S.)** • **NEW** ● • ☌♂♆	*have*
8	Sa.	Winterberry fruits especially showy now. • { 6.2 / 5.8	*to mush!*
9	**G**	**2nd S. of Advent** • ☾ RUNS LOW • ☌♄☾ • ☌♇☾ • { 6.1 / 5.7	*A*
10	M.	St. Eulalia • ☾ AT ☋ • *One ounce of discretion is worth a pound of wit.* • { 6.0 / 5.6	*snow*
11	Tu.	Astronomer Annie Jump Cannon born, 1863 • *Dec. 11–12:* Ice storm hit Northeast, 2008 • { 5.8 / 5.5	*event*
12	W.	**Our Lady of Guadalupe** • ☾ AT APO. • U.S. diplomat Joel Roberts Poinsett died, 1851	*may*
13	Th.	St. Lucia • Wilson first U.S. president to visit Europe while in office, 1918 • { 5.4 / —	*leave*
14	Fr.	Halcyon Days begin. • ☌♂☾ • ☌♆☾ • "Diplogen" suggested for isotope name, 1933	*us*
15	Sa.	☿ GR. ELONG. (21° WEST) • Architect Alexandre Gustave Eiffel born, 1832 • Tides { 5.3 / 5.0	*wan,*
16	**G**	**3rd S. of Advent** • ☾ ON EQ. • Boston Tea Party occurred, 1773	*spent.*
17	M.	☌⛢☾ • *When the snow falls dry, it means to lie; But flakes light and soft bring rain oft.* • { 5.4 / 4.9	*Arctic*
18	Tu.	Beware the Pogonip. • Actress Zsa Zsa Gabor died, 2016	*blast*
19	W.	Ember Day • *Intelsat III F-2* communications satellite launched, 1968 • { 5.8 / 5.3	*is*
20	Th.	Industrialist Harvey S. Firestone born, 1868 • { 6.1 / 5.6	*quickly*
21	Fr.	St. Thomas • Ember Day • **WINTER SOLSTICE** • ☌☿♃ • { 6.4 / 5.9	*past,*
22	Sa.	Ember Day • **FULL COLD** ○ • Writer Beatrix Potter died, 1943	*so*
23	**G**	**4th S. of Advent** • ☾ RIDES HIGH • Van Gogh cut off most of left ear, 1888	*Santa's*
24	M.	☾ AT ☊ • ☾ AT PERIG. • Pepper, a Bolivian gray titi monkey, born at Philadelphia Zoo, Pa., 2012	*not*
25	Tu.	**Christmas** • G. Washington's troops crossed Delaware R., Am. Revolution, 1776	*despondent.*
26	W.	St. Stephen • **Boxing Day** • **First Day of Kwanzaa** • { 6.5 / 6.2	*Snowy*
27	Th.	St. John • Ill diarist, N.Y., 1864: *I don't see no need of being sick now that school is out. Darn it!*	*and shivery*
28	Fr.	Holy Innocents • First sudden-death overtime game in NFL, Baltimore Colts vs. N.Y. Giants, 1958	*for*
29	Sa.	☾ ON EQ. • Lake Washington Floating Bridge construction began, Seattle, Wash., 1938	*infant*
30	**G**	**1st S. af. Ch.** • *Good to begin well, better to end well.* • Tides { 5.8 / 5.2	*'19's*
31	M.	St. Sylvester • Helium-filled sun shade patented, 1991	*delivery!*

Farmer's Calendar

Those of us who lived through the Great New England Ice Storm of December 11–12, 2008, still have posttraumatic stress disorder. The storm lasted 2 days, but the power was out for more than a week at our house. Now, when ice is predicted, we check our water supplies, our batteries, our candles. We sleep with a flashlight; we unplug the computers. We lie awake listening for the chatter of sleet on the windows or, God forbid, the rifle shots of branches breaking or the chandelier-fall crash of a treetop.

But in many ways this was the most joyous holiday season ever. People checked on their neighbors. The General Store contributed 200 turkey dinners to a supper at the elementary school so that people could enjoy a hot meal and some company. One couple went ahead with a church wedding, lit by candles. Bundled up like fur trappers, they left little puffs of fog when they said their vows.

We're just not quite ready to go through it all again. The worst part was going a week without a shower. Come to think of it: No, it was hauling water up from the creek in buckets. Actually: No, it was using up half a winter's firewood in a fortnight!

This ice storm followed the last big one by 12 years. We're about due for another.

JANUARY

SKY WATCH: The year begins with a predawn string of pearls: Some 40 minutes before sunrise on the 1st, the Moon, Venus, Jupiter, and Mercury hover from upper right to lower left, low in the eastern sky. Venus is now at its brightest of the year. The alignment on the 2nd finds the Moon between Venus and Jupiter. On the 3rd, the Moon is to the left of Jupiter. Through January, Venus sinks lower at first light but Jupiter is higher; their opposing motions cause them to meet from the 20th to the 26th. At nightfall all month, Mars in Pisces is due south at a bright magnitude 0. A total lunar eclipse on the 20th, visible from the entire United States and Canada, begins at 10:34 P.M., with totality starting at 11:41 P.M.

● **NEW MOON** 5th day 8:28 P.M.   ○ **FULL MOON** 21st day 12:16 A.M.
◐ **FIRST QUARTER** 14th day 1:46 A.M.   ◑ **LAST QUARTER** 27th day 4:10 P.M.

All times are given in Eastern Standard Time.

GET THESE PAGES WITH TIMES SET TO YOUR POSTAL CODE AT ALMANAC.CA/ACCESS.

DAY OF YEAR	DAY OF MONTH	DAY OF WEEK	☼ RISES H. M.	RISE KEY	☼ SETS H. M.	SET KEY	LENGTH OF DAY H. M.	SUN FAST M.	SUN DECLINATION ° '	HIGH TIDE TIMES HALIFAX		☾ RISES H. M.	RISE KEY	☾ SETS H. M.	SET KEY	☾ ASTRON. PLACE	☾ AGE
1	1	Tu.	7:43	E	4:30	A	8 47	*6	22 s. 58	4¼	4¾	3:14	D	1:45	B	LIB	25
2	2	W.	7:43	E	4:31	A	8 48	*7	22 s. 53	5	5¾	4:20	D	2:18	B	LIB	26
3	3	Th.	7:43	E	4:32	A	8 49	*7	22 s. 47	6	6½	5:23	E	2:55	A	OPH	27
4	4	Fr.	7:42	E	4:33	A	8 51	*8	22 s. 41	6¾	7¼	6:22	E	3:37	A	OPH	28
5	5	Sa.	7:42	E	4:34	A	8 52	*8	22 s. 35	7½	8	7:16	E	4:25	A	SAG	0
6	6	**F**	7:42	E	4:35	A	8 53	*9	22 s. 28	8	8¾	8:04	E	5:17	A	SAG	1
7	7	M.	7:42	E	4:36	A	8 54	*9	22 s. 20	8¾	9½	8:46	E	6:14	A	CAP	2
8	8	Tu.	7:42	E	4:37	A	8 55	*9	22 s. 12	9½	10	9:22	E	7:12	A	CAP	3
9	9	W.	7:41	E	4:39	A	8 58	*10	22 s. 04	10	10¾	9:53	D	8:12	B	CAP	4
10	10	Th.	7:41	E	4:40	A	8 59	*10	21 s. 55	10¾	11¼	10:21	D	9:13	B	AQU	5
11	11	Fr.	7:41	E	4:41	A	9 00	*11	21 s. 46	11¼	—	10:46	D	10:14	B	AQU	6
12	12	Sa.	7:40	E	4:42	A	9 02	*11	21 s. 36	12	12	11:10	C	11:15	C	PSC	7
13	13	**F**	7:40	E	4:43	A	9 03	*11	21 s. 26	12½	12¾	11:34	C	—	-	CET	8
14	14	M.	7:39	E	4:45	A	9 06	*12	21 s. 15	1¼	1½	11:59	B	12:18	C	PSC	9
15	15	Tu.	7:39	E	4:46	A	9 07	*12	21 s. 04	2¼	2½	12:26	B	1:23	D	CET	10
16	16	W.	7:38	E	4:47	A	9 09	*12	20 s. 53	3	3¾	12:57	B	2:31	D	ARI	11
17	17	Th.	7:38	E	4:48	A	9 10	*13	20 s. 41	4	5	1:35	A	3:41	D	TAU	12
18	18	Fr.	7:37	E	4:50	A	9 13	*13	20 s. 29	5	6	2:21	A	4:52	E	TAU	13
19	19	Sa.	7:36	E	4:51	A	9 15	*13	20 s. 17	6	6¾	3:18	A	6:00	E	ORI	14
20	20	**F**	7:36	E	4:52	A	9 16	*14	20 s. 04	6¾	7½	4:24	A	7:03	E	GEM	15
21	21	M.	7:35	E	4:54	A	9 19	*14	19 s. 51	7¾	8½	5:39	A	7:57	E	CAN	16
22	22	Tu.	7:34	E	4:55	A	9 21	*14	19 s. 37	8½	9¼	6:58	B	8:43	D	CAN	17
23	23	W.	7:33	E	4:57	A	9 24	*15	19 s. 23	9½	10	8:16	B	9:21	D	LEO	18
24	24	Th.	7:32	E	4:58	A	9 26	*15	19 s. 09	10¼	11	9:32	B	9:54	D	LEO	19
25	25	Fr.	7:31	E	4:59	B	9 28	*15	18 s. 54	11	11¾	10:46	C	10:24	C	VIR	20
26	26	Sa.	7:30	E	5:01	B	9 31	*15	18 s. 39	12	—	11:57	C	10:52	C	VIR	21
27	27	**F**	7:29	E	5:02	B	9 33	*15	18 s. 24	12½	12¾	—	-	11:19	B	VIR	22
28	28	M.	7:28	E	5:04	B	9 36	*16	18 s. 08	1½	1¾	1:06	D	11:48	B	LIB	23
29	29	Tu.	7:27	E	5:05	B	9 38	*16	17 s. 52	2½	3	2:12	D	12:20	B	LIB	24
30	30	W.	7:26	E	5:07	B	9 41	*16	17 s. 36	3½	4¼	3:16	E	12:55	A	OPH	25
31	31	Th.	7:25	D	5:08	B	9 43	*16	17 s. 19	4½	5½	4:16	E	1:36	A	OPH	26

JANUARY

Ring on, ring yet more gladly, merry bells,
Peal the new lord of days glad welcoming.
–Augusta Webster

DAY OF MONTH	DAY OF WEEK	DATES, FEASTS, FASTS, ASPECTS, TIDE HEIGHTS, AND WEATHER	
1	Tu.	Holy Name • **NEW YEAR'S DAY** • ♂♀☉• First U.S. electronic hwy. toll collection, Okla., 1991	*Grab*
2	W.	♂♄☉ • *A still tongue makes a wise head.* • Tides {5.8 / 5.2	*a*
3	Th.	♂♃☉ • ⊕ AT PERIHELION • Alaska became 49th state, 1959 • {5.8 / 5.3	*sled*
4	Fr.	St. Elizabeth Ann Seton • ♂♀☉• Ctrl-Alt-Delete computer code author David Bradley born, 1949	*and*
5	Sa.	Twelfth Night • **NEW ●** • **ECLIPSE** ☉ • ☾ RUNS LOW • ♂♄☾ • ♀ GR. ELONG. (47° WEST)	
6	**F**	**Epiphany** • ☾ AT ☋ • ♂♇☾ • ♁ STAT. • {6.0 / 5.6	*head for*
7	M.	Distaff Day • Plough Monday • *Surveyor VII* spacecraft launched, 1968 • {6.0 / 5.6	*the*
8	Tu.	☾ AT APO. • Physicist Stephen Hawking born, 1942 • Tides {5.9 / 5.6	*hills!*
9	W.	UN headquarters opened in N.Y.C., 1951 • {5.8 / 5.6	*Chillier:*
10	Th.	♂♆☉ • U.S. Army first to bounce radar signals off Moon (Project Diana), Wall, N.J., 1946	*Swill*
11	Fr.	♂♇☉ • Canadian prime minister Jean Chrétien born, 1934 • Tides {5.5 / 5.5	*your*
12	Sa.	♂♂☉ • *A thousand probabilities do not make one truth.* • Tides {5.3 / —	*cocoa*
13	**F**	**1st ☽. af. Ep.** • ☾ ON EQ. • ♂♀♄ • Tides {5.5 / 5.1	*before*
14	M.	♂☉☾ • First nonstop trans-Canada flight completed, 1949 • Tides {5.4 / 4.9	*it*
15	Tu.	Great Molasses Flood, Boston, Mass., 1919 • Writer André Alexis born, 1957 • {5.4 / 4.8	*spills!*
16	W.	−40°F, Coggon, Iowa, 2009 • Tides {5.5 / 4.9	*Rain*
17	Th.	U.S. statesman Benjamin Franklin born, 1706 • 6.7 earthquake, Northridge, Calif., 1994	*pelting*
18	Fr.	♂♀♇ • NASA and NOAA announced that 2016 was hottest year globally on record, 2017	*down*
19	Sa.	☾ RIDES HIGH • Writer Edgar Allan Poe born, 1809 • Tides {6.3 / 5.7	*and*
20	**F**	**2nd ☽. af. Ep.** • ☾ AT ☋ • *20–21:* **ECLIPSE** ☾	*snowmen*
21	M.	Martin Luther King Jr.'s Birthday, observed (U.S.) • **FULL WOLF** ○ • ☾ AT PERIG. • {6.8 / 6.3	*are*
22	Tu.	St. Vincent • ♂♀♃ • *If the Sun shines on January 22, there shall be much wind.*	*melting*
23	W.	Bob Keeshan (Captain Kangaroo) died, 2004 • {6.8 / 6.4	*down!*
24	Th.	Apple's Macintosh personal computer introduced, 1984 • Tides {6.6 / 6.4	*Flakes,*
25	Fr.	Conversion of Paul • ☾ ON EQ. • January thaw traditionally begins around now.	*flurries*
26	Sa.	Sts. Timothy & Titus • Rocky Mountain National Park established, Colo., 1915	*again,*
27	**F**	**3rd ☽. af. Ep.** • National Recording Registry's first 50 selections announced, 2003	*bring*
28	M.	St. Thomas Aquinas • −132°F windchill, Pelly Bay, N.W.T., 1989 • {5.8 / 5.1	*out*
29	Tu.	☿ IN SUP. ♂ • Raccoons mate now. • *All covet, all lose.*	*those*
30	W.	♂♃☾ • 31-lb. 12-oz. bluefish caught, Hatteras, N.C., 1972 • Tides {5.4 / 4.8	*furries*
31	Th.	♂♀☾ • Ice hockey player Tyler Seguin born, 1992 • {5.4 / 4.9	*again.*

Farmer's Calendar

The cottages around the lake are locked, their pipes drained, shades pulled. Where just months ago kayakers floated on silky waters, now a pickup truck zooms onto the frozen lake, towing something that looks like a deluxe privy. A handful of shanties are sprinkled across the ice— a spontaneous colony of mostly quiet anglers. I find one of them crouched over his fishing hole, withdrawing his line. The monofilament is so slender, it's hard to see; it's as if he's pantomiming the act with his hands. Finally, he crooks a finger in the emerging fish's gill as he pulls out a lake trout. Its scales are emerald, mottled with iridescent, leopard-like spots. The man has just executed a magic trick, pulling this shimmering creature from the lake's bottom—a gambler's payoff in the coldest, least hospitable casino. He measures the fish against his tackle box ruler: just barely legal. He studies his treasure once more, then lets it slip back through the hole. In a swish, it is gone. The only sounds are the shushing wind, the buzzing of a gas-powered auger, and then, in odd moments, the booming ice. It's a low bass sound, *lubb-dub*—the beat of a lake-size heart.

FEBRUARY

SKY WATCH: The heavens offer a new alignment before dawn on the 1st: Low in the east, from highest to lowest, stand Jupiter, Venus, the Moon, and Saturn. On the 2nd, the order is Jupiter, Venus, Saturn, and the Moon. On the 18th and 19th, quite low at first light, Venus meets Saturn. Throughout February, just as darkness falls, bright orange Mars stands halfway up the southwestern sky. To its left, also in Pisces, Uranus dimly shines at magnitude 5.8, just visible to the naked eye in unpolluted skies early and again late in the month. It is easily identified as the only green "star" by those who sweep binoculars leftward from Mars.

● NEW MOON	4th day	4:04 P.M.
◐ FIRST QUARTER	12th day	5:26 P.M.
○ FULL MOON	19th day	10:54 A.M.
◑ LAST QUARTER	26th day	6:28 A.M.

All times are given in Eastern Standard Time.

GET THESE PAGES WITH TIMES SET TO YOUR POSTAL CODE AT ALMANAC.CA/ACCESS.

Day of Year	Day of Month	Day of Week	☼ Rises	Rise Key	☼ Sets	Set Key	Length of Day	Sun Fast	Sun Declination		High Tide Times Halifax		☾ Rises	Rise Key	☾ Sets	Set Key	☾ Astron. Place	☾ Age
			H. M.		H. M.		H. M.	M.	°	'			H. M.		H. M.			
32	1	Fr.	7:24	D	**5:09**	B	9 45	*16	17	s. 02	5½	**6¼**	5:12	E	**2:21**	A	SAG	27
33	2	Sa.	7:23	D	**5:11**	B	9 48	*16	16	s. 45	6¼	**7¼**	6:02	E	**3:12**	A	SAG	28
34	3	**F**	7:21	D	**5:12**	B	9 51	*17	16	s. 27	7	**7¾**	6:45	E	**4:07**	A	SAG	29
35	4	M.	7:20	D	**5:14**	B	9 54	*17	16	s. 09	7¾	**8½**	7:23	E	**5:05**	A	CAP	0
36	5	Tu.	7:19	D	**5:15**	B	9 56	*17	15	s. 51	8½	**9**	7:56	D	**6:05**	B	CAP	1
37	6	W.	7:18	D	**5:17**	B	9 59	*17	15	s. 33	9	**9½**	8:24	D	**7:05**	B	AQU	2
38	7	Th.	7:16	D	**5:18**	B	10 02	*17	15	s. 14	9¾	**10¼**	8:50	D	**8:06**	B	AQU	3
39	8	Fr.	7:15	D	**5:20**	B	10 05	*17	14	s. 55	10¼	**10¾**	9:14	C	**9:07**	C	AQU	4
40	9	Sa.	7:13	D	**5:21**	B	10 08	*17	14	s. 36	10¾	**11¼**	9:38	C	**10:09**	C	CET	5
41	10	**F**	7:12	D	**5:23**	B	10 11	*17	14	s. 16	11½	—	10:02	C	**11:12**	D	PSC	6
42	11	M.	7:11	D	**5:24**	B	10 13	*17	13	s. 57	12	**12¼**	10:27	B	—	-	CET	7
43	12	Tu.	7:09	D	**5:25**	B	10 16	*17	13	s. 37	12½	**1**	10:56	B	12:17	D	ARI	8
44	13	W.	7:08	D	**5:27**	B	10 19	*17	13	s. 17	1¼	**2**	11:29	B	1:23	D	TAU	9
45	14	Th.	7:06	D	**5:28**	B	10 22	*17	12	s. 56	2¼	**3¼**	**12:09**	A	2:31	E	TAU	10
46	15	Fr.	7:05	D	**5:30**	B	10 25	*17	12	s. 36	3¼	**4½**	**12:59**	A	3:39	E	TAU	11
47	16	Sa.	7:03	D	**5:31**	B	10 28	*17	12	s. 15	4½	**5½**	**1:59**	A	4:43	E	GEM	12
48	17	**F**	7:02	D	**5:33**	B	10 31	*17	11	s. 54	5½	**6½**	**3:09**	A	5:41	E	GEM	13
49	18	M.	7:00	D	**5:34**	B	10 34	*17	11	s. 33	6½	**7¼**	**4:25**	A	6:30	E	CAN	14
50	19	Tu.	6:58	D	**5:36**	B	10 38	*17	11	s. 12	7½	**8¼**	**5:45**	B	7:13	D	LEO	15
51	20	W.	6:57	D	**5:37**	B	10 40	*16	10	s. 50	8¼	**9**	**7:05**	B	7:49	D	LEO	16
52	21	Th.	6:55	D	**5:38**	B	10 43	*16	10	s. 29	9¼	**9¾**	**8:23**	C	8:21	C	VIR	17
53	22	Fr.	6:53	D	**5:40**	B	10 47	*16	10	s. 07	10	**10½**	**9:38**	C	8:50	C	VIR	18
54	23	Sa.	6:52	D	**5:41**	B	10 49	*16	9	s. 45	10¾	**11¼**	**10:51**	D	9:19	B	VIR	19
55	24	**F**	6:50	D	**5:43**	B	10 53	*16	9	s. 23	11½	—	—	-	9:48	B	LIB	20
56	25	M.	6:48	D	**5:44**	B	10 56	*16	9	s. 00	12	**12½**	12:00	D	10:20	B	LIB	21
57	26	Tu.	6:47	D	**5:45**	B	10 58	*16	8	s. 38	12¾	**1¼**	1:07	D	10:55	A	SCO	22
58	27	W.	6:45	D	**5:47**	B	11 02	*15	8	s. 16	1¾	**2½**	2:10	E	11:34	A	OPH	23
59	28	Th.	6:43	D	**5:48**	B	11 05	*15	7	s. 53	2¾	**3¾**	3:08	E	**12:18**	A	SAG	24

FEBRUARY

Here delicate snow-stars, out of the cloud,
Come floating downward in airy play.
–William Cullen Bryant

DAY OF MONTH	DAY OF WEEK	DATES, FEASTS, FASTS, ASPECTS, TIDE HEIGHTS, AND WEATHER	
1	Fr.	St. Brigid • ☾ RUNS LOW • –50°F, Gavilan, N.Mex., 1951 • {5.4 5.1	*Groundhogs*
2	Sa.	Candlemas • Groundhog Day • ☌♄☾ • ☌♇☾ • {5.6 5.2	*blinded,*
3	**F**	☾ AT ☋ • Artist Norman Rockwell born, 1894 • Tides {5.7 5.3	*more*
4	M.	NEW ● • *Codex Sinaiticus* discovered, St. Catherine's Monastery, Mt. Sinai, Egypt, 1859	*winter,*
5	Tu.	St. Agatha • **CHINESE NEW YEAR (PIG)** • ☾ AT APO. • ☌☿☾ • {5.9 5.6	*we're*
6	W.	Woodrow Wilson became first U.S. president to be buried in D.C., 1924 • Tides {5.9 5.6	*reminded.*
7	Th.	☌♆☾ • Manufacturer John Deere born, 1804 • *Stardust* probe launched, Cape Canaveral, Fla., 1999	
8	Fr.	Politician Thelma Chalifoux born, 1929 • Tides {5.7 5.7	*Whiteout, then*
9	Sa.	☾ ON EQ. • First train passed through Hoosac Tunnel, Mass., 1875 • Tides {5.5 5.6	*bright*
10	**F**	☌♂☾ • ☌♅☾ • Olympic swimmer Victor Davis born, 1964 • {5.4 5.6	*out!*
11	M.	First joint U.S.-Russian space shuttle mission completed, 1994 • Tides {5.2 —	*Snow*
12	Tu.	U.S. president Abraham Lincoln born, 1809 • {5.5 5.0	*on and*
13	W.	☌♂♅ • *Absence sharpens love; presence strengthens it.* –Thomas Fuller • {5.5 4.8	*offing, coats*
14	Th.	Sts. Cyril & Methodius • **VALENTINE'S DAY** • {5.5 4.8	*doffing.*
15	Fr.	**NATIONAL FLAG OF CANADA DAY** • Astronomer Galileo Galilei born, 1564 • Social reformer Susan B. Anthony born, 1820	
16	Sa.	☾ RIDES HIGH • 250-hr., 3-min., 20-sec. ice hockey marathon ended, Saiker's Acres, Alta., 2015	*Mercury*
17	**F**	**Septuagesima** • ☾ AT ☊ • Winter's back breaks. • {6.0 5.7	*plummets,*
18	M.	**PRESIDENTS' DAY (U.S.)** • ☌♀♄ • "Firenado" captured on video, Platte County, Mo., 2016	*more*
19	Tu.	**FULL SNOW** ○ • ☾ AT PERIG. • ☌☿♆ • {6.6 6.4	*flurries*
20	W.	*It is wise not to seek a secret, and honest not to reveal it.* • Tides {6.7 6.6	*come; it's*
21	Th.	Polaroid instant camera first demonstrated, 1947 • Tides {6.7 6.6	*suddenly*
22	Fr.	☾ ON EQ. • U.S. president George Washington born, 1732 • "Florida Purchase" treaty signed, 1819	*springlike!*
23	Sa.	☌♀♇ • 97°F, San Antonio, Tex., 1996 • Tides {6.2 6.3	*Who*
24	**F**	**Sexagesima** • Skunks mate now. • Tides {5.8 —	*would*
25	M.	St. Matthias[T] • 49.3" snow fell, Mt. Washington, N.H., 1969 • {6.0 5.4	*guess*
26	Tu.	☿ GR. ELONG. (18° EAST) • Grand Canyon National Park established, Ariz., 1919 • {5.6 5.0	*a*
27	W.	☌♃☾ • *When gnats dance in February, the husbandman becomes a beggar.* • {5.3 4.8	*thing like*
28	Th.	St. Romanus • Radio broadcaster Paul Harvey died, 2009 • Tides {5.1 4.7	*this?*

What's the fastest vegetable? A runner bean.

Farmer's Calendar

While snow levels fluctuate or mostly rise, our winter stores subside. The woodshed looks like a mouth of broken teeth, and the chest freezer has new cavities, too. The same goes for our livestock supplies. Our cows wait out the days gazing at snow that they can't eat covering fields that they used to graze—thank heavens for hay. Last summer we stuffed the mow with a winter's worth (one bale per cow, per day, plus extra, just in case). As I deliver flakes to the Jersey and her yearling calf, I second-guess what's left, wondering if it'll last until they're back on pasture; so much depends on winter's strength and length. Years ago, when I worked on a bigger farm, each morning I climbed into the loft, where the bales were stacked to the rafters. Summiting the steep pile, I'd pry down a dozen, clenching them by their twine. As winter days ticked by and the mountain of dried grass dwindled, the barn's walls re-emerged. One day in mid-February, by luck or barn maker's design, I saw a sign I took to mean that we'd reached the season's halfway mark: Sunlight streamed through a hole bored near the roof's peak, a vent in the shape of a valentine.

Listen to the Farmer's Calendar at Almanac.ca/Podcast.

MARCH

SKY WATCH: Mercury hovers low in the west during the first few evenings of March. On the 1st, in the east just before dawn, a line of celestial objects becomes visible above Sagittarius's "Teapot" asterism (pattern of stars). From right to left, these are Jupiter, the Moon, Saturn, and Venus. On the morning of the 2nd, the thin crescent Moon passes to the right of Venus, which presents a gibbous shape through binoculars and small telescopes. Earth stands sideways to the Sun on the 20th. This is the vernal equinox, marking the start of spring, which occurs at 5:58 P.M., shortly before the Sun sets at precisely the cardinal direction of due west.

● **NEW MOON** 6th day 11:04 A.M. ○ **FULL MOON** 20th day 9:43 P.M.

◑ **FIRST QUARTER** 14th day 6:27 A.M. ◐ **LAST QUARTER** 28th day 12:10 A.M.

After 2:00 A.M. on March 10, Eastern Daylight Time is given.

GET THESE PAGES WITH TIMES SET TO YOUR POSTAL CODE AT ALMANAC.CA/ACCESS.

DAY OF YEAR	DAY OF MONTH	DAY OF WEEK	☼ RISES H. M.	RISE KEY	☼ SETS H. M.	SET KEY	LENGTH OF DAY H. M.	SUN FAST M.	SUN DECLINATION ° ′	HIGH TIDE TIMES HALIFAX		☾ RISES H. M.	RISE KEY	☾ SETS H. M.	SET KEY	☾ ASTRON. PLACE	☾ AGE
60	1	Fr.	6:41	D	5:50	B	11 09	*15	7 s. 30	4	5	3:59	E	1:07	A	SAG	25
61	2	Sa.	6:40	D	5:51	B	11 11	*15	7 s. 07	5	6	4:45	E	2:01	A	SAG	26
62	3	F	6:38	D	5:52	C	11 14	*15	6 s. 44	6	6¾	5:24	E	2:58	A	CAP	27
63	4	M.	6:36	D	5:54	C	11 18	*14	6 s. 21	6¾	7½	5:58	D	3:57	B	CAP	28
64	5	Tu.	6:34	C	5:55	C	11 21	*14	5 s. 58	7½	8	6:28	D	4:58	B	AQU	29
65	6	W.	6:32	C	5:56	C	11 24	*14	5 s. 35	8	8½	6:54	D	5:59	B	AQU	0
66	7	Th.	6:31	C	5:58	C	11 27	*14	5 s. 11	8¾	9	7:19	C	7:00	C	AQU	1
67	8	Fr.	6:29	C	5:59	C	11 30	*13	4 s. 48	9¼	9½	7:42	C	8:02	C	PSC	2
68	9	Sa.	6:27	C	6:01	C	11 34	*13	4 s. 25	9¾	10	8:06	C	9:05	C	CET	3
69	10	F	7:25	C	7:02	C	11 37	*13	4 s. 01	11½	11¾	9:31	B	11:09	D	PSC	4
70	11	M.	7:23	C	7:03	C	11 40	*13	3 s. 38	12	—	9:58	B	—	-	ARI	5
71	12	Tu.	7:21	C	7:05	C	11 44	*12	3 s. 14	12¼	12¾	10:29	B	12:15	D	TAU	6
72	13	W.	7:19	C	7:06	C	11 47	*12	2 s. 50	1	1½	11:05	A	1:21	E	TAU	7
73	14	Th.	7:18	C	7:07	C	11 49	*12	2 s. 27	1¾	2½	11:50	A	2:27	E	TAU	8
74	15	Fr.	7:16	C	7:09	C	11 53	*12	2 s. 03	2¾	3¾	12:43	A	3:30	E	GEM	9
75	16	Sa.	7:14	C	7:10	C	11 56	*11	1 s. 39	3¾	5	1:46	A	4:28	E	GEM	10
76	17	F	7:12	C	7:11	C	11 59	*11	1 s. 16	5¼	6¼	2:58	A	5:20	E	CAN	11
77	18	M.	7:10	C	7:12	C	12 02	*11	0 s. 52	6¼	7¼	4:15	B	6:04	D	LEO	12
78	19	Tu.	7:08	C	7:14	C	12 06	*10	0 s. 28	7¼	8	5:34	B	6:42	D	LEO	13
79	20	W.	7:06	C	7:15	C	12 09	*10	0 s. 04	8¼	8¾	6:53	B	7:15	D	LEO	14
80	21	Th.	7:04	C	7:16	C	12 12	*10	0 N. 18	9	9½	8:10	C	7:46	C	VIR	15
81	22	Fr.	7:02	C	7:18	C	12 16	*10	0 N. 42	9¾	10¼	9:26	C	8:15	C	VIR	16
82	23	Sa.	7:01	C	7:19	C	12 18	*9	1 N. 06	10¾	11	10:40	D	8:45	B	VIR	17
83	24	F	6:59	C	7:20	C	12 21	*9	1 N. 29	11½	11¾	11:51	D	9:16	B	LIB	18
84	25	M.	6:57	C	7:22	C	12 25	*9	1 N. 53	12¼	—	—	-	9:50	A	LIB	19
85	26	Tu.	6:55	C	7:23	C	12 28	*8	2 N. 16	12½	1	12:58	E	10:28	A	OPH	20
86	27	W.	6:53	C	7:24	C	12 31	*8	2 N. 40	1¼	2	1:59	E	11:12	A	OPH	21
87	28	Th.	6:51	C	7:25	C	12 34	*8	3 N. 03	2¼	3	2:55	E	12:00	A	SAG	22
88	29	Fr.	6:49	C	7:27	C	12 38	*8	3 N. 27	3¼	4¼	3:43	E	12:53	A	SAG	23
89	30	Sa.	6:47	C	7:28	C	12 41	*7	3 N. 50	4¼	5½	4:25	E	1:49	A	CAP	24
90	31	F	6:45	C	7:29	C	12 44	*7	4 N. 13	5½	6½	5:00	E	2:48	A	CAP	25

The warring hosts of Winter and of Spring
Are hurtling o'er the plains.
–Christopher Pearse Cranch

Farmer's Calendar

When the bird with black-and-white–flecked feathers and a poinsettia-red head swooped into our yard, I didn't need binoculars to observe it. North America's largest woodpecker, the pileated is notorious for clinging to trees and hammering with its beak, sending blonde splinters sprinkling onto the snow. Viewed up close, this avian air hammer strikes me as faintly spooky. So when this one latched on to my favorite silver maple and began its carpentry, I felt uneasy. We'd lost an ancient oak to lightning the year before, and I was averse to uninvited things alighting in our remaining trees. Pileateds can be beneficial, extracting insects and larvae lurking under the bark, even when the cavities they bore are wide and deep. Still, I wanted to preclude its excavation. Therefore, when the bird commenced to drill and a pile of bark chips began to accrue, I tried to shoo it off, hooting and waving my arms. But this only deterred it momentarily. So I opened my laptop to play a recording of its species at maximum volume. Did the digital voice express a curse or hex? Whatever it proclaimed halted the yard bird in midpeck. Then it trilled a reply, flapped off, and hasn't been back.

DAY OF MONTH	DAY OF WEEK	DATES, FEASTS, FASTS, ASPECTS, TIDE HEIGHTS, AND WEATHER		
1	Fr.	St. David • ☾ RUNS LOW • ♂♓☾ • ♂♇☾ • Tides {5.0 / 4.7	*Wintry*
2	Sa.	St. Chad • ☾ AT ☋ • ♂♀☾ • Writer Theodor Seuss Geisel born, 1904	*reentry:*
3	F	**Quinquagesima** • *A good life keeps off wrinkles.* • {5.3 / 5.1	*sunny,*
4	M.	☾ AT APO. • *Voyager I* spacecraft revealed rings of Jupiter, 1979 • Playwright Horton Foote died, 2009	*but*
5	Tu.	Shrove Tuesday • St. Piran • ☿ STAT. • Tides {5.6 / 5.5	*hard*
6	W.	**Ash Wednesday** • NEW ● • ♂♆☉ • ♂♆☾	*to*
7	Th.	St. Perpetua • ♂♀☾ • Horticulturist Luther Burbank born, 1849 • {5.8 / 5.7	*feel*
8	Fr.	☾ ON EQ. • Baseball player Joe DiMaggio died, 1999 • {5.7 / 5.8	*cheery in*
9	Sa.	♂☌☾ • Hummingbirds migrate north now. • Tides {5.7 / 5.8	*(after*
10	F	1st �};. in Lent • **DAYLIGHT SAVING TIME BEGINS, 2:00 A.M.** • {5.6 / 5.8	*some*
11	M.	Clean Monday • ♂♂☾ • 9.0 earthquake moved Honshu, Japan, 8' east, 2011	*rain),*
12	Tu.	*Winds that change against the Sun Are always sure to backward run.* • Tides {5.7 / 5.3	*it's*
13	W.	Ember Day • Geomagnetic storm collapsed Hydro-Québec power grid, 1989 • {5.6 / 5.1	*Siberian!*
14	Th.	☿ IN INF. • Physicist Albert Einstein born, 1879 • {5.5 / 4.9	*Snowstorm*
15	Fr.	Ember Day • Beware the ides of March. • ☾ RIDES HIGH • American Legion org. founded, 1919	*enormous*
16	Sa.	Ember Day • ☾ AT ☋ • Norman Thagard first American to visit Russian space station *Mir*, 1995	*to*
17	F	2nd �};. in Lent • **ST. PATRICK'S DAY** • {5.5 / 5.3	*flurries*
18	M.	$500 million in artwork stolen, Isabella Stewart Gardner Museum, Boston, 1990 • {5.8 / 5.8	*diminishing;*
19	Tu.	St. Joseph • ☾ AT PERIG. • 1,383-sq. ft. omelet made, 1994 • {6.1 / 6.2	*south*
20	W.	**VERNAL EQUINOX** • **FULL WORM** ○ • Musician John Lennon wed Yoko Ono, 1969	*winds*
21	Th.	☾ ON EQ. • "Royals" winning name for new Kansas City baseball team, 1968 • {6.5 / 6.7	*will*
22	Fr.	♂♀♆ • Alaska's Mt. Redoubt volcano began series of eruptions, 2009 • {6.5 / 6.7	*warm*
23	Sa.	NHL player Wayne Gretzky scored 802nd career goal, 1994 • Tides {6.3 / 6.5	*us,*
24	F	3rd �};. in Lent • Maser patented, 1959 • {6.0 / 6.2	*soft*
25	M.	Annunciation • *Mar. 25–26: 20.6" snow fell in 24 hours, Amarillo, Tex., 1934* • {5.7 / —	*rains*
26	Tu.	♂♃☾ • "Melissa" macro computer virus released, disrupting email systems worldwide, 1999	*inform*
27	W.	☿ STAT. • Chipmunks emerge from hibernation now. • Tides {5.4 / 5.1	*us*
28	Th.	☾ RUNS LOW • Partial meltdown of Three Mile Island nuclear power station, Pa., 1979	*that*
29	Fr.	☾ AT ☋ • ♂♓☾ • ♂♇☾ • First performance of Ringling Bros. and Barnum & Bailey Circus, 1919	
30	Sa.	*A kind word is like a spring day.* • Tides {4.8 / 4.7	*winter is*
31	F	4th �};. in Lent • ☾ AT APO. • Nfld. became 10th province, 1949	*finishing.*

CALENDAR

APRIL

SKY WATCH: Mercury is now a morning star and on the 1st participates in an alignment low in the east some 40 minutes before sunrise: Look to see, from highest to lowest, the Moon, Venus, and Mercury. On the 2nd, the Moon is below Venus, with Mercury to their left. Jupiter, brightening steadily, now appears several hours before sunrise, high enough for useful telescopic observation at dawn. Saturn is marginally high enough, too, but its rings are not as wide open as they've been in recent years. Mars, now in Taurus and fading, stands above the fat waxing crescent Moon on the 8th.

● **NEW MOON** 5th day 4:50 A.M. ○ **FULL MOON** 19th day 7:12 A.M.
◐ **FIRST QUARTER** 12th day 3:06 P.M. ◑ **LAST QUARTER** 26th day 6:18 P.M.

All times are given in Eastern Daylight Time.

GET THESE PAGES WITH TIMES SET TO YOUR POSTAL CODE AT ALMANAC.CA/ACCESS.

DAY OF YEAR	DAY OF MONTH	DAY OF WEEK	☼ RISES H. M.	RISE KEY	☼ SETS H. M.	SET KEY	LENGTH OF DAY H. M.	SUN FAST M.	SUN DECLINATION ° '	HIGH TIDE TIMES HALIFAX		☾ RISES H. M.	RISE KEY	☾ SETS H. M.	SET KEY	☾ ASTRON. PLACE	☾ AGE
91	1	M.	6:44	C	7:31	C	12 47	*7	4 N. 37	6½	7¼	5:31	D	**3:49**	B	CAP	26
92	2	Tu.	6:42	C	7:32	C	12 50	*6	5 N. 00	7¼	7¾	5:58	D	**4:50**	B	AQU	27
93	3	W.	6:40	C	7:33	D	12 53	*6	5 N. 23	8	8½	6:23	D	**5:51**	B	AQU	28
94	4	Th.	6:38	C	7:35	D	12 57	*6	5 N. 46	8½	9	6:47	C	**6:54**	C	PSC	29
95	5	Fr.	6:36	B	7:36	D	13 00	*5	6 N. 08	9¼	9½	7:10	C	**7:57**	C	CET	0
96	6	Sa.	6:34	B	7:37	D	13 03	*5	6 N. 31	9¾	10	7:34	B	**9:02**	D	PSC	1
97	7	**F**	6:32	B	7:38	D	13 06	*5	6 N. 54	10½	10½	8:01	B	**10:08**	D	CET	2
98	8	M.	6:31	B	7:40	D	13 09	*5	7 N. 16	11	11¼	8:30	B	**11:14**	D	ARI	3
99	9	Tu.	6:29	B	7:41	D	13 12	*4	7 N. 39	11¾	11¾	9:05	A	—	-	TAU	4
100	10	W.	6:27	B	7:42	D	13 15	*4	8 N. 01	12½	—	9:46	A	12:21	E	TAU	5
101	11	Th.	6:25	B	7:44	D	13 19	*4	8 N. 23	12½	1¼	10:36	A	1:25	E	GEM	6
102	12	Fr.	6:23	B	7:45	D	13 22	*4	8 N. 45	1½	2¼	11:35	A	2:24	E	GEM	7
103	13	Sa.	6:21	B	7:46	D	13 25	*3	9 N. 07	2¼	3½	**12:42**	A	3:16	E	CAN	8
104	14	**F**	6:20	B	7:47	D	13 27	*3	9 N. 28	3½	4¾	**1:54**	A	4:01	E	CAN	9
105	15	M.	6:18	B	7:49	D	13 31	*3	9 N. 50	4¾	6	**3:10**	B	4:40	D	LEO	10
106	16	Tu.	6:16	B	7:50	D	13 34	*3	10 N. 11	6	6¾	**4:27**	B	5:13	D	LEO	11
107	17	W.	6:14	B	7:51	D	13 37	*2	10 N. 32	7	7½	**5:44**	C	5:44	C	VIR	12
108	18	Th.	6:13	B	7:53	D	13 40	*2	10 N. 53	8	8½	**7:00**	C	6:12	C	VIR	13
109	19	Fr.	6:11	B	7:54	D	13 43	*2	11 N. 14	8¾	9	**8:15**	D	6:41	B	VIR	14
110	20	Sa.	6:09	B	7:55	D	13 46	*2	11 N. 35	9½	9¾	**9:29**	D	7:11	B	LIB	15
111	21	**F**	6:07	B	7:56	D	13 49	*2	11 N. 55	10¼	10½	**10:39**	D	7:44	B	LIB	16
112	22	M.	6:06	B	7:58	D	13 52	*1	12 N. 15	11	11¼	**11:45**	E	8:21	A	OPH	17
113	23	Tu.	6:04	B	7:59	D	13 55	*1	12 N. 35	12	—	—	-	9:02	A	OPH	18
114	24	W.	6:02	B	8:00	D	13 58	*1	12 N. 55	12	12¾	**12:45**	E	9:50	A	SAG	19
115	25	Th.	6:01	B	8:02	D	14 01	*1	13 N. 15	12¾	1½	**1:38**	E	10:42	A	SAG	20
116	26	Fr.	5:59	B	8:03	D	14 04	*1	13 N. 34	1½	2½	**2:23**	E	11:38	A	SAG	21
117	27	Sa.	5:58	B	8:04	D	14 06	*1	13 N. 53	2½	3½	**3:01**	E	**12:37**	A	CAP	22
118	28	**F**	5:56	B	8:05	D	14 09	0	14 N. 12	3½	4¾	**3:33**	D	**1:37**	B	CAP	23
119	29	M.	5:55	B	8:07	D	14 12	0	14 N. 31	4¾	5¾	**4:02**	D	**2:38**	B	AQU	24
120	30	Tu.	5:53	B	8:08	D	14 15	0	14 N. 49	6	6½	**4:27**	D	**3:39**	B	AQU	25

To use this page, see p. 116; for Key Letters, see p. 238. LIGHT = A.M. BOLD = P.M.

CALENDAR

The gray hills deepen in green again;
The rainbow hangs in heaven.
–Emma Lazarus

DAY OF MONTH	DAY OF WEEK	DATES, FEASTS, FASTS, ASPECTS, TIDE HEIGHTS, AND WEATHER	
1	M.	**ALL FOOLS'** • *It is a great point of wisdom to find out one's own folly.* • {5.0 / 5.2}	Snow
2	Tu.	☌♀☿ • ☌♀♅ • ☌♂☽ • ☌♀♆ • Tides {5.2 / 5.4}	a foot
3	W.	St. Richard of Chichester • First mobile phone call made, 1973 • {5.4 / 5.6}	thick!
4	Th.	☽ ON EQ. • *Apr. 3–4:* "Super Outbreak" of 148 tornadoes hit 13 U.S. states and Ont., 1974	How's
5	Fr.	**NEW** ● • Actor Charlton Heston died, 2008 • {5.6 / 5.8}	that
6	Sa.	☌☽☉ • Explorer Robert Peary's party reached what was believed to be North Pole, 1909	for a
7	**F**	**5th S. in Lent** • World Health Organization established, 1948 • {5.7 / 5.9}	trick?
8	M.	Gallaudet University founded, D.C., 1864 • Hank Aaron broke Babe Ruth's record w/ 715th home run, 1974	Promise
9	Tu.	☌♀♆ • ☌☌☽ • Names of first 7 NASA astronauts announced, 1959 • {5.5 / 5.8}	of
10	W.	♃ STAT. • Walter Hunt rec'd patent for safety pin, 1849 • Tides {5.4 / —}	better
11	Th.	☽ RIDES HIGH • ☿ GR. ELONG. (28° WEST) • Geneva, Switz., chosen as League of Nations location, 1919	times,
12	Fr.	☽ AT ☊ • *Sour grapes can ne'er make sweet wine.* • Tides {5.5 / 5.0}	but first
13	Sa.	U.S. president Thomas Jefferson born, 1743 • Tides {5.3 / 5.0}	some
14	**F**	**Palm Sunday** • Noah Webster's *American Dict. of the English Language* printed, 1828	wetter
15	M.	Canadian thanksgiving day held after Prince of Wales recovered from serious illness, 1872 • {5.3 / 5.5}	times.
16	Tu.	☽ AT PERIG. • Toronto Maple Leafs won 3rd consecutive NHL Stanley Cup, 1949	Sunshine
17	W.	Discovery of first Earth-size planet in "Habitable Zone" publicized, 2014 • Tides {5.8 / 6.2}	enraptures
18	Th.	**Maundy Thursday** • ☽ ON EQ. • First U.S. public laundromat opened, Fort Worth, Tex., 1934	
19	Fr.	**Good Friday** • Passover begins at sundown • **FULL PINK** ○ {6.1 / 6.6}	us,
20	Sa.	Daredevil Felix Baumgartner born, 1969 • Tides {6.1 / 6.5}	then
21	**F**	**Easter** • Half-dollar–size hail fell near Marion, S.C., 2012 • Tides {6.0 / 6.3}	showers
22	M.	**Easter Monday** • ☌☽☉ • R. Keech drove 207.552 mph in "White Triplex" car, 1928	will
23	Tu.	☌♃☽ • Guelph, Ont., incorporated as city, 1879 • Tides {5.6 / —}	capture
24	W.	☽ RUNS LOW • *The Old Farmer's Almanac* founder Robert B. Thomas born, 1766 • {5.7 / 5.4}	us.
25	Th.	☽ AT ☊ • ☌♄☽ • ☌♇☽ • ♇ STAT. • Tides {5.4 / 5.1}	Steadily
26	Fr.	*If ants their walls do frequent build, Rain will from the clouds be spilled.* • Tides {5.1 / 4.9}	soaking
27	Sa.	Odd green light shot across night sky, experts concluded likely meteor, southern Calif., 2016 • {4.8 / 4.8}	and
28	**F**	**2nd S. of Easter** • **Orthodox Easter** • ☽ AT APO.	we're
29	M.	St. George[T] • ♄ STAT. • Poplars leaf out about now. • Tides {4.7 / 5.0}	not
30	Tu.	St. Mark[T] • ☌♀♆ • George Washington inaugurated as first U.S. president, 1789	joking.

CALENDAR

Farmer's Calendar

Winter's true finish is anyone's guess—precisely the point of the annual contest on Joe's Pond in West Danville, Vermont. This year, I'm betting it's April 2 at 11:27 A.M. This guess cost me a buck. So if I'm correct and if the "ice-out" contraption—a pallet, a cinder block, and a flag tethered by 250 feet of nylon rope to a power source for the clock on land—if that wacky raft hunkered on the frozen pond should slump during the thaw of a warm March and begin to sink beneath the pond's waters around breakfast on April 2, and its descent strains the rope such that it finally breaks the electrical connection, stopping the clock at precisely 11:27 A.M., as the raft submerges into the newly liquefied pond, then I stand to collect half the betting cash. What's more, come July, no matter who won, everybody in the vicinity of Joe's Pond gets a prize: On the evening of Independence Day, the sky will fill with sparkles and crackles and scintillating falling stars. This fireworks display is funded with the remaining money from those hunches, those best guesses when our winter went out not with a bang, but with a gurgle.

MAY

SKY WATCH: This is a transition month. At nightfall on the 1st, Orion stands upright on the western horizon but vanishes by month's end. Mars, fading rapidly, starts this month in Taurus but zooms into Gemini by midmonth. Jupiter, in the "13th zodiac constellation," Ophiuchus, now rises well before midnight and is near the Moon on the 20th and 21st. Saturn, in Sagittarius, rises at about 1:00 A.M. on the 1st and is well placed for the rest of the short night. In the predawn east, the planetary alignments have ended; only Venus remains, hovering low to float above the waning crescent Moon on the 2nd.

● **NEW MOON** 4th day 6:46 P.M.   ○ **FULL MOON** 18th day 5:11 P.M.
◐ **FIRST QUARTER** 11th day 9:12 P.M.   ◑ **LAST QUARTER** 26th day 12:34 P.M.

All times are given in Eastern Daylight Time.

GET THESE PAGES WITH TIMES SET TO YOUR POSTAL CODE AT ALMANAC.CA/ACCESS.

DAY OF YEAR	DAY OF MONTH	DAY OF WEEK	☼ RISES H. M.	RISE KEY	☼ SETS H. M.	SET KEY	LENGTH OF DAY H. M.	SUN FAST M.	SUN DECLINATION ° '	HIGH TIDE TIMES HALIFAX		☾ RISES H. M.	RISE KEY	☾ SETS H. M.	SET KEY	☾ ASTRON. PLACE	☾ AGE
121	1	W.	5:51	B	8:09	D	14 18	0	15 N. 08	6¾	7¼	4:51	C	4:42	C	PSC	26
122	2	Th.	5:50	B	8:10	D	14 20	0	15 N. 26	7½	7¾	5:14	C	5:45	C	CET	27
123	3	Fr.	5:48	B	8:12	D	14 24	0	15 N. 43	8	8¼	5:38	C	6:50	D	PSC	28
124	4	Sa.	5:47	B	8:13	D	14 26	0	16 N. 01	8¾	9	6:03	B	7:56	D	CET	0
125	5	**F**	5:46	B	8:14	D	14 28	0	16 N. 18	9½	9½	6:31	B	9:04	D	ARI	1
126	6	M.	5:44	B	8:15	D	14 31	0	16 N. 35	10	10	7:04	A	10:13	E	TAU	2
127	7	Tu.	5:43	B	8:17	E	14 34	1	16 N. 52	10¾	10¾	7:44	A	11:19	E	TAU	3
128	8	W.	5:41	B	8:18	E	14 37	1	17 N. 08	11½	11½	8:32	A	—	-	ORI	4
129	9	Th.	5:40	B	8:19	E	14 39	1	17 N. 24	12¼	—	9:28	A	12:21	E	GEM	5
130	10	Fr.	5:39	B	8:20	E	14 41	1	17 N. 40	12¼	1¼	10:33	A	1:15	E	GEM	6
131	11	Sa.	5:38	B	8:22	E	14 44	1	17 N. 55	1¼	2	11:43	A	2:02	E	CAN	7
132	12	**F**	5:36	A	8:23	E	14 47	1	18 N. 11	2¼	3¼	12:57	B	2:42	D	LEO	8
133	13	M.	5:35	A	8:24	E	14 49	1	18 N. 25	3¼	4½	2:11	B	3:16	D	LEO	9
134	14	Tu.	5:34	A	8:25	E	14 51	1	18 N. 40	4¾	5½	3:26	C	3:46	D	VIR	10
135	15	W.	5:33	A	8:26	E	14 53	1	18 N. 54	5¾	6½	4:40	C	4:14	C	VIR	11
136	16	Th.	5:32	A	8:27	E	14 55	1	19 N. 08	6¾	7¼	5:54	C	4:41	C	VIR	12
137	17	Fr.	5:30	A	8:29	E	14 59	1	19 N. 22	7¾	8	7:07	D	5:10	B	VIR	13
138	18	Sa.	5:29	A	8:30	E	15 01	1	19 N. 35	8½	8¾	8:19	D	5:40	B	LIB	14
139	19	**F**	5:28	A	8:31	E	15 03	1	19 N. 48	9¼	9½	9:28	E	6:14	A	SCO	15
140	20	M.	5:27	A	8:32	E	15 05	1	20 N. 01	10	10¼	10:32	E	6:54	A	OPH	16
141	21	Tu.	5:26	A	8:33	E	15 07	0	20 N. 13	10¾	11	11:29	E	7:39	A	SAG	17
142	22	W.	5:25	A	8:34	E	15 09	0	20 N. 25	11½	11¾	—	-	8:29	A	SAG	18
143	23	Th.	5:25	A	8:35	E	15 10	0	20 N. 36	12¼	—	12:18	E	9:25	A	SAG	19
144	24	Fr.	5:24	A	8:36	E	15 12	0	20 N. 48	12½	1	12:59	E	10:24	A	CAP	20
145	25	Sa.	5:23	A	8:37	E	15 14	0	20 N. 58	1¼	2	1:34	E	11:24	A	CAP	21
146	26	**F**	5:22	A	8:38	E	15 16	0	21 N. 09	2	2¾	2:04	D	12:25	B	AQU	22
147	27	M.	5:21	A	8:39	E	15 18	0	21 N. 19	2¾	3¾	2:30	D	1:26	B	AQU	23
148	28	Tu.	5:20	A	8:40	E	15 20	0	21 N. 29	4	4¾	2:54	C	2:28	C	AQU	24
149	29	W.	5:20	A	8:41	E	15 21	0	21 N. 38	5	5¾	3:17	C	3:30	C	CET	25
150	30	Th.	5:19	A	8:42	E	15 23	0	21 N. 47	6	6¼	3:40	C	4:34	C	CET	26
151	31	Fr.	5:18	A	8:43	E	15 25	*1	21 N. 56	6¾	7	4:05	B	5:40	D	PSC	27

To use this page, see p. 116; for Key Letters, see p. 238. LIGHT = A.M. **BOLD = P.M.** 2019

CALENDAR

THE FIFTH MONTH • 2019 MAY MAY HATH 31 DAYS

Then came fair May, the fairest maid on ground,
Decked all with dainties of her season's pride.
–Edmund Spenser

DAY OF MONTH	DAY OF WEEK	DATES, FEASTS, FASTS, ASPECTS, TIDE HEIGHTS, AND WEATHER	
1	W.	Sts. Philip & James • May Day • Existence of Van Allen radiation belts announced, 1958	*Wet*
2	Th.	St. Athanasius • ☾ on Eq. • ☌♀☾ • Horse *Mine That Bird* won Kentucky Derby, 2009	*as*
3	F.	☌☿☾ • ☌♅☾ • Tornado outbreak struck Okla. and Kans., 1999 • {5.3/5.8	*we*
4	Sa.	New ● • Royal Canadian Mint produced its last penny, 2012 • {5.5/5.9	*can*
5	**F**	**3rd S. of Easter** • Ramadan begins at sundown • *After black clouds, clear weather.*	*get,*
6	M.	State of emergency declared due to flooding, Winnipeg, Man., 1950 • Tides {5.6/6.1	*we*
7	Tu.	☌♂☾ • 9.4-inch-long, 14-lb. pearl found in giant clam, set world record, Philippines, 1934	*regret.*
8	W.	St. Julian of Norwich • ☌☿♅ • Baseball player Dom DiMaggio died, 2009 • {5.6/5.9	*Brilliant,*
9	Th.	St. Gregory of Nazianzus • ☾ rides high • ☾ at ☊ • {5.5/—	*but*
10	Fr.	Golden spike linked Union Pacific and Central Pacific railroads, Promontory Point, Utah, 1869	*briefly;*
11	Sa.	James Monroe first U.S. president to ride on steamboat (SS *Savannah*), 1819 • Three • {5.6/5.3	*more*
12	**F**	**4th S. of Easter** • Mother's Day • Chilly • {5.4/5.3	*showers,*
13	M.	☾ at perig. • Cranberries in bud now. • Saints • {5.2/5.4	*chiefly.*
14	Tu.	Entrepreneur Henry John Heinz died, 1919 • Filmmaker George Lucas born, 1944 • Tides {5.2/5.7	*No*
15	W.	☾ on Eq. • 4 bear cubs playing on backyard trampoline caught on video, Avon, Conn., 2017	*signs*
16	Th.	*Night is the mother of thought.* • Discovery of 2.6-billion-year-old water in Ont. mine announced, 2013	*of*
17	Fr.	Allan Ganz honored for 67-year career as ice-cream man, 2014 • Tides {5.7/6.3	*relief,*
18	Sa.	Vesak • Full Flower ○ • ☌♀♅ • 116°F, Death Valley, Calif., 2006 • {5.8/6.3	*we*
19	**F**	**5th S. of Easter** • U.S. First Lady Jacqueline Kennedy Onassis died, 1994	*report,*
20	M.	Victoria Day • ☌♃☾ • 6" snow, Lexington, Ky., 1894 • {5.7/6.1	*to*
21	Tu.	☿ in sup. ☌ • Painter Henri Rousseau born, 1844 • {5.6/5.8	*our*
22	W.	☾ runs low • ☾ at ☋ • ☌♄☾ • ☌♇☾ • {5.5/5.6	*grief.*
23	Th.	Townsend-Purnell Plant Patent Act first in U.S. to grant patent protection to plant breeders, 1930	*Be*
24	Fr.	Britain's Queen Victoria born, 1819 • Samuel Morse sent first telegraphic message, "What hath God wrought," 1844	*of*
25	Sa.	St. Bede • First shave in space, *Apollo 10,* 1969 • Tides {5.1/5.0	*good*
26	**F**	**Rogation Sunday** • ☾ at apo. • Tides {4.9/5.0	
27	M.	Memorial Day, observed (U.S.) • ☌♆☾ • Lightning struck storm chaser in car, S.Dak., 2014	*cheer!*
28	Tu.	R. H. Macy & Co. incorporated, 1919 • Tides {4.6/5.1	*Summer*
29	W.	☾ on Eq. • *If the brain sows not corn, it plants thistles.* • Tides {4.6/5.2	*appears*
30	Th.	**Ascension** • Musician Benny Goodman born, 1909 • {4.8/5.4	*to be*
31	Fr.	Visit. of Mary • ☌♅☾ • Waterspout formed, Dollar Lake, Riverton, Wyo., 2014	*here!*

Farmer's Calendar

Sometimes I get lonesome for a moose to lumber through the back field, if only to prove that they really do exist, that these aren't mythic beasts. Maine drivers are believers and, sadly, all too familiar with humongous ungulates who come strolling out of the woods and onto the highway. Vermonters often have to hunt for an encounter, as a few of us did one spring when the leaves were still as tender as the muzzle of an *Alces alces*. We rose before dawn and piled into a car, friends on a mission to glimpse the gangly cousins of lovely deer. We drove to their favored habitat, a patch of swampy woods. As the Sun's rays broke over the hills, we pulled off by a "Moose Crossing" sign and waited like fools for our improbable quarry. When I think back now, I wonder: What were the odds of us spotting the apocryphal animal? But as luck would have it, within minutes, a shaggy specimen came stilting across the asphalt. Cell-phone cameras were still years away, so we have no photograph of the hulking bull who nonchalantly swiveled to consider our vehicle and then plodded on, leaving hoofprints the size of our amazed faces.

JUNE

SKY WATCH: The thin crescent Moon hangs to the right of Venus on the 1st, very low in the east during dawn's first light. Mercury is an evening star, not difficult to see in the west during the first half of the month. It closely meets Mars on the 18th, but both are low in evening twilight; use binoculars. Jupiter reaches opposition on the 10th and shines at magnitude –2.6, its brightest of the year, in the constellation Ophiuchus; it is joined by the full Moon on the 16th. Rising at sunset, Jupiter dominates as the night's brightest "star." Far to its right floats Antares, the supergiant alpha star of Scorpius. Far to Jupiter's left hovers bright but not dazzling Saturn, which now rises at nightfall. Summer begins with the solstice on the 21st at 11:54 A.M.

● **NEW MOON** 3rd day 6:02 A.M. ○ **FULL MOON** 17th day 4:31 A.M.
◑ **FIRST QUARTER** 10th day 1:59 A.M. ◐ **LAST QUARTER** 25th day 5:46 A.M.

All times are given in Eastern Daylight Time.

GET THESE PAGES WITH TIMES SET TO YOUR POSTAL CODE AT ALMANAC.CA/ACCESS.

DAY OF YEAR	DAY OF MONTH	DAY OF WEEK	☼ RISES H. M.	RISE KEY	☼ SETS H. M.	SET KEY	LENGTH OF DAY H. M.	SUN FAST M.	SUN DECLINATION ° '	HIGH TIDE TIMES HALIFAX		☾ RISES H. M.	RISE KEY	☾ SETS H. M.	SET KEY	☾ ASTRON. PLACE	☾ AGE
152	1	Sa.	5:18	A	8:44	E	15 26	*1	22 N. 04	7½	7¾	4:31	B	6:48	D	ARI	28
153	2	**F**	5:17	A	8:45	E	15 28	*1	22 N. 12	8¼	8¼	5:02	B	7:57	E	TAU	29
154	3	M.	5:17	A	8:45	E	15 28	*1	22 N. 20	9	9	5:39	A	9:06	E	TAU	0
155	4	Tu.	5:16	A	8:46	E	15 30	*1	22 N. 27	9¾	9¾	6:24	A	10:12	E	TAU	1
156	5	W.	5:16	A	8:47	E	15 31	*1	22 N. 33	10½	10½	7:19	A	11:11	E	GEM	2
157	6	Th.	5:16	A	8:48	E	15 32	*2	22 N. 40	11¼	11¼	8:22	A	—	-	GEM	3
158	7	Fr.	5:15	A	8:48	E	15 33	*2	22 N. 46	12¼	—	9:33	A	12:02	E	CAN	4
159	8	Sa.	5:15	A	8:49	E	15 34	*2	22 N. 51	12¼	1	10:47	B	12:44	D	LEO	5
160	9	**F**	5:15	A	8:50	E	15 35	*2	22 N. 56	1	2	**12:01**	B	1:20	D	LEO	6
161	10	M.	5:14	A	8:50	E	15 36	*2	23 N. 01	2	3	**1:16**	B	1:51	D	LEO	7
162	11	Tu.	5:14	A	8:51	E	15 37	*3	23 N. 05	3¼	4	**2:29**	C	2:19	C	VIR	8
163	12	W.	5:14	A	8:52	E	15 38	*3	23 N. 09	4¼	5	**3:41**	C	2:45	C	VIR	9
164	13	Th.	5:14	A	8:52	E	15 38	*3	23 N. 13	5½	6	**4:53**	D	3:12	B	VIR	10
165	14	Fr.	5:14	A	8:53	E	15 39	*3	23 N. 16	6½	6¾	**6:04**	D	3:41	B	LIB	11
166	15	Sa.	5:14	A	8:53	E	15 39	*3	23 N. 18	7½	7½	**7:13**	E	4:13	B	LIB	12
167	16	**F**	5:14	A	8:53	E	15 39	*4	23 N. 21	8¼	8¼	**8:18**	E	4:49	A	OPH	13
168	17	M.	5:14	A	8:54	E	15 40	*4	23 N. 22	9	9	**9:18**	E	5:31	A	OPH	14
169	18	Tu.	5:14	A	8:54	E	15 40	*4	23 N. 24	9¾	9¾	**10:11**	E	6:19	A	SAG	15
170	19	W.	5:14	A	8:54	E	15 40	*4	23 N. 25	10½	10½	**10:56**	E	7:13	A	SAG	16
171	20	Th.	5:14	A	8:55	E	15 41	*4	23 N. 25	11¼	11¼	**11:33**	E	8:11	A	CAP	17
172	21	Fr.	5:14	A	8:55	E	15 41	*5	23 N. 26	12	—	—	-	9:11	A	CAP	18
173	22	Sa.	5:15	A	8:55	E	15 40	*5	23 N. 25	12	12¾	12:05	D	10:12	B	CAP	19
174	23	**F**	5:15	A	8:55	E	15 40	*5	23 N. 25	12¾	1¼	12:33	D	11:13	B	AQU	20
175	24	M.	5:15	A	8:55	E	15 40	*5	23 N. 24	1½	2	12:58	D	**12:14**	B	AQU	21
176	25	Tu.	5:15	A	8:55	E	15 40	*6	23 N. 22	2¼	3	1:21	C	**1:16**	C	PSC	22
177	26	W.	5:16	A	8:55	E	15 39	*6	23 N. 20	3	3¾	1:43	C	**2:18**	C	CET	23
178	27	Th.	5:16	A	8:55	E	15 39	*6	23 N. 18	4	4¾	2:06	C	**3:22**	D	PSC	24
179	28	Fr.	5:17	A	8:55	E	15 38	*6	23 N. 15	5¼	5½	2:31	B	**4:28**	D	CET	25
180	29	Sa.	5:17	A	8:55	E	15 38	*6	23 N. 12	6¼	6¼	3:00	B	**5:37**	D	ARI	26
181	30	**F**	5:18	A	8:55	E	15 37	*7	23 N. 09	7	7	3:34	A	**6:46**	E	TAU	27

To use this page, see p. 116; for Key Letters, see p. 238. LIGHT = A.M. BOLD = P.M.

CALENDAR

On the grass the fallen apple blossoms
Heap a pillow rosy-hued and rare.
–Elizabeth Anne Chase Akers Allen

DAY OF MONTH	DAY OF WEEK	DATES, FEASTS, FASTS, ASPECTS, TIDE HEIGHTS, AND WEATHER	
1	Sa.	☌♀☾ • 1" snow, Delta Junction, Alaska, 2015 • { 5.1 5.8	*Hot*
2	**F**	1st S. af. Asc. • Grover Cleveland became first U.S. president to wed in White House, 1886	*stuff!*
3	M.	NEW ● • *Sweet discourse makes short days and nights.* • Tides { 5.5 6.1	*Cool*
4	Tu.	☌☿☾ • Writer Joyce Meyer born, 1943 • Tides { 5.6 6.2	*enough*
5	W.	St. Boniface • ☾ RIDES HIGH • ☾ AT ☊ • ☌♂☾ • { 5.7 6.1	*to*
6	Th.	Orthodox Ascension • D-Day, 1944 • *Tetris* video game released, 1984 • { 5.7 6.0	*dampen*
7	Fr.	☾ AT PERIG. • King George VI, with Queen Elizabeth, first reigning British monarch to visit U.S., 1939	*campers.*
8	Sa.	Shavuot begins at sundown • Tornado struck National Weather Service office in Oklahoma City, 1974	*Warmer,*
9	**F**	Whit S. • Pentecost • Donald Duck debuted in "The Wise Little Hen," 1934	*but*
10	M.	♃ AT ☍ • "Maunder Minimum" astronomer John Eddy died, 2009 • { 5.4 5.5	*watch*
11	Tu.	St. Barnabas • ☾ ON EQ. • Marine explorer Jacques-Yves Cousteau born, 1910 • { 5.2 5.6	*out*
12	W.	Ember Day • Writer Anne Frank born, 1929 • { 5.1 5.7	*for*
13	Th.	Alexander the Great died, 323 B.C. • Deadly hurricane hit Labrador, 1871 • { 5.1 5.8	*a*
14	Fr.	St. Basil • Ember Day • FLAG DAY (U.S.) • Composer Henry Mancini died, 1994	*storm or*
15	Sa.	Ember Day • Charles Goodyear granted patent for process to strengthen rubber, 1844	*two!*
16	**F**	Trinity • Orthodox Pentecost • FATHER'S DAY • ☌♃☾ • { 5.4 5.9	*Rainy*
17	M.	FULL STRAWBERRY ○ • 15th FIFA World Cup soccer games began, first time held in U.S., 1994	*and*
18	Tu.	☾ RUNS LOW • ☾ AT ☋ • ☌☿♂ • ☌♄☾ • { 5.5 5.8	*cool,*
19	W.	☌♇☾ • 100°F, Billings, Mont., 1989 • Tides { 5.5 5.7	*friend,*
20	Th.	Danielle formed, setting record for earliest 4th tropical storm in Atlantic basin, 2016 • { 5.4 5.5	*for*
21	Fr.	NATIONAL INDIGENOUS PEOPLES DAY • SUMMER SOLSTICE • ♆ STAT. • { 5.4 5.4	*school's*
22	Sa.	St. Alban • 102°F, Vero Beach, Fla., 2009 • Tides { 5.3 —	*end.*
23	**F**	Corpus Christi • Orthodox All Saints' • ☾ AT APO. • ☿ GR. ELONG. (25° EAST) • ☌♆☾	*Chance*
24	M.	Nativ. John the Baptist • MIDSUMMER DAY • *Rain on St. John's Day, damage to nuts.* • { 4.9 5.1	*of*
25	Tu.	☾ ON EQ. • Five English monks saw "flaming torch" spew "fire, hot coals, and sparks" on Moon, 1178	*noisy*
26	W.	Physicist Lord Kelvin born, 1824 • St. Lawrence Seaway officially opened, 1959	*precipitation*
27	Th.	☌♅☾ • British scientist James Smithson died, leaving will that led to founding of Smithsonian Institution, 1829	*for*
28	Fr.	St. Irenaeus • Labor Day made official U.S. holiday, 1894 • Treaty of Versailles signed, WWI, 1919	*high*
29	Sa.	Sts. Peter & Paul • *If you would enjoy the fruit, pluck not the flower.* • { 4.8 5.5	*school*
30	**F**	3rd S. af. P. • Canada's loonie coin entered circulation, 1987 • { 5.0 5.8	*graduation!*

Farmer's Calendar

Far from Wall Street, our rural stock exchange thrives with unlisted commodities and functions at all hours. On Saturday, I might swap my extra laying hens for my neighbor's spare vacuum cleaner, and then on Sunday trade a box of frozen beef for pork. But every so often, a transaction occurs that at first seems an outright loss, such as on the morning when I awoke at dawn to a strange noise outside. On the single occasion that I'd neglected to electrify the turkeys' fence, a fox had feasted; telltale white feathers were strewn about like leaves. Still on the premises, the fox, seeing me, attempted to flee. Having already devoured a 10-pound fowl, the intruder toted another as it approached the electric mesh encircling the birds' yard. It botched its leap, dropped its prey, and became entangled in the fence. Instead of fury, I felt awe for its audacity and, now, for its predicament. As the fox thrashed and panted, whining slightly in its panic, I stared at its lavish tail, elegant paws, and auburn coat—I'd never seen a fox this close. Was this a swindle? I wondered, as the animal twisted and, at last, leapt free. Or a barter: two of my flock for hearing the fox's getaway huff.

JULY

SKY WATCH: On the 2nd, a total solar eclipse sweeps across central Chile and Argentina. Mercury and Mars hover just above the thin crescent Moon on the 3rd, low in dusk's western twilight. Earth is farthest from the Sun (at aphelion) on the 4th. Saturn reaches opposition on the 9th, in Sagittarius, at a bright but not brilliant magnitude 0.1; the Ringed Planet rises at sunset to the left of Sagittarius's "Teapot" asterism and is highest at about 1:00 A.M. It is next to the Moon on the 15th. Meanwhile, Jupiter remains optimally placed and is nicely up in the southeast at nightfall as the night's brightest "star." Mars is gone by month's end.

● **NEW MOON** 2nd day 3:16 P.M.	☾ **LAST QUARTER** 24th day 9:18 P.M.	
☽ **FIRST QUARTER** 9th day 6:55 A.M.	● **NEW MOON** 31st day 11:12 P.M.	
○ **FULL MOON** 16th day 5:38 P.M.		

All times are given in Eastern Daylight Time.

GET THESE PAGES WITH TIMES SET TO YOUR POSTAL CODE AT ALMANAC.CA/ACCESS.

DAY OF YEAR	DAY OF MONTH	DAY OF WEEK	☼ RISES H. M.	RISE KEY	☼ SETS H. M.	SET KEY	LENGTH OF DAY H. M.	SUN FAST M.	SUN DECLINATION ° '	HIGH TIDE TIMES HALIFAX		☾ RISES H. M.	RISE KEY	☾ SETS H. M.	SET KEY	☾ ASTRON. PLACE	☾ AGE
182	1	M.	5:18	A	8:55	E	15 37	*7	23 N. 05	7¾	7¾	4:15	A	7:55	E	TAU	28
183	2	Tu.	5:19	A	8:55	E	15 36	*7	23 N. 01	8¾	8¾	5:05	A	8:58	E	GEM	0
184	3	W.	5:19	A	8:54	E	15 35	*7	22 N. 56	9½	9½	6:06	A	9:54	E	GEM	1
185	4	Th.	5:20	A	8:54	E	15 34	*7	22 N. 51	10¼	10¼	7:16	A	10:41	E	CAN	2
186	5	Fr.	5:21	A	8:54	E	15 33	*7	22 N. 45	11	11¼	8:31	A	11:21	D	CAN	3
187	6	Sa.	5:21	A	8:53	E	15 32	*8	22 N. 39	12	—	9:48	B	11:54	D	LEO	4
188	7	**F**	5:22	A	8:53	E	15 31	*8	22 N. 33	12	12¾	11:04	B	—	-	LEO	5
189	8	M.	5:23	A	8:53	E	15 30	*8	22 N. 26	1	1½	12:19	C	12:23	C	VIR	6
190	9	Tu.	5:24	A	8:52	E	15 28	*8	22 N. 19	1¾	2½	1:32	C	12:50	C	VIR	7
191	10	W.	5:24	A	8:52	E	15 28	*8	22 N. 12	2¾	3½	2:44	D	1:17	B	VIR	8
192	11	Th.	5:25	A	8:51	E	15 26	*8	22 N. 04	4	4½	3:54	D	1:45	B	LIB	9
193	12	Fr.	5:26	A	8:50	E	15 24	*9	21 N. 56	5¼	5½	5:03	D	2:15	B	LIB	10
194	13	Sa.	5:27	A	8:50	E	15 23	*9	21 N. 47	6¼	6½	6:08	E	2:49	A	OPH	11
195	14	**F**	5:28	A	8:49	E	15 21	*9	21 N. 38	7¼	7¼	7:09	E	3:28	A	OPH	12
196	15	M.	5:29	A	8:48	E	15 19	*9	21 N. 29	8	8	8:04	E	4:14	A	SAG	13
197	16	Tu.	5:30	A	8:48	E	15 18	*9	21 N. 19	8¾	8¾	8:52	E	5:05	A	SAG	14
198	17	W.	5:31	A	8:47	E	15 16	*9	21 N. 09	9½	9½	9:32	E	6:01	A	SAG	15
199	18	Th.	5:32	A	8:46	E	15 14	*9	20 N. 59	10¼	10¼	10:06	D	7:00	A	CAP	16
200	19	Fr.	5:33	A	8:45	E	15 12	*9	20 N. 48	11	11	10:35	D	8:01	B	CAP	17
201	20	Sa.	5:34	A	8:44	E	15 10	*9	20 N. 37	11½	11½	11:01	D	9:03	B	AQU	18
202	21	**F**	5:35	A	8:43	E	15 08	*9	20 N. 25	12¼	—	11:24	C	10:04	B	AQU	19
203	22	M.	5:36	A	8:42	E	15 06	*9	20 N. 13	12¼	12¾	11:47	C	11:04	C	PSC	20
204	23	Tu.	5:37	A	8:41	E	15 04	*9	20 N. 01	12¾	1¼	—	-	12:05	C	CET	21
205	24	W.	5:38	A	8:40	E	15 02	*9	19 N. 49	1½	2	12:09	C	1:08	C	PSC	22
206	25	Th.	5:39	A	8:39	E	15 00	*9	19 N. 36	2¼	2¾	12:33	B	2:11	D	CET	23
207	26	Fr.	5:40	A	8:38	E	14 58	*9	19 N. 23	3¼	3¾	12:59	B	3:17	D	ARI	24
208	27	Sa.	5:41	A	8:37	E	14 56	*9	19 N. 09	4½	4¾	1:29	B	4:25	E	TAU	25
209	28	**F**	5:42	A	8:36	E	14 54	*9	18 N. 55	5½	5½	2:06	A	5:33	E	TAU	26
210	29	M.	5:43	A	8:35	E	14 52	*9	18 N. 41	6½	6½	2:51	A	6:39	E	TAU	27
211	30	Tu.	5:44	A	8:33	E	14 49	*9	18 N. 27	7½	7½	3:46	A	7:39	E	GEM	28
212	31	W.	5:45	A	8:32	E	14 47	*9	18 N. 12	8¼	8¼	4:53	A	8:31	E	GEM	0

CALENDAR

JULY

JULY HATH 31 DAYS

All the heat was singing,
The insect chorus hummed in undertone.
–Herman Charles Merivale

DAY OF MONTH	DAY OF WEEK	DATES, FEASTS, FASTS, ASPECTS, TIDE HEIGHTS, AND WEATHER	
1	M.	Canada Day • ☌♀☾ • NASA's *Cassini* spacecraft first to orbit Saturn, 2004	*Fireworks*
2	Tu.	New ● • Eclipse ⊙ • ☾ rides high • Tides {5.5 6.2	*fizzle*
3	W.	Dog Days begin. • ☾ at ☊ • First cog-driven train ride up Mt. Washington, N.H., 1869 • {5.7 6.3	*in*
4	Th.	Independence Day (U.S.) • ☌☿☾ • ☌♂☾ • ⊕ at aphelion	*foggy*
5	Fr.	☾ at perig. • Football's Winnipeg Blue Bombers beat Saskatchewan Roughriders, 56-0, 1986	*drizzle.*
6	Sa.	First east-to-west Atlantic crossing by dirigible (*R34*) completed, Scotland to N.Y., 1919 • {5.9 —	*It's*
7	F	4th S. af. P. • ☌☿♂ • ☿ stat. • Tides {6.0 5.9	*fine*
8	M.	☾ on Eq. • *In the morning, mountains, In the evening, fountains.* • Tides {5.7 5.8	*on*
9	Tu.	♄ at ☍ • 96°F, Glennallen, Alaska, 2009 • Tides {5.4 5.7	*the*
10	W.	Orchestra conductor Arthur Fiedler died, 1979 • "Whipped Cream King" Aaron Lapin died, 1999	*front*
11	Th.	Black-eyed Susans in bloom now. • Last slide rule manufactured in U.S., 1976 • {4.9 5.6	*nine.*
12	Fr.	U.S. statesman Alexander Hamilton died, 1804 • Tides {4.9 5.6	*Cool*
13	Sa.	☌♃☾ • Lightning strike triggered 24-hour blackout, N.Y.C., 1977 • Tides {4.9 5.6	*air*
14	F	5th S. af. P. • Bastille Day • ♇ at ☍ • {5.0 5.6	*prevails*
15	M.	St. Swithin • ☾ runs low • Ice hockey player Bryan Helmer born, 1972 • {5.1 5.6	*on*
16	Tu.	Full Buck ○ • Eclipse ☾ • ☌♄☾ • ☌♇☾ • ☾ at ☋	*mountain*
17	W.	Newscaster Walter Cronkite died, 2009 • *Two of a trade seldom agree.* • Tides {5.3 5.7	*trails.*
18	Th.	Armadillos mate now. • First day of storm that brought flooding to Saguenay region, Que., 1996	*Picknickers*
19	Fr.	Fire began near Circus Maximus that destroyed 2/3 of Rome, Italy, A.D. 64 • Tides {5.4 5.5	*beware*
20	Sa.	☾ at apo. • Sir Edmund Hillary (one of first to summit Mt. Everest) born, 1919 • {5.4 5.4	*of*
21	F	6th S. af P. • ☌♆☾ • ☿ in inf. ☌ • {5.4 —	*cornscateous*
22	M.	St. Mary Magdalene • Cornscateous air is everywhere. • {5.2 5.3	*air!*
23	Tu.	☾ on Eq. • *Tarzan,* Disney's first all-digital film, released, 1999 • {5.0 5.3	*Hot*
24	W.	☌☿♀ • 67-lb. 8-oz. muskellunge caught, Lac Courte Oreilles, Hayward, Wisc., 1949 • {4.8 5.2	*enough*
25	Th.	St. James • ☌♅☾ • 5.6 earthquake struck western Mont., 2005 • Tides {4.7 5.2	*to*
26	Fr.	St. Anne • First Moon rock samples analyzed, Lunar Receiving Laboratory, Houston, Tex., 1969	*melt*
27	Sa.	Northern white rhino Nabire died, leaving just 4 others on Earth, 2015 • Adult gypsy moths emerge.	*butter.*
28	F	7th S. af. P. • Coffee rationing in U.S. ended, WWII, 1943 • {4.7 5.5	*Listen*
29	M.	St. Martha • *Neither heat nor cold abides always in the sky.* • Tides {4.9 5.7	*to*
30	Tu.	☾ rides high • ☌☿☾ • ☾ at ☊ • USS *Indianapolis* sunk, WWII, 1945	*thunder's*
31	W.	St. Ignatius of Loyola • New ● • ☌♀☾ • ☿ stat. • {5.6 6.3	*mutter.*

Farmer's Calendar

Soon a tractor will rumble up the road, its motorized growl growing louder, as its sidebar mower makes its first and only pass, lancing through roadside grasses. This annual act creates a "before" and "after." Prior to the mower's arrival, summer stretches endlessly. The timothy, switch, and orchard grasses have been rising since they first poked through the soil in April. Some mingle with the lowest branches of the maples and apples. Not for long. One pass of that tractor—the tin reaper of summer—and all that growth will cascade back to earth. Sure, its stubble will resume a skyward journey, but it won't achieve this same kind of height. Since June's summer solstice, each day's been snipped of a minute. Night will have lopped off nearly half an hour of light by the time the tractor sidles up in mid-July. Which leads me to anticipate this smooth operator who wields the roadside mower: Is he the tardy barber of spring or the first shearer of autumn? Perhaps it's the latter, for in the wake of the blades, beneath the flat top of collapsed grass, the crickets' murmur grows louder, as if they too are whetting their scythes.

SKY WATCH: Venus passes behind the Sun in superior conjunction on the 14th, marking its transition to an evening star for the rest of the year. It is 5 degrees from the Sun even at month's end and hopelessly lost in solar glare. Mars is lost behind the Sun, too. Jupiter and Saturn are wonderfully positioned at nightfall, in the south. Although both have far southern declinations and neither ascends more than a third of the way up the sky this year, they are both easy viewing targets all night long throughout the summer. The Moon is strikingly close to Jupiter on the 9th. The fat gibbous Moon hovers to the right of Saturn on the 11th and to its left on the 12th. These bright lunar phases will spoil the Perseid meteor showers.

| ◗ FIRST QUARTER | 7th day | 1:31 P.M. | ◖ LAST QUARTER | 23rd day | 10:56 A.M. |
| ○ FULL MOON | 15th day | 8:29 A.M. | ● NEW MOON | 30th day | 6:37 A.M. |

All times are given in Eastern Daylight Time.

GET THESE PAGES WITH TIMES SET TO YOUR POSTAL CODE AT ALMANAC.CA/ACCESS.

DAY OF YEAR	DAY OF MONTH	DAY OF WEEK	☼ RISES H. M.	RISE KEY	☼ SETS H. M.	SET KEY	LENGTH OF DAY H. M.	SUN FAST M.	SUN DECLINATION ° '	HIGH TIDE TIMES HALIFAX		☾ RISES H. M.	RISE KEY	☾ SETS H. M.	SET KEY	☾ ASTRON. PLACE	☾ AGE
213	1	Th.	5:47	B	8:31	E	14 44	*9	17 N. 57	9	9¼	6:07	A	9:15	D	CAN	1
214	2	Fr.	5:48	B	8:30	E	14 42	*9	17 N. 42	10	10	7:26	B	9:52	D	LEO	2
215	3	Sa.	5:49	B	8:28	E	14 39	*9	17 N. 26	10¾	10¾	8:45	B	10:24	D	LEO	3
216	4	F	5:50	B	8:27	E	14 37	*9	17 N. 10	11½	11¾	10:03	B	10:53	C	VIR	4
217	5	M.	5:51	B	8:26	E	14 35	*9	16 N. 54	12¼	—	11:19	C	11:20	C	VIR	5
218	6	Tu.	5:52	B	8:24	E	14 32	*9	16 N. 38	12½	1¼	12:33	C	11:48	B	VIR	6
219	7	W.	5:54	B	8:23	D	14 29	*9	16 N. 21	1½	2	1:45	D	—	-	LIB	7
220	8	Th.	5:55	B	8:21	D	14 26	*8	16 N. 04	2½	3	2:55	D	12:18	B	LIB	8
221	9	Fr.	5:56	B	8:20	D	14 24	*8	15 N. 47	3½	4	4:02	E	12:51	A	SCO	9
222	10	Sa.	5:57	B	8:18	D	14 21	*8	15 N. 29	4¾	5	5:04	E	1:28	A	OPH	10
223	11	F	5:58	B	8:17	D	14 19	*8	15 N. 12	6	6	6:00	E	2:11	A	SAG	11
224	12	M.	6:00	B	8:15	D	14 15	*8	14 N. 54	7	7	6:50	E	3:00	A	SAG	12
225	13	Tu.	6:01	B	8:14	D	14 13	*8	14 N. 36	7¾	7¾	7:32	E	3:54	A	SAG	13
226	14	W.	6:02	B	8:12	D	14 10	*7	14 N. 17	8½	8½	8:08	E	4:52	A	CAP	14
227	15	Th.	6:03	B	8:10	D	14 07	*7	13 N. 59	9¼	9¼	8:38	D	5:53	B	CAP	15
228	16	Fr.	6:04	B	8:09	D	14 05	*7	13 N. 40	9¾	9¾	9:05	D	6:54	B	AQU	16
229	17	Sa.	6:06	B	8:07	D	14 01	*7	13 N. 21	10½	10½	9:29	D	7:55	B	AQU	17
230	18	F	6:07	B	8:06	D	13 59	*7	13 N. 01	11	11	9:51	C	8:56	B	AQU	18
231	19	M.	6:08	B	8:04	D	13 56	*6	12 N. 42	11½	11¾	10:13	C	9:57	C	CET	19
232	20	Tu.	6:09	B	8:02	D	13 53	*6	12 N. 22	12	—	10:36	B	10:58	C	CET	20
233	21	W.	6:11	B	8:00	D	13 49	*6	12 N. 02	12¼	12¾	11:00	B	12:00	D	PSC	21
234	22	Th.	6:12	B	7:59	D	13 47	*6	11 N. 42	1	1¼	11:28	B	1:04	D	ARI	22
235	23	Fr.	6:13	B	7:57	D	13 44	*5	11 N. 22	1¾	2	—	-	2:10	D	TAU	23
236	24	Sa.	6:14	B	7:55	D	13 41	*5	11 N. 01	2½	2¾	12:00	A	3:16	E	TAU	24
237	25	F	6:15	B	7:53	D	13 38	*5	10 N. 41	3¾	4	12:40	A	4:21	E	TAU	25
238	26	M.	6:17	B	7:52	D	13 35	*5	10 N. 20	5	5	1:30	A	5:23	E	GEM	26
239	27	Tu.	6:18	B	7:50	D	13 32	*4	9 N. 59	6	6	2:29	A	6:18	E	GEM	27
240	28	W.	6:19	B	7:48	D	13 29	*4	9 N. 38	7	7	3:39	A	7:05	D	CAN	28
241	29	Th.	6:20	B	7:46	D	13 26	*4	9 N. 17	8	8	4:56	A	7:45	D	LEO	29
242	30	Fr.	6:22	B	7:45	D	13 23	*3	8 N. 55	8¾	9	6:17	B	8:20	D	LEO	0
243	31	Sa.	6:23	B	7:43	D	13 20	*3	8 N. 34	9½	9¾	7:38	B	8:51	C	LEO	1

AUGUST

Then waxed the heavens black,
Until the lightning leapt from cloud to cloud.
–**William Morris**

DAY OF MONTH	DAY OF WEEK	DATES, FEASTS, FASTS, ASPECTS, TIDE HEIGHTS, AND WEATHER	
1	Th.	Lammas Day • ☌♂☾ • Writer Herman Melville born, 1819 • Tides {5.9 6.4	*These*
2	F.	☾ at perig. • Viking ship replica *Gaia* arrived at L'Anse aux Meadows, Nfld., 1991 • {6.1 6.4	*are*
3	Sa.	115°F, Fort Smith, Ark., 2011 • Tides {6.2 6.3	*the*
4	**F**	**8th S. af. P.** • U.S. president Barack Obama born, 1961 • Tides {6.3 6.1	*climes*
5	M.	**Civic Holiday** • ☾ on Eq. • *A good neighbor is a precious thing.* • {6.2 —	*that*
6	Tu.	Transfiguration • Sonic boom broke windows in Kelowna, B.C., 1969 • {5.8 6.0	*fry*
7	W.	Gray squirrels have second litters now. • Low temperature of 40°F, Valentine, Nebr., 1989 • {5.4 5.8	*men's*
8	Th.	St. Dominic • Tornado touched down in Brooklyn, N.Y., 2007 • Tides {5.1 5.5	*soles.*
9	Fr.	☌♃☾ • ☿ Gr. Elong. (19° West) • Smokey Bear chosen fire prevention symbol, 1944	*Sweltering!*
10	Sa.	St. Lawrence • Coldest temp. on Earth at time: –135.8°F, East Antarctic Plateau, Antarctica, 2010	*Perseid*
11	**F**	**9th S. af. P.** • Dog Days end. • ♃ stat. • Tides {4.8 5.3	*meteors*
12	M.	☾ runs low • ☾ at ☋ • ☌♄☾ • ☌♇☾ • ⛢ stat. • {4.9 5.4	*streak*
13	Tu.	Samuel Leeds Allen granted patent for Flexible Flyer sled, 1889 • Chef Julia Child died, 2004	*the*
14	W.	♀ in sup. ☌ • *A good nut year, a good corn year.* • Tides {5.2 5.6	*sky*
15	Th.	Assumption • Full Sturgeon ○ • 1,224-lb. cupcake set world record, 2009	*with*
16	Fr.	Ragweed in bloom. • Element 110 named "darmstadtium," 2003 • Tides {5.4 5.6	*fiery*
17	Sa.	Cat Nights commence. • ☾ at apo. • ☌♆☾ • {5.5 5.6	*letters.*
18	**F**	**10th S. af. P.** • Woodstock Festival ended, Bethel, N.Y., 1969 • {5.5 5.4	*It's*
19	M.	☾ on Eq. • Gymnast Carly Patterson won women's all-around Olympic gold medal, 2004 • {5.5 5.3	*turning*
20	Tu.	Parade of 83 tow trucks set world record, Wenatchee, Wash., 2004 • Tides {5.5 —	*cool*
21	W.	☌⛢☾ • Singer Kenny Rogers born, 1938 • Tides {5.1 5.4	*enough*
22	Th.	1¼" hail, Castle Rock, Colo., 2007 • Tides {5.0 5.4	*for*
23	Fr.	2-lb. blue lobster caught off Pine Point, Scarborough, Maine, 2014 • *Every shoe fits not every foot.*	*sweaters.*
24	Sa.	St. Bartholomew • ☌♀♂ • White House set on fire (War of 1812), D.C., 1814	*Summer's*
25	**F**	**11th S. af. P.** • Hurricane Harvey made landfall, Corpus Christi, Tex., 2017	*buglers*
26	M.	☾ rides high • ☾ at ☊ • Starch process that led to puffed grain cereals patented, 1902	*blow*
27	Tu.	Largest trade at time in NBA, 11 players, 3 teams, 1999 • Tides {5.0 5.7	*their*
28	W.	St. Augustine of Hippo • Hummingbirds migrate south. • Tides {5.4 6.1	*last*
29	Th.	St. John the Baptist • ☌☿☾ • Astronaut Chris Hadfield born, 1959 • {5.8 6.3	*call;*
30	Fr.	First of Muharram begins at sundown • New ● • ☾ at perig. • ☌♀☾ • ☌♂☾	*enter*
31	Sa.	Comet Howard-Koomur-Michels collided with Sun, 1979 • Tides {6.4 6.5	*fall.*

Farmer's Calendar

I follow tiny hand-painted signs, each depicting a blueberry, from the paved straightaway of Wild Branch Road onto a dirt road winding through Collinsville. Day, lovers of the small blue fruit travel this route to arrive at Arnold Brown's gravel drive, sign the guest log, grab a bucket, and traipse into a field teeming with hundreds of mature berry bushes. Last year was a light one, as only 15,000 pounds of berries were gleaned. The year before, pickers hauled out 10 tons! I find, as usual, that Brown's hillside is abuzz with people; their voices carry easily. I overhear snippets of heart-to-heart conversations, as well as an excited child discovering a "big one!" But none of us could be gathering these sweet surprises if not for an overeager man with a tractor mower. Back in the 1990s, Arnold had just planted this hillside with 7,500 Christmas tree saplings. All was proceeding according to plan until the man hired to cut the east field did Arnold a misinformed favor. He thought: "Arnold would probably like me to mow this field. He just forgot to ask." So, here we are with our buckets, gossiping across the bushes, harvesting Plan B.

Listen to the Farmer's Calendar at Almanac.ca/Podcast.

SEPTEMBER

SKY WATCH: The September Moon offers both an easy spectacle and a difficult challenge. The easy part is a series of conjunctions with brilliant Jupiter and bright Saturn at nightfall. The Moon floats to the right of Jupiter on the 5th, left of Jupiter on the 6th, right of Saturn on the 7th, and left of Saturn on the 8th. The visually challenging portion of the program occurs on the 29th, when the thin crescent Moon, very low in the west soon after sunset, forms a triangle with Mercury to its lower left and bright returning Venus to its lower right. Autumn begins with the equinox on the 23rd at 3:50 A.M.

◑ **FIRST QUARTER** 5th day 11:10 P.M.   ◐ **LAST QUARTER** 21st day 10:41 P.M.
○ **FULL MOON** 14th day 12:33 A.M.   ● **NEW MOON** 28th day 2:26 P.M.

All times are given in Eastern Daylight Time.

GET THESE PAGES WITH TIMES SET TO YOUR POSTAL CODE AT ALMANAC.CA/ACCESS.

DAY OF YEAR	DAY OF MONTH	DAY OF WEEK	☀ RISES H.M.	RISE KEY	☀ SETS H.M.	SET KEY	LENGTH OF DAY H.M.	SUN FAST M.	SUN DECLINATION ° '	HIGH TIDE TIMES HALIFAX		☾ RISES H.M.	RISE KEY	☾ SETS H.M.	SET KEY	☾ ASTRON. PLACE	☾ AGE
244	1	**F**	6:24	B	**7:41**	D	13 17	*3	8 N. 12	10¼	**10½**	8:57	C	**9:20**	C	VIR	2
245	2	M.	6:25	B	**7:39**	D	13 14	*2	7 N. 50	11	**11½**	10:15	C	**9:48**	B	VIR	3
246	3	Tu.	6:26	B	**7:37**	D	13 11	*2	7 N. 28	11¾	—	11:30	D	**10:18**	B	VIR	4
247	4	W.	6:28	B	**7:35**	D	13 07	*2	7 N. 06	12¼	**12¾**	**12:43**	D	**10:50**	B	LIB	5
248	5	Th.	6:29	B	**7:33**	D	13 04	*1	6 N. 44	1	**1½**	**1:53**	E	**11:27**	A	LIB	6
249	6	Fr.	6:30	B	**7:31**	D	13 01	*1	6 N. 21	2	**2½**	**2:58**	E	—	-	OPH	7
250	7	Sa.	6:31	B	**7:30**	D	12 59	*1	5 N. 59	3	**3½**	**3:57**	E	12:08	A	SAG	8
251	8	**F**	6:32	C	**7:28**	D	12 56	0	5 N. 36	4¼	**4½**	**4:48**	E	12:56	A	SAG	9
252	9	M.	6:34	C	**7:26**	D	12 52	0	5 N. 14	5¾	**5¾**	**5:32**	E	1:49	A	SAG	10
253	10	Tu.	6:35	C	**7:24**	C	12 49	0	4 N. 51	6¾	**6¾**	**6:10**	E	2:46	A	CAP	11
254	11	W.	6:36	C	**7:22**	C	12 46	1	4 N. 28	7½	**7½**	**6:41**	D	3:46	A	CAP	12
255	12	Th.	6:37	C	**7:20**	C	12 43	1	4 N. 06	8¼	**8¼**	**7:09**	D	4:47	B	AQU	13
256	13	Fr.	6:38	C	**7:18**	C	12 40	1	3 N. 43	8¾	**8¾**	**7:33**	D	5:48	B	AQU	14
257	14	Sa.	6:40	C	**7:16**	C	12 36	2	3 N. 20	9¼	**9½**	**7:56**	C	6:49	B	AQU	15
258	15	**F**	6:41	C	**7:14**	C	12 33	2	2 N. 57	9¾	**10**	**8:18**	C	7:50	C	PSC	16
259	16	M.	6:42	C	**7:12**	C	12 30	2	2 N. 33	10¼	**10½**	**8:40**	C	8:51	C	CET	17
260	17	Tu.	6:43	C	**7:10**	C	12 27	3	2 N. 10	11	**11¼**	**9:03**	B	9:53	D	PSC	18
261	18	W.	6:45	C	**7:09**	C	12 24	3	1 N. 47	11½	**11¾**	**9:30**	B	10:56	D	CET	19
262	19	Th.	6:46	C	**7:07**	C	12 21	3	1 N. 24	12	—	**10:00**	A	**12:01**	D	TAU	20
263	20	Fr.	6:47	C	**7:05**	C	12 18	4	1 N. 01	12½	**12¾**	**10:36**	A	**1:06**	E	TAU	21
264	21	Sa.	6:48	C	**7:03**	C	12 15	4	0 N. 37	1¼	**1½**	**11:20**	A	**2:10**	E	TAU	22
265	22	**F**	6:49	C	**7:01**	C	12 12	4	0 N. 14	2	**2¼**	—	-	**3:11**	E	GEM	23
266	23	M.	6:51	C	**6:59**	C	12 08	5	0 s. 08	3¼	**3½**	12:13	A	**4:07**	E	GEM	24
267	24	Tu.	6:52	C	**6:57**	C	12 05	5	0 s. 32	4½	**4¾**	1:17	A	**4:56**	E	CAN	25
268	25	W.	6:53	C	**6:55**	C	12 02	6	0 s. 55	5¾	**5¾**	2:29	A	**5:38**	D	CAN	26
269	26	Th.	6:54	C	**6:53**	C	11 59	6	1 s. 19	6¾	**6¾**	3:46	B	**6:14**	D	LEO	27
270	27	Fr.	6:56	C	**6:51**	C	11 55	6	1 s. 42	7½	**7¾**	5:06	B	**6:46**	D	LEO	28
271	28	Sa.	6:57	C	**6:49**	C	11 52	7	2 s. 05	8¼	**8½**	6:27	B	**7:16**	C	VIR	0
272	29	**F**	6:58	C	**6:47**	C	11 49	7	2 s. 29	9	**9½**	7:47	C	**7:45**	C	VIR	1
273	30	M.	6:59	C	**6:45**	C	11 46	7	2 s. 52	9¾	**10¼**	9:06	D	**8:14**	B	VIR	2

To use this page, see p. 116; for Key Letters, see p. 238. LIGHT = A.M. BOLD = P.M.   **2019**

SEPTEMBER

The sheaves flew fast and thick
From fork to fork, to feed the growing rick.
–Charles Tennyson Turner

DAY OF MONTH	DAY OF WEEK	DATES, FEASTS, FASTS, ASPECTS, TIDE HEIGHTS, AND WEATHER	
1	**F**	**12th S. af. P.** • ☾ ON EQ. • Sundance Fire intensified, Idaho, 1967	*Children*
2	M.	**Labour Day** • ☌♂☉ • Evacuation began for 2.8 million people, Hurricane Frances, Fla., 2004	*board*
3	Tu.	☌☿♂ • ☿ IN SUP. ☌ • *When the fog falls, fair weather follows.* • {6.4 —	*buses*
4	W.	A 127-lb. cabbage won prize at Alaska State Fair, 2009 • Tides {5.8 6.1	*in*
5	Th.	102°F, Portland, Oreg., 1944 • Missionary Saint Teresa of Calcutta died, 1997 • {5.5 5.7	*yellow*
6	F.	☌♃☾ • Basketball player John Wall born, 1990 • Tides {5.1 5.4	*slickers;*
7	Sa.	First Canadian Official Languages Act went into effect, 1969 • Tides {4.8 5.1	*orchards*
8	**F**	**13th S. af. P.** • ☾ RUNS LOW • ☾ AT ☋ • ☌♄☾ • ☌♇☾	*are*
9	M.	Continental Congress declared "United States of America" name of new nation, 1776 • {4.8 5.1	*filled*
10	Tu.	♆ AT ☍ • Cranberry bog harvest begins, Cape Cod, Mass. • Tides {4.9 5.3	*with*
11	W.	**Patriot Day (U.S.)** • *Queen Elizabeth 2* ocean liner struck by approx. 90-ft.-high rogue wave, 1995	*pickers.*
12	Th.	*Pride often borrows the cloak of humility.* • Tides {5.3 5.6	*Rain*
13	Fr.	☾ AT APO. • ☌☿♀ • ☌♆☾ • Writer Roald Dahl born, 1916 • {5.5 5.6	*gives*
14	Sa.	Holy Cross • **FULL HARVEST** ○ • World Series canceled due to strike, 1994 • {5.6 5.7	*way*
15	**F**	**14th S. af. P.** • ☾ ON EQ. • First successful portable MP3 player debuted, 1998	*to*
16	M.	Physicist/educator Ursula Franklin born, 1921 • {5.7 5.5	*northern*
17	Tu.	☌♅☾ • First powered flight of X-15 rocket plane, 1959 • Tides {5.7 5.4	*gales*
18	W.	Ember Day • ♄ STAT. • Cosmonaut Arnaldo Tamayo Méndez first Latin American in space, 1980	*as*
19	Th.	International Talk Like a Pirate Day • Astronomer Jean Baptiste Joseph Delambre born, 1749 • {5.6 —	*they*
20	Fr.	Ember Day • Navigator Ferdinand Magellan left Sanlúcar de Barrameda, Spain, for Spice Islands, 1519	*fill*
21	Sa.	St. Matthew • Ember Day • N.Y. Jets' Steve O'Neal's 98-yd. punt longest in NFL history, 1969	*their*
22	**F**	**15th S. af. P.** • ☾ RIDES HIGH • Mime Marcel Marceau died, 2007 • {4.8 5.3	*pails*
23	M.	Harvest Home • **AUTUMNAL EQUINOX** • ☾ AT ☊ • Tides {4.8 5.3	*with*
24	Tu.	*When a friend asketh, there is no tomorrow.* • {4.9 5.4	*autumn's*
25	W.	Woodchucks hibernate now. • Tides {5.2 5.7	*riches*
26	Th.	Nurseryman Johnny "Appleseed" Chapman born, 1774 • {5.6 6.1	*and*
27	Fr.	St. Vincent de Paul • ☾ AT PERIG. • ☌♂☾ • Tides {6.1 6.3	*showers*
28	Sa.	NEW ● • 437 people dressed as Superman set world record, Calgary, Alta., 2011	*swell*
29	**F**	**16th S. af. P.** • Rosh Hashanah begins at sundown • ☾ ON EQ. • ☌☿☾ • ☌♀☾	*the*
30	M.	St. Michael[T] • U.S. Navy's first nuclear sub, USS *Nautilus,* commissioned, 1954 • {6.8 6.4	*ditches.*

Farmer's Calendar

"A cold pocket" sounds like something a snowman might have. Meteorologically, I live where chilly-heavy air will linger on a breezeless night. Hence, one evening sooner than most, I'll wake to find the pocket's white lint—our first deep frost—lining each blade of grass, crystallizing flower petals, glazing pumpkins' platter-like leaves. Denizens of Zone 5, we expect our first brush with frost to arrive anytime after the second week of September. I can try to avert damage to tender plants by casting blankets across the basil and tomatoes, by swaddling the fragile cuffs of morning glories in hopes of seeing one more bloom, but no amount of bedding will cushion the sharpening truth: Our growing season is over. Soon we'll have the kind of frigid night that fringes all of our vegetation in a hoary ice. Certain plants' cells can't withstand this drastic temperature change. When the rising Sun warms a morning glory's frozen leaves, its cell walls will break, irreparably. Eventually, the frostbitten garden will be blanketed with flakes. By then, we won't be able to discern any difference between the snowman's pocket and his voluminous white coat.

Listen to the Farmer's Calendar at Almanac.ca/Podcast.

OCTOBER

SKY WATCH: Returning Venus, barely brightening and climbing, may be glimpsed very low in the west in evening twilight. When will you first spot it? Mercury is down there, too, this month and, although less brilliant, is higher up and may be easier to see. Mars, at an unimpressive magnitude 1.8, starts to rise ahead of the morning Sun, but it's still subdued in solar glare. This leaves Jupiter and Saturn to strut unchallenged in the southern sky nearly all night long, although both start to set before dawn. Green Uranus comes into opposition on the 28th; in Pisces at magnitude 5.7, the seventh planet from the Sun is dimly visible to the naked eye away from city lights.

◐ **FIRST QUARTER** 5th day 12:47 P.M. ◑ **LAST QUARTER** 21st day 8:39 A.M.
○ **FULL MOON** 13th day 5:08 P.M. ● **NEW MOON** 27th day 11:38 P.M.

All times are given in Eastern Daylight Time.

GET THESE PAGES WITH TIMES SET TO YOUR POSTAL CODE AT ALMANAC.CA/ACCESS.

DAY OF YEAR	DAY OF MONTH	DAY OF WEEK	☀ RISES H. M.	RISE KEY	☀ SETS H. M.	SET KEY	LENGTH OF DAY H. M.	SUN FAST M.	SUN DECLINATION ° '	HIGH TIDE TIMES HALIFAX		☽ RISES H. M.	RISE KEY	☽ SETS H. M.	SET KEY	☽ ASTRON. PLACE	☽ AGE
274	1	Tu.	7:01	C	6:44	C	11 43	8	3 s. 15	10½	11	10:23	D	8:46	B	LIB	3
275	2	W.	7:02	C	6:42	C	11 40	8	3 s. 38	11½	12	11:37	D	9:22	A	LIB	4
276	3	Th.	7:03	C	6:40	C	11 37	8	4 s. 02	12	12¼	12:46	E	10:02	A	OPH	5
277	4	Fr.	7:04	C	6:38	C	11 34	8	4 s. 25	12¾	1	1:50	E	10:49	A	OPH	6
278	5	Sa.	7:06	C	6:36	C	11 30	9	4 s. 48	1½	1¾	2:45	E	11:41	A	SAG	7
279	6	**F**	7:07	C	6:34	C	11 27	9	5 s. 11	2½	3	3:32	E	—	-	SAG	8
280	7	M.	7:08	C	6:32	C	11 24	9	5 s. 34	3¾	4	4:12	E	12:38	A	CAP	9
281	8	Tu.	7:09	C	6:30	C	11 21	10	5 s. 57	5¼	5¼	4:45	E	1:37	A	CAP	10
282	9	W.	7:11	D	6:29	C	11 18	10	6 s. 20	6¼	6¼	5:13	D	2:38	B	CAP	11
283	10	Th.	7:12	D	6:27	C	11 15	10	6 s. 42	7	7	5:38	D	3:40	B	AQU	12
284	11	Fr.	7:13	D	6:25	B	11 12	10	7 s. 05	7½	7¾	6:01	C	4:41	B	AQU	13
285	12	Sa.	7:15	D	6:23	B	11 08	11	7 s. 28	8¼	8¼	6:23	C	5:42	C	PSC	14
286	13	**F**	7:16	D	6:21	B	11 05	11	7 s. 50	8¾	9	6:45	C	6:44	C	CET	15
287	14	M.	7:17	D	6:20	B	11 03	11	8 s. 12	9¼	9½	7:08	B	7:46	C	PSC	16
288	15	Tu.	7:19	D	6:18	B	10 59	11	8 s. 35	9¾	10¼	7:33	B	8:49	D	CET	17
289	16	W.	7:20	D	6:16	B	10 56	12	8 s. 57	10¼	10¾	8:01	B	9:54	D	ARI	18
290	17	Th.	7:21	D	6:14	B	10 53	12	9 s. 19	11	11½	8:35	A	10:59	E	TAU	19
291	18	Fr.	7:23	D	6:13	B	10 50	12	9 s. 40	11½	—	9:16	A	12:04	E	TAU	20
292	19	Sa.	7:24	D	6:11	B	10 47	12	10 s. 02	12¼	12¼	10:06	A	1:06	E	TAU	21
293	20	**F**	7:25	D	6:09	B	10 44	12	10 s. 24	1	1	11:04	A	2:03	E	GEM	22
294	21	M.	7:27	D	6:08	B	10 41	13	10 s. 45	1¾	2	—	-	2:53	E	GEM	23
295	22	Tu.	7:28	D	6:06	B	10 38	13	11 s. 06	3	3	12:11	A	3:36	E	CAN	24
296	23	W.	7:29	D	6:04	B	10 35	13	11 s. 27	4¼	4¼	1:24	A	4:12	D	LEO	25
297	24	Th.	7:31	D	6:03	B	10 32	13	11 s. 48	5½	5½	2:41	A	4:44	D	LEO	26
298	25	Fr.	7:32	D	6:01	B	10 29	13	12 s. 09	6¼	6½	3:59	B	5:14	C	LEO	27
299	26	Sa.	7:33	D	5:59	B	10 26	13	12 s. 30	7¼	7½	5:18	C	5:42	C	VIR	28
300	27	**F**	7:35	D	5:58	B	10 23	13	12 s. 50	8	8¼	6:36	C	6:10	B	VIR	0
301	28	M.	7:36	D	5:56	B	10 20	13	13 s. 10	8¾	9	7:55	D	6:40	B	VIR	1
302	29	Tu.	7:38	D	5:55	B	10 17	13	13 s. 30	9½	10	9:12	D	7:14	A	LIB	2
303	30	W.	7:39	D	5:53	B	10 14	14	13 s. 50	10¼	10¾	10:26	E	7:53	A	SCO	3
304	31	Th.	7:40	D	5:52	B	10 12	14	14 s. 09	11	11½	11:35	E	8:38	A	OPH	4

To use this page, see p. 116; for Key Letters, see p. 238. LIGHT = A.M. **BOLD** = P.M. 2019

OCTOBER

The small red maple leaves, keen-scented, mute,
Here fleck the stream, to grape-dark purple hushed.
–Bliss Carman

DAY OF MONTH	DAY OF WEEK	DATES, FEASTS, FASTS, ASPECTS, TIDE HEIGHTS, AND WEATHER	
1	Tu.	U.S. president Jimmy Carter born, 1924 • Water polo player/coach Rosanna Tomiuk born, 1984 • {6.7 6.2	*Under*
2	W.	♇ STAT. • Watch for banded woolly bear caterpillars now. • Tides {6.4 5.9	*clouds*
3	Th.	☌♃☾ • F4 tornado struck Windsor Locks, Conn., 1979 • Tides {6.1 —	*leaden,*
4	Fr.	St. Francis of Assisi • Astronaut Gordon Cooper died, 2004 • {5.6 5.7	*swamp*
5	Sa.	☾ RUNS LOW • ☾ AT ☋ • ☌♄☾ • First space shuttle launch w/oceanographer, 1984	*maples*
6	**F**	**17th S. af. P.** • ☌♇☾ • *It is the tone that makes the music.* • {5.0 5.1	*redden.*
7	M.	Adrienne Clarkson became 26th governor-general of Canada, 1999 • Tides {4.8 5.0	*Bright*
8	Tu.	Yom Kippur begins at sundown • California wildfires began in wine country, 2017 • {4.9 5.0	*skies*
9	W.	Hailstorms hit Mont., damaging crops, 1944 • Tides {5.1 5.2	*are*
10	Th.	☾ AT APO. • ☌♆☾ • Asteroid Cruithne (quasi-satellite of Earth) discovered, 1986	*pluses*
11	Fr.	Little brown bats hibernate now. • *Honor the tree that gives you shelter.* • Tides {5.5 5.5	*for*
12	Sa.	U.S. Navy Cross recipient Doris Miller born, 1919 • Tides {5.7 5.6	*foliage*
13	**F**	**18th S. af. P.** • Sukkoth begins at sundown • FULL HUNTER'S ○ • ☾ ON EQ.	*buses,*
14	M.	THANKSGIVING DAY • COLUMBUS DAY, OBSERVED (U.S.) • ☌⛢☾ • {5.9 5.7	*and*
15	Tu.	Edison Electric Light Co. established, N.Y.C., 1878 • Tides {5.9 5.7	*early*
16	W.	7.1 earthquake near Hector Mine, Mojave Desert, Calif., 1999 • Tides {6.0 5.6	*snow*
17	Th.	St. Ignatius of Antioch • Frank Giannino completed run across U.S. (46 days, 8 hrs., 36 mins.), 1980	*thrills*
18	Fr.	St. Luke • Canadian prime minister Pierre Trudeau born, 1919 • St. Luke's little summer. • {5.9 —	*in*
19	Sa.	First object ('Oumuamua) from another solar system detected in ours, 2017 • {5.4 5.7	*the*
20	**F**	**19th S. af. P.** • ☾ RIDES HIGH • ☾ AT ☊ • ☿ GR. ELONG. (25° EAST)	*northern*
21	M.	*Better to give the wool than the sheep.* • Tides {5.1 5.5	*hills. But*
22	Tu.	Writer Jean-Paul Sartre rejected Nobel Prize for Literature, 1964 • Tides {5.1 5.4	*the*
23	W.	St. James of Jerusalem • Football coach John Heisman born, 1869 • {5.2 5.5	*old-timers*
24	Th.	Actor Richard Burton bought $1.1 million, 69-carat Cartier diamond ring for wife Elizabeth Taylor, 1969	*sneer,*
25	Fr.	Timber rattlesnakes move to winter dens. • Tides {6.0 6.0	*"You*
26	Sa.	☾ ON EQ. • ☾ AT PERIG. • ☌♂☾ • Ballet conductor George Crum born, 1926	*shoulda*
27	**F**	**20th S. af. P.** • NEW ● • 32-lb. bull trout caught, Lake Pend Oreille, Idaho, 1949	
28	M.	Sts. Simon & Jude • ⛢ AT ☍ • Cyclone 05B became Cat. 5, Indian Ocean, 1999	*seen*
29	Tu.	☌☿☾ • ☌♀☾ • First commencement of first U.S. coeducational college (Oberlin), 1834 • {6.8 6.3	*it*
30	W.	☌☿♀ • Patent granted to Daniel Cooper for "workman's time recorder," 1894 • {6.7 6.1	*last*
31	Th.	All Hallows' Eve • Reformation Day • ☌♃☾ • ☿ STAT. • {6.4 5.9	*year."*

Farmer's Calendar

Every fall, I bucket up some apples and haul them over to Dave's garage to make cider on his hand-cranked press. Whether he likes it or not, I've appointed my unassuming neighbor—a careful homesteader who's tended his forest and fields for nearly 40 years—my godfather in sustainability and simple living. I am perpetually on his doorstep with questions about how to make better sauerkraut or to ascertain how frequently he mulches his trees. He brushes off my studious worship as if I were a fly pesking a loaf of his wood-fired oven–baked bread. Now Dave helps me to fit the crank on the press and I begin turning. Soon the hopper full of apple mash is forced to become juice. At first the cider trickles out, but soon it gushes and fills the collecting pot to the brim. Then we swap in a new pot, until all's been squeezed from this batch of apples. Before unscrewing the press and emptying the sack of tawny mush called pomace, before we reset the press and begin the whole process again, we each fill a cup and drink a toast: to a good crop of apples, to the revolving seasons, and to my neighbor's sustaining sweetness.

Listen to the Farmer's Calendar at Almanac.ca/Podcast.

NOVEMBER

SKY WATCH: Mercury transits the Sun's face on the 11th, starting at 7:37 A.M. and continuing for over 5 hours. All of the United States (except Alaska) and Canada can see at least part of it (a "solar telescope" is required). From the 1st to the 14th, low in the predawn east, returning orange Mars meets Virgo's blue star, Spica. During the month's second half, bright Mercury appears below Mars. On the 24th, the crescent Moon hovers to the left of Mars, with Mercury below. On the 25th, a predawn lineup has blue Spica highest, above orange Mars, then orange Mercury, and finally the Moon, lowest. In the west after sunset, Venus and Jupiter hover side-by-side on the 23rd and 24th but quite low in twilight. The Moon floats just above brilliant Venus on the 28th.

◐ FIRST QUARTER	4th day	5:23 A.M.	◑ LAST QUARTER	19th day	4:11 P.M.
○ FULL MOON	12th day	8:34 A.M.	● NEW MOON	26th day	10:06 A.M.

After 2:00 A.M. on November 3, Eastern Standard Time is given.

GET THESE PAGES WITH TIMES SET TO YOUR POSTAL CODE AT ALMANAC.CA/ACCESS.

DAY OF YEAR	DAY OF MONTH	DAY OF WEEK	☼ RISES H. M.	RISE KEY	☼ SETS H. M.	SET KEY	LENGTH OF DAY H. M.	SUN FAST M.	SUN DECLINATION °	'	HIGH TIDE TIMES HALIFAX		☾ RISES H. M.	RISE KEY	☾ SETS H. M.	SET KEY	☾ ASTRON. PLACE	☾ AGE
305	1	Fr.	7:42	D	**5:50**	B	10 08	14	14	s. 29	11¾	—	**12:36**	E	**9:29**	A	SAG	5
306	2	Sa.	7:43	D	**5:49**	B	10 06	14	14	s. 48	12¼	**12½**	**1:28**	E	**10:26**	A	SAG	6
307	3	**F**	6:45	D	**4:48**	B	10 03	14	15	s. 07	1¼	**12½**	**1:11**	E	**10:26**	A	SAG	7
308	4	M.	6:46	D	**4:46**	B	10 00	14	15	s. 25	1¼	**1¼**	**1:47**	E	**11:27**	A	CAP	8
309	5	Tu.	6:47	D	**4:45**	B	9 58	14	15	s. 43	2¼	**2½**	**2:17**	D	—	-	CAP	9
310	6	W.	6:49	D	**4:44**	B	9 55	14	16	s. 01	3½	**3¾**	**2:43**	D	12:29	B	AQU	10
311	7	Th.	6:50	D	**4:42**	B	9 52	14	16	s. 19	4½	**4¾**	**3:06**	D	1:30	B	AQU	11
312	8	Fr.	6:52	D	**4:41**	B	9 49	13	16	s. 37	5¼	**5½**	**3:28**	C	2:32	B	PSC	12
313	9	Sa.	6:53	D	**4:40**	B	9 47	13	16	s. 54	6	**6¼**	**3:50**	C	3:33	C	CET	13
314	10	**F**	6:54	D	**4:39**	B	9 45	13	17	s. 11	6½	**7**	**4:12**	B	4:35	C	PSC	14
315	11	M.	6:56	D	**4:37**	B	9 41	13	17	s. 28	7	**7½**	**4:36**	B	5:39	D	CET	15
316	12	Tu.	6:57	E	**4:36**	B	9 39	13	17	s. 44	7¾	**8**	**5:03**	B	6:44	D	ARI	16
317	13	W.	6:58	E	**4:35**	B	9 37	13	18	s. 00	8¼	**8¾**	**5:36**	A	7:51	D	TAU	17
318	14	Th.	7:00	E	**4:34**	B	9 34	13	18	s. 16	8¾	**9½**	**6:14**	A	8:57	E	TAU	18
319	15	Fr.	7:01	E	**4:33**	B	9 32	13	18	s. 31	9½	**10¼**	**7:01**	A	10:01	E	TAU	19
320	16	Sa.	7:03	E	**4:32**	B	9 29	12	18	s. 46	10¼	**11**	**7:57**	A	11:00	E	GEM	20
321	17	**F**	7:04	E	**4:31**	B	9 27	12	19	s. 01	11	**11¾**	**9:02**	A	11:52	E	GEM	21
322	18	M.	7:05	E	**4:30**	A	9 25	12	19	s. 15	11¾	—	**10:12**	A	**12:37**	E	CAN	22
323	19	Tu.	7:07	E	**4:29**	A	9 22	12	19	s. 29	12½	**12¾**	**11:26**	B	**1:14**	D	LEO	23
324	20	W.	7:08	E	**4:28**	A	9 20	12	19	s. 43	1¾	**1¾**	—	-	**1:47**	D	LEO	24
325	21	Th.	7:09	E	**4:27**	A	9 18	11	19	s. 56	2¾	**3**	12:41	B	**2:16**	C	LEO	25
326	22	Fr.	7:11	E	**4:27**	A	9 16	11	20	s. 09	4	**4¼**	1:57	C	**2:43**	C	VIR	26
327	23	Sa.	7:12	E	**4:26**	A	9 14	11	20	s. 22	5	**5¼**	3:13	C	**3:09**	C	VIR	27
328	24	**F**	7:13	E	**4:25**	A	9 12	11	20	s. 34	5¾	**6¼**	4:30	D	**3:37**	B	VIR	28
329	25	M.	7:15	E	**4:25**	A	9 10	10	20	s. 46	6½	**7**	5:46	D	**4:09**	B	LIB	29
330	26	Tu.	7:16	E	**4:24**	A	9 08	10	20	s. 58	7¼	**7¾**	7:01	D	**4:44**	A	LIB	0
331	27	W.	7:17	E	**4:23**	A	9 06	10	21	s. 09	8	**8½**	8:14	E	**5:26**	A	OPH	1
332	28	Th.	7:18	E	**4:23**	A	9 05	9	21	s. 19	8¾	**9½**	9:20	E	**6:15**	A	SAG	2
333	29	Fr.	7:19	E	**4:22**	A	9 03	9	21	s. 30	9½	**10¼**	10:18	E	**7:10**	A	SAG	3
334	30	Sa.	7:21	E	**4:22**	A	9 01	9	21	s. 40	10¼	**11**	11:06	E	**8:10**	A	SAG	4

 To use this page, see p. 116; for Key Letters, see p. 238. LIGHT = A.M. **BOLD** = P.M.

NOVEMBER

Chill winds sweep down the mountain way,
The skies are leaden-like and gray.
–James Berry Bensel

DAY OF MONTH	DAY OF WEEK	DATES, FEASTS, FASTS, ASPECTS, TIDE HEIGHTS, AND WEATHER	
1	Fr.	All Saints' • ☾ RUNS LOW • ☾ AT ☋ • U.S. First Lady Mamie Eisenhower died, 1979	*An*
2	Sa.	All Souls' • Sadie Hawkins Day • ☌♄☾ • ☌♇☾ • Tides {5.6 / 5.7	*echo*
3	**F**	**21st S. af. P.** • DAYLIGHT SAVING TIME ENDS, 2:00 A.M. • Tides {5.4 / 5.4	*of*
4	M.	Manufacturer Benjamin F. Goodrich born, 1841 • {5.2 / 5.1	*summer,*
5	Tu.	ELECTION DAY (U.S) • GPS system patented, 1996 • {5.0 / 5.0	*before*
6	W.	☌♆☾ • Posthumous Victoria Cross recipient James Robertson died, 1917 • {5.1 / 5.0	*rain's*
7	Th.	☾ AT APO. • U.S. president FDR re-elected for 4th term, 1944 • {5.2 / 5.1	*drummer*
8	Fr.	Mont. statehood (Dakotas, Nov. 2; Wash., Nov. 11), 1889 • Tides {5.4 / 5.3	*sends*
9	Sa.	☾ ON EQ. • First documented Canadian gridiron football game played, Univ. of Toronto, Ont., 1861	*the*
10	**F**	**22nd S. af. P.** • ☌♅☾ • TV's *Sesame Street* debuted, 1969 • {5.8 / 5.5	*last*
11	M.	St. Martin of Tours • REMEMBRANCE DAY • ☿ IN INF. ☌ • ☿ TRANSIT OVER ☉	*leaves*
12	Tu.	Indian Summer • FULL BEAVER ○ • Voters OK'd creation of Nunavut territory, 1992 • {6.1 / 5.7	*fleeing.*
13	W.	*Set trees poor, and they will grow rich; set them rich, and they will grow poor.* • Tides {6.2 / 5.7	*Rain*
14	Th.	Just after launch, *Apollo 12* struck twice by lightning, 1969 • Tides {6.2 / 5.7	*turns*
15	Fr.	Judge Joseph Wapner born, 1919 • Tides {6.2 / 5.7	*to*
16	Sa.	☾ RIDES HIGH • ☾ AT ☊ • Meteor fireball turned night into day, Finland, 2017 • {6.1 / 5.6	*snow*
17	**F**	**23rd S. af. P.** • 1800s champagne sampled from Baltic Sea shipwreck, 2010 • {6.0 / 5.5	*and*
18	M.	St. Hilda of Whitby • *November take flail, Let ships no more sail.* • {5.8 / —	*thoughts*
19	Tu.	David L. Pickens granted patent for "registered pedigree stuffed animals," 2002 • {5.4 / 5.6	*turn*
20	W.	☿ STAT. • Tucson Municipal Flying Field, Ariz., first municipal airport in U.S., 1919 • {5.4 / 5.5	*to*
21	Th.	N.C. statehood, 1789 • Dusting of snow, central Fla., 2006 • Tides {5.6 / 5.4	*skiing.*
22	Fr.	☾ ON EQ. • Humane Society of the United States founded, 1954 • Writer George Eliot born, 1819	*Turkey's*
23	Sa.	St. Clement • ☾ AT PERIG. • Thespis first actor on record in Greek drama, 534 B.C. • {6.1 / 5.8	*been*
24	**F**	**24th S. af. P.** • ☌☿☾ • ☌♀♃ • ☌♂☾ • Tides {6.4 / 5.9	*fixed;*
25	M.	U.S. chess champion John Donaldson wed Soviet champion Elena Akhmilovskaya, 1988	*precipitation's*
26	Tu.	NEW ● • 1.5" rain fell in 1 minute, setting world record, Barot, Guadeloupe, 1970 • {6.7 / 6.1	*mixed.*
27	W.	♆ STAT. • *Better some of a pudding than none of a pie.* • Tides {6.7 / 6.1	*So*
28	Th.	THANKSGIVING DAY (U.S.) • ☾ AT ☋ • ☌♀☾ • ☌♃☾ • ☿ GR. ELONG. (20° WEST)	*are*
29	Fr.	☾ RUNS LOW • ☌♄☾ • ☌♇☾ • First governor-general of Canada, Sir Charles Stanley, died, 1894	*our*
30	Sa.	St. Andrew • Discovery of 215 fossilized pterosaur eggs in Gobi Desert, China, announced, 2017	*feelings.*

Farmer's Calendar

The rungs had rattled my mind for months, as I wondered what I might see from the silo's cusp. One night shy of the full Moon, I climbed up. During the growing season, a homesteader is devoted to the ground: trundling hoses, sinking fence posts, dumping manure, stooping to tend everything. And then, suddenly, there is nothing left to weed or harvest and her focus can drift upward. Twice I'd queried the neighbors for permission to scale their tower of corn silage and twice they'd declined. So, what happened next might just be a lie. At dusk, I crept to the silo with a friend who boosted me to the ladder's bottom rung. From there, I scrambled up to where the view was generous, expansive. At height, the three nearby farmhouses appeared as diminutive as butter pats. The neighbors' dairy barn seemed no bigger than a mailbox amid the shorn cornfield with its plaid of tractor ruts. As the neighbors' lights snapped out, my friend waited gamely by the ladder's start. Maybe I was the highest living thing in our valley? Just then a Canada goose squawked, correcting me, as it soared over the silo toward the Milky Way.

Listen to the Farmer's Calendar at Almanac.ca/Podcast.

DECEMBER

SKY WATCH: The year ends with a planetary whimper. All of the superior planets are on the far side of the Sun, near their dimmest magnitudes and further diminished by solar glare. Several farewell conjunctions provide compensation. On the 1st, low in the west at evening twilight, float Jupiter (highest), Venus, Saturn, and the crescent Moon. Venus meets Saturn on the 10th and 11th. Meanwhile, Mars rises a bit higher as a predawn morning star, but it's still low and shines at a mere magnitude 2. The Geminid meteors on the 13th are spoiled by a nearly full Moon parked in Gemini that very night. Winter begins with the solstice on the 21st at 11:19 P.M.

◑ FIRST QUARTER	4th day	1:58 A.M.	◐ LAST QUARTER	18th day	11:57 P.M.
○ FULL MOON	12th day	12:12 A.M.	● NEW MOON	26th day	12:13 A.M.

All times are given in Eastern Standard Time.

GET THESE PAGES WITH TIMES SET TO YOUR POSTAL CODE AT ALMANAC.CA/ACCESS.

DAY OF YEAR	DAY OF MONTH	DAY OF WEEK	☼ RISES H. M.	RISE KEY	☼ SETS H. M.	SET KEY	LENGTH OF DAY H. M.	SUN FAST M.	SUN DECLINATION ° '	HIGH TIDE TIMES HALIFAX		☾ RISES H. M.	RISE KEY	☾ SETS H. M.	SET KEY	☾ ASTRON. PLACE	☾ AGE
335	1	F	7:22	E	4:21	A	8 59	8	21 s. 49	11	11¾	11:46	E	9:12	A	CAP	5
336	2	M.	7:23	E	4:21	A	8 58	8	21 s. 58	11¾	—	12:19	E	10:15	B	CAP	6
337	3	Tu.	7:24	E	4:21	A	8 57	7	22 s. 07	12¾	12¾	12:46	D	11:17	B	AQU	7
338	4	W.	7:25	E	4:20	A	8 55	7	22 s. 15	1½	1½	1:10	D	—	-	AQU	8
339	5	Th.	7:26	E	4:20	A	8 54	7	22 s. 23	2½	2¾	1:33	C	12:19	B	AQU	9
340	6	Fr.	7:27	E	4:20	A	8 53	6	22 s. 30	3½	3¾	1:54	C	1:20	C	CET	10
341	7	Sa.	7:28	E	4:20	A	8 52	6	22 s. 37	4½	4¾	2:15	C	2:22	C	CET	11
342	8	F	7:29	E	4:20	A	8 51	5	22 s. 43	5¼	5¾	2:38	B	3:24	C	PSC	12
343	9	M.	7:30	E	4:20	A	8 50	5	22 s. 49	5¾	6¼	3:04	B	4:29	D	ARI	13
344	10	Tu.	7:31	E	4:20	A	8 49	4	22 s. 55	6½	7	3:34	A	5:35	D	TAU	14
345	11	W.	7:32	E	4:20	A	8 48	4	23 s. 00	7	7¾	4:10	A	6:43	E	TAU	15
346	12	Th.	7:33	E	4:20	A	8 47	4	23 s. 05	7¾	8½	4:55	A	7:50	E	TAU	16
347	13	Fr.	7:34	E	4:20	A	8 46	3	23 s. 09	8½	9	5:49	A	8:53	E	GEM	17
348	14	Sa.	7:35	E	4:20	A	8 45	3	23 s. 13	9¼	9¾	6:52	A	9:49	E	GEM	18
349	15	F	7:35	E	4:20	A	8 45	2	23 s. 16	10	10¾	8:02	A	10:37	E	CAN	19
350	16	M.	7:36	E	4:20	A	8 44	2	23 s. 19	10¾	11½	9:16	B	11:17	E	CAN	20
351	17	Tu.	7:37	E	4:21	A	8 44	1	23 s. 21	11½	—	10:31	B	11:51	D	LEO	21
352	18	W.	7:38	E	4:21	A	8 43	1	23 s. 23	12¼	12½	11:46	B	12:20	D	LEO	22
353	19	Th.	7:38	E	4:21	A	8 43	0	23 s. 24	1¼	1½	—		12:47	C	VIR	23
354	20	Fr.	7:39	E	4:22	A	8 43	0	23 s. 25	2½	2¾	1:00	C	1:13	C	VIR	24
355	21	Sa.	7:39	E	4:22	A	8 43	*1	23 s. 26	3½	4	2:14	C	1:40	B	VIR	25
356	22	F	7:40	E	4:23	A	8 43	*1	23 s. 26	4½	5	3:28	D	2:08	B	LIB	26
357	23	M.	7:40	E	4:23	A	8 43	*2	23 s. 25	5¼	6	4:42	D	2:41	A	LIB	27
358	24	Tu.	7:41	E	4:24	A	8 43	*2	23 s. 24	6¼	6¾	5:54	E	3:19	A	SCO	28
359	25	W.	7:41	E	4:25	A	8 44	*3	23 s. 23	7	7¾	7:03	E	4:04	A	OPH	29
360	26	Th.	7:41	E	4:25	A	8 44	*3	23 s. 21	7¾	8½	8:04	E	4:56	A	SAG	0
361	27	Fr.	7:42	E	4:26	A	8 44	*4	23 s. 18	8½	9¼	8:57	E	5:54	A	SAG	1
362	28	Sa.	7:42	E	4:27	A	8 45	*4	23 s. 16	9¼	10	9:41	E	6:56	A	CAP	2
363	29	F	7:42	E	4:27	A	8 45	*5	23 s. 12	10	10¾	10:17	E	8:00	A	CAP	3
364	30	M.	7:42	E	4:28	A	8 46	*5	23 s. 09	10¾	11¼	10:47	D	9:03	B	CAP	4
365	31	Tu.	7:42	E	4:29	A	8 47	*6	23 s. 04	11½	—	11:13	D	10:05	B	AQU	5

CALENDAR

DECEMBER

DECEMBER HATH 31 DAYS

Send the ruddy firelight higher;
Draw your easy chair up nigher.
–Ina Donna Coolbrith

DAY OF MONTH	DAY OF WEEK	DATES, FEASTS, FASTS, ASPECTS, TIDE HEIGHTS, AND WEATHER	
1	**F**	**1st S. of Advent** • Winnie (bear Pooh named after) donated to London Zoo, 1919	*Deck*
2	M.	St. Viviana • First T. Eaton Co. Santa Claus parade, Toronto, Ont., 1905 • Tides {5.5/—	*the*
3	Tu.	*Pioneer 11* Jupiter flyby, 1974 • 68°F, Portland, Maine, 2009 • Tides {5.4/5.2	*halls;*
4	W.	☽ AT APO. • ☌♆☽ • French statesman Armand-Jean du Plessis (Cardinal de Richelieu) died, 1642	*hit*
5	Th.	Pusuke, a Shiba Inu mix and world's oldest dog at time (26 yrs., 8 mos.), died, 2011 • Tides {5.2/4.9	*the*
6	Fr.	St. Nicholas • ☽ ON EQ. • Kitty Hambleton reached 512.71 mph land speed, 1976	*malls;*
7	Sa.	St. Ambrose • **Nat'l Pearl Harbor Remembrance Day (U.S.)** • {5.4/5.0	*scan*
8	**F**	**2nd S. of Advent** • ☌⛢☽ • Astronaut John Glenn died, 2016 • {5.6/5.1	*the*
9	M.	Quebec adopted new coat of arms, 1939 • Tides {5.8/5.3	*Web*
10	Tu.	St. Eulalia • ☌♀♄ • *All doors open to courtesy.* –Thomas Fuller • {5.9/5.5	*with*
11	W.	United Nations International Children's Emergency Fund (UNICEF) established, 1946 • {6.1/5.6	*passion!*
12	Th.	**Our Lady of Guadalupe** • FULL COLD ○ • Paul Martin became Canada's 21st prime minister, 2003	*These*
13	Fr.	St. Lucia • ☽ RIDES HIGH • ☽ AT ☊ • ☌♀♇ • Tides {6.4/5.8	*mild*
14	Sa.	Halcyon Days begin. • Ala. statehood, 1819 • Millau Viaduct opened, France, 2004	*days*
15	**F**	**3rd S. of Advent** • *Dec. 14–15:* Windstorm caused flooding/power outages, Wash./Oreg., 2006	*are*
16	M.	9,000th episode of *All My Children* aired, 2004 • Tides {6.2/5.8	*flashin' by—*
17	Tu.	Project Blue Book (UFO investigations) terminated, 1969 • {6.0/—	*Snowstorm's*
18	W.	Ember Day • ☽ AT PERIG. • Freezing rain caused 170 auto accidents, Memphis, Tenn., 1989	*crashin'*
19	Th.	Beware the Pogonip. • *A snow year, a rich year.* • {5.7/5.5	*Santa's*
20	Fr.	Ember Day • ☽ ON EQ. • Calif. angler caught 230-lb. Nile perch, Lake Nasser, Egypt, 2000 • {5.8/5.3	*party!*
21	Sa.	St. Thomas • Ember Day • **WINTER SOLSTICE** • Tides {5.9/5.3	*May*
22	**F**	**4th S. of Advent** • Chanukah begins at sundown • ☌♂☽ • {6.1/5.4	*your*
23	M.	Entrepreneur Madam C. J. Walker born, 1867 • –50°F, Williston, N.Dak., 1983 • Tides {6.2/5.6	*Yule*
24	Tu.	Clement Moore's "A Visit From St. Nicholas" likely written, 1822 • Tides {6.3/5.7	*be filled*
25	W.	**Christmas** • ☌☿☽ • *Be merry and wise.* • Tides {6.4/5.8	*with*
26	Th.	**Boxing Day** • **1st day of Kwanzaa** • **NEW ● ECLIPSE ☉** • ☽ RUNS LOW • ☽ AT ☋ • ☌♃☽	
27	Fr.	St. John • ☌♃☉ • ☌♄☽ • ☌♇☽ • ALH 84001 Mars meteorite found, Antarctica, 1984	*plenty*
28	Sa.	Holy Innocents • ☌♀☽ • 2nd U.S. chewing gum patent went to William Semple, 1869 • {6.2/5.8	*and*
29	**F**	**1st S. af. Ch.** • American Meteorological Society founded, 1919 • {6.0/5.7	*likewise*
30	M.	Social reformer Amelia Bloomer died, 1894 • Tides {5.8/5.6	*your*
31	Tu.	St. Sylvester • ☌♆☽ • *Plan your life at New Year's eve, your day at dawn.* • {5.6/—	*2020!*

Farmer's Calendar

"Can you tell the difference between a balsam and a Fraser?" Steve Moffatt grills his tree hauler, Seth Johnson, a young farmer. "Yep," replies Seth, who grows beans and wheat, raises beef and horses, and moonlights as a trucker when his growing season stalls. Together they load the culmination of Steve's decade of labor—planting, fertilizing, weeding, grooming, harvesting, and baling. Now Seth climbs onto his trailer and begins driving in the bed stakes that will gird this precious cargo. Then Steve hands over the first of 500 eight-foot balsams and Fraser firs. Seth lays them in like shingles, butts and tips sheltering each other, protecting each tree's topmost branch. In the cold, it can snap like glass, and a tree without a tip, as both driver and grower know, is useless. The cold air fills with a balsam perfume as the Christmas tree layers accrue. Finally, Seth stretches his cables and cinches the load. He climbs into his cab, equipped with his CB radio, Thermos, and Santa hat. As Seth's truck eases onto Wild Branch Road, Steve watches the results of his labor—the forest he began 10 years ago—glide off in a diesel sleigh.

HOLIDAYS AND OBSERVANCES

2019 HOLIDAYS

JAN. 1: New Year's Day*

FEB. 2: Groundhog Day

FEB. 14: Valentine's Day

FEB. 15: National Flag of Canada Day

FEB. 18: Family Day *(Alta., B.C., N.B., Ont., Sask.)*
Louis Riel Day *(Man.)*
Nova Scotia Heritage Day *(N.S.)*
Islander Day *(P.E.I.)*

FEB. 22: Heritage Day *(Y.T.)*

MAR. 8: International Women's Day

MAR. 11: Commonwealth Day

APR. 19: Good Friday

APR. 22: Easter Monday
Earth Day
St. George's Day, observed *(N.L.)*

MAY 12: Mother's Day

MAY 20: Victoria Day

JUNE 5: World Environment Day

JUNE 16: Father's Day

JUNE 21: National Indigenous Peoples Day

JUNE 24: Discovery Day *(N.L.)*
Fête Nationale *(Qué.)*

JULY 1: Canada Day*

JULY 9: Nunavut Day

JULY 15: Orangemen's Day, observed *(N.L.)*

AUG. 5: Civic Holiday *(Alta., B.C., Man., N.B., N.W.T., N.S., Nunavut, Ont., P.E.I., Sask.)*

AUG. 19: Discovery Day *(Y.T.)*

SEPT. 2: Labour Day

OCT. 14: Thanksgiving Day

OCT. 31: Halloween

NOV. 11: Remembrance Day*

NOV. 20: National Child Day

DEC. 25: Christmas Day*

DEC. 26: Boxing Day
First day of Kwanzaa

*When this day falls on a Saturday or Sunday, the following Monday is observed as a holiday.

–PGC photo/Jacob Dingel

GROUNDHOG DAY

Traditionally, on February 2, farmers looked for signs of what the weather would be for the next 6 weeks. They believed that if an animal came out of hibernation on this day and saw its shadow, winter would continue.

For centuries, farmers in France and England looked to a bear; in Germany, they kept their eye on the badger. In the 1800s, German immigrants to Pennsylvania brought the tradition with them. Finding no badgers there, they adopted the groundhog to fit the lore. Pennsylvania's Punxsutawney Phil has predicted spring's arrival since 1887.

Since 1956, albino groundhogs named Wiarton Willie have made annual weather prognostications in Wiarton, Ontario. Several other groundhogs are employed across the nation, including Nova Scotia's Shubenacadie Sam, who, because of location and special training, has the honor of making the first groundhog end-of-winter prediction for North America.

(continued)

CALENDAR

Why Viagra Is Failing Men

Soaring demand expected for new scientific advance made just for older men. Works on both men's physical ability and their desire in bed.

New men's pill overwhelms your senses with sexual desire as well as firmer, long-lasting erections. There's never been anything like it before.

By Harlan S. Waxman
Health News Syndicate

New York – If you're like the rest of us guys over 50; you probably already know the truth… Prescription ED pills don't work! Simply getting an erection doesn't fix the problem" says Dr. Bassam Damaj, chief scientific officer at the world famous Innovus Pharma Laboratories.

As we get older, we need more help in bed. Not only does our desire fade; but erections can be soft or feeble, one of the main complaints with prescription pills. Besides, they're expensive… costing as much as $50.00 each

Plus, it does nothing to stimulate your brain to want sex. "I don't care what you take, if you aren't interested in sex, you can't get or keep an erection. It's physiologically impossible," said Dr. Damaj.

MADE JUST FOR MEN OVER 50

But now, for the first time ever, there's a pill made just for older men. It's called Vesele®. A new pill that helps you get an erection by stimulating your body and your brainwaves. So Vesele® can work even when nothing else worked before.

The new men's pill is not a drug. It's something completely different Because you don't need a prescription for Vesele®, sales are exploding. The maker just can't produce enough of it to keep up with demand. Even doctors are having a tough time getting their hands on it. So what's all the fuss about?

WORKS ON YOUR HEAD AND YOUR BODY

The new formula takes on erectile problems with a whole new twist. It doesn't just address the physical problems of getting older; it works on the mental part of sex too. Unlike the expensive prescriptions, the new

pill stimulates your sexual brain chemistry as well. Actually helping you regain the passion and burning desire you had for your partner again.

THE BRAIN/ERECTION CONNECTION

Vesele takes off where Viagra® only begins. Thanks to a discovery made by 3 Nobel-Prize winning scientists; Vesele® has become the first ever patented supplement to harden you and your libido. So you regain your desire as well as the ability to act on it.

JAW-DROPPING CLINICAL PROOF

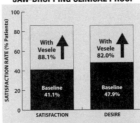

	Vesele	Baseline
Satisfaction	88.1%	41.4%
Frequency	79.5%	44.9%
Desire	82%	47.9%
Hardness	85.7%	36.2%
Duration	79.5%	35%
Ability to Satisfy	83.3%	44.1%

In a 16-week clinical study; scientists from the U.S.A. joined forces to prove Nitric Oxide's effects on the cardio vascular system. They showed that Nitric Oxide could not only increase your ability to get an erection, it would also work on your brainwaves to stimulate your desire for sex. The results were remarkable and published in the world's most respected medical journals.

THE SCIENCE OF SEX

The study asked men, 45 to 65 years old to take the main ingredient in

Vesele® once a day. Then they were instructed not to change the way they eat or exercise but to take Vesele® twice a day. What happened next was remarkable. Virtually every man in the study who took Vesele® twice a day reported a huge difference in their desire for sex. They also experienced harder erections that lasted for almost 20 minutes. The placebo controlled group (who received sugar pills) mostly saw no difference.

The study results even showed an impressive increase in the energy, brain-power and memory of the participants.

"VESELE® PASSED THE TEST"

"As an expert in the development of sexual dysfunction, I've studied the effectiveness of Nitric Oxide on the body and the brain. I'm impressed by the way it increases cerebral and penile blood flow. The result is evident in the creation of Vesele®. It's sure-fire proof that the mind/body connection is unbeatable when achieving and maintaining an erection and the results are remarkable" said Dr. Damaj.

HOW TO GET VESELE®

In order to get the word out about Vesele®, Innovus Pharma is offering special introductory discounts to all who call. Discounts will automatically be applied to all callers, but don't wait. This offer may not last forever. **Call toll-free: 1-800-611-1445.**

U.S. FEDERAL HOLIDAYS

JAN. 1: New Year's Day

JAN. 21: Martin Luther King Jr.'s Birthday, observed

FEB. 18: Presidents' Day

MAY 27: Memorial Day, observed

JULY 4: Independence Day

SEPT. 2: Labor Day

OCT. 14: Columbus Day, observed

NOV. 11: Veterans Day

NOV. 28: Thanksgiving Day

DEC. 25: Christmas Day

Movable Religious Observances

FEB. 17: Septuagesima Sunday

MAR. 5: Shrove Tuesday

MAR. 6: Ash Wednesday

APR. 14: Palm Sunday

APR. 19: Good Friday
Passover begins at sundown

APR. 21: Easter

APR. 28: Orthodox Easter

MAY 5: Ramadan begins at sundown

MAY 26: Rogation Sunday

MAY 30: Ascension Day

JUNE 9: Whitsunday–Pentecost

JUNE 16: Trinity Sunday

JUNE 23: Corpus Christi

SEPT. 29: Rosh Hashanah begins at sundown

OCT. 8: Yom Kippur begins at sundown

DEC. 1: First Sunday of Advent

DEC. 22: Chanukah begins at sundown

–Beth Krommes

CHRONOLOGICAL CYCLES

Dominical Letter **F**

Epact **24**

Golden Number (Lunar Cycle) **6**

Roman Indiction **12**

Solar Cycle **12**

Year of Julian Period **6732**

ERAS

ERA	YEAR	BEGINS
Byzantine	7528	September 14
Jewish (A.M.)*	5780	September 29
Chinese (Lunar) [Year of the Pig]	4717	February 5
Roman (A.U.C.)	2772	January 14
Nabonassar	2768	April 19
Japanese	2679	January 1
Grecian (Seleucidae)	2331	September 14 (or October 14)
Indian (Saka)	1941	March 22
Diocletian	1736	September 12
Islamic (Hegira)* [FCNA date]	1441	August 30

*Year begins at sundown.

NEW PROSTATE PILL HELPS RELIEVE SYMPTOMS WITHOUT DRUGS OR SURGERY

Combats all-night bathroom urges and embarrassment... *Yet most doctors don't even know about it!*

By Health Writer, Peter Metler

Thanks to a brand new discovery made from a rare prostate relief plant; thousands of men across America are taking their lives back from "prostate hell". This remarkable new natural supplement helps you:

- **MINIMIZE** constant urges to urinate
- **END** embarrassing sexual "let-downs"
- **SUPPORT** a strong, healthy urine flow
- **GET** a restful night of uninterrupted sleep
- **STOP** false alarms, dribbles
- **ENJOY** a truly empty bladder

More men than ever before are dealing with prostate problems that range from annoying to downright EMBARRASSING! But now, research has discovered a new solution so remarkable that helps alleviate symptoms associated with an enlarged prostate (sexual failure, lost sleep, bladder discomfort and urgent runs to the bathroom). Like nothing before!

Yet 9 out of 10 doctors don't know about it! Here's why: Due to strict managed health care constrictions, many MD's are struggling to keep their practices afloat. "Unfortunately, there's no money in prescribing natural products. They aren't nearly as profitable," says a confidential source. Instead, doctors rely on toxic drugs that help, but could leave you sexually "powerless" (or a lot worse)!

On a CNN Special, Medical Correspondent Dr. Steve Salvatore shocked America by quoting a statistic from the prestigious Journal of American Medical Association that stated, "... about 60% of men who go under the knife for a prostatectomy are left UNABLE to perform sexually!"

PROSTATE PROBLEM SOLVED!

But now you can now beat the odds. And enjoy better sleep, a powerful urine stream and a long and healthy love life. The secret? You need to load your diet with essential Phyto-Nutrients, (traditionally found in certain fruits, vegetables and grains).

The problem is, most Phyto-Nutrients never get into your bloodstream. They're destroyed

HERE ARE 6 WARNING SIGNS YOU BETTER NOT IGNORE

- ✓ Waking up 2 to 6 times a night to urinate
- ✓ A constant feeling that you have to "go"... but can't
- ✓ A burning sensation when you do go
- ✓ A weak urine stream
- ✓ A feeling that your bladder is never completely empty
- ✓ Embarrassing sputtering, dripping & staining

by today's food preparation methods (cooking, long storage times and food additives).

YEARS OF RESEARCH

Thankfully, a small company (Wellness Logix™) out of Maine, is on a mission to change that. They've created a product that arms men who suffer with prostate inflammation with new hope. And it's fast becoming the #1 Prostate formula in America.

Prostate IQ™ gives men the super-concentrated dose of Phyto-Nutrients they need to beat prostate symptoms. "You just can't get them from your regular diet" say Daniel. It's taken a long time to understand how to capture the prostate relieving power of this amazing botanical. But their hard work paid off. *Prostate IQ*™ is different than any other prostate supplement on the market...

DON'T BE FOOLED BY CHEAP FORMULATIONS!

Many hope you won't notice, but a lot of prostate supplements fall embarrassingly short with their dosages. The formulas may be okay, but they won't do a darn thing for you unless you take 10 or more tablets a day. *Prostate IQ*™ contains a whopping 300mg of this special "Smart Prostate Plant". So it's loaded with Phyto-Nutrients. Plus, it gets inside your bloodstream faster and stays inside for maximum results!

TRY IT RISK-FREE

SPECIAL OPPORTUNITY

Get a risk-free trial supply of *Prostate IQ*™ today - just for asking. But you must act now, supplies are limited!

Call Now, Toll-Free at:

1-800-380-0925

THESE STATEMENTS HAVE NOT BEEN EVALUATED BY THE FDA. THESE PRODUCTS ARE NOT INTENDED TO DIAGNOSE, TREAT, CURE OR PREVENT ANY DISEASE.. OFFER NOT AVAILABLE TO RESIDENTS OF IOWA

GLOSSARY OF ALMANAC ODDITIES

Many readers have expressed puzzlement over the rather obscure entries that appear on our **Right-Hand Calendar Pages, 121–147.** These "oddities" have long been fixtures in the Almanac, and we are pleased to provide some definitions. Once explained, they may not seem so odd after all!

EMBER DAYS: These are the Wednesdays, Fridays, and Saturdays that occur in succession following (1) the First Sunday in Lent; (2) Whitsunday–Pentecost; (3) the Feast of the Holy Cross, September 14; and (4) the Feast of St. Lucia, December 13. The word *ember* is perhaps a corruption of the Latin *quatuor tempora,* "four times." The four periods are observed by some Christian denominations for prayer, fasting, and the ordination of clergy.

Folklore has it that the weather on each of the 3 days foretells the weather for the next 3 months; that is, in September, the first Ember Day, Wednesday, forecasts the weather for October; Friday predicts November; and Saturday foretells December.

DISTAFF DAY (JANUARY 7): This was the day after Epiphany, when women were expected to return to their spinning following the Christmas holiday. A distaff is the staff that women used for holding the flax or wool in spinning. (Hence the term "distaff" refers to women's work or the maternal side of the family.)

PLOUGH MONDAY (JANUARY): Traditionally, the first Monday after Epiphany was called Plough Monday because it was the day when men returned to their plough, or daily work, following the Christmas holiday. (Every few years, Plough Monday and Distaff Day fall on the same day.) It was customary at this time for farm laborers to draw a plough through the village, soliciting money for a "plough light,"

which was kept burning in the parish church all year. This traditional verse captures the spirit of it:

> *Yule is come and Yule is gone,*
> *and we have feasted well;*
> *so Jack must to his flail again*
> *and Jenny to her wheel.*

THREE CHILLY SAINTS (MAY): Mamertus, Pancras, and Gervais were three early Christian saints whose feast days, on May 11, 12, and 13, respectively, are traditionally cold; thus they have come to be known as the Three Chilly Saints. An old French saying translates to "St. Mamertus, St. Pancras, and St. Gervais do not pass without a frost."

MIDSUMMER DAY (JUNE 24): To the farmer, this day is the midpoint of the growing season, halfway between planting and harvest. The Anglican Church considered it a "Quarter Day," one of the four major divisions of the liturgical year. It also marks the feast day of St. John the Baptist. (Midsummer Eve is an occasion for festivity and celebrates fertility.)

CORNSCATEOUS AIR (JULY): First used by early almanac makers, this term signifies warm, damp air. Although it signals ideal climatic conditions for growing corn, warm, damp air poses

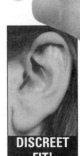
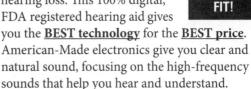
2019   The Old Farmer's Almanac   153

a danger to those affected by asthma and other respiratory problems.

DOG DAYS (JULY 3–AUGUST 11): These 40 days are traditionally the year's hottest and unhealthiest. They once coincided with the year's heliacal (at sunrise) rising of the Dog Star, Sirius. Ancient folks thought that the "combined heat" of Sirius and the Sun caused summer's swelter.

LAMMAS DAY (AUGUST 1): Derived from the Old English *hlaf maesse,* meaning "loaf mass," Lammas Day marked the beginning of the harvest. Traditionally, loaves of bread were baked from the first-ripened grain and brought to the churches to be consecrated. In Scotland, Lammastide fairs became famous as the time when trial marriages could be made. These marriages could end after a year with no strings attached.

CAT NIGHTS COMMENCE (AUGUST 17): This term harks back to the days when people believed in witches. An Irish legend says that a witch could turn into a cat and regain herself eight times, but on the ninth time (August 17), she couldn't change back and thus began her final life permanently as a cat. Hence the saying "A cat has nine lives."

HARVEST HOME (SEPTEMBER): In Britain and other parts of Europe, this marked the conclusion of the harvest and a period of festivals for feasting and thanksgiving. It was also a time to hold elections, pay workers, and collect rents. These festivals usually took place around the autumnal equinox. Certain groups in the United States, e.g., the Pennsylvania Dutch, have kept the tradition alive.

ST. LUKE'S LITTLE SUMMER (OCTOBER): This is a period of warm weather that occurs on or near St. Luke's feast day (October 18) and is sometimes called Indian summer.

INDIAN SUMMER (NOVEMBER): A period of warm weather following a cold spell or a hard frost, Indian summer can occur between St. Martin's Day (November 11) and November 20. Although there are differing dates for its occurrence, for more than 225 years the Almanac has adhered to the saying "If All Saints' (November 1) brings out winter, St. Martin's brings out Indian summer." The term may have come from early Native Americans, some of whom believed that the condition was caused by a warm wind sent from the court of their southwestern god, Cautantowwit.

HALCYON DAYS (DECEMBER): This period of about 2 weeks of calm weather often follows the blustery winds at autumn's end. Ancient Greeks and Romans experienced this weather at around the time of the winter solstice, when the halcyon, or kingfisher, was thought to brood in a nest floating on the sea. The bird was said to have charmed the wind and waves so that waters were especially calm at this time.

BEWARE THE POGONIP (DECEMBER): The word *pogonip* refers to frozen fog and was coined by Native Americans to describe the frozen fogs of fine ice needles that occur in the mountain valleys of the western United States and Canada. According to tradition, breathing the fog is injurious to the lungs. ∎

—Beth Krommes

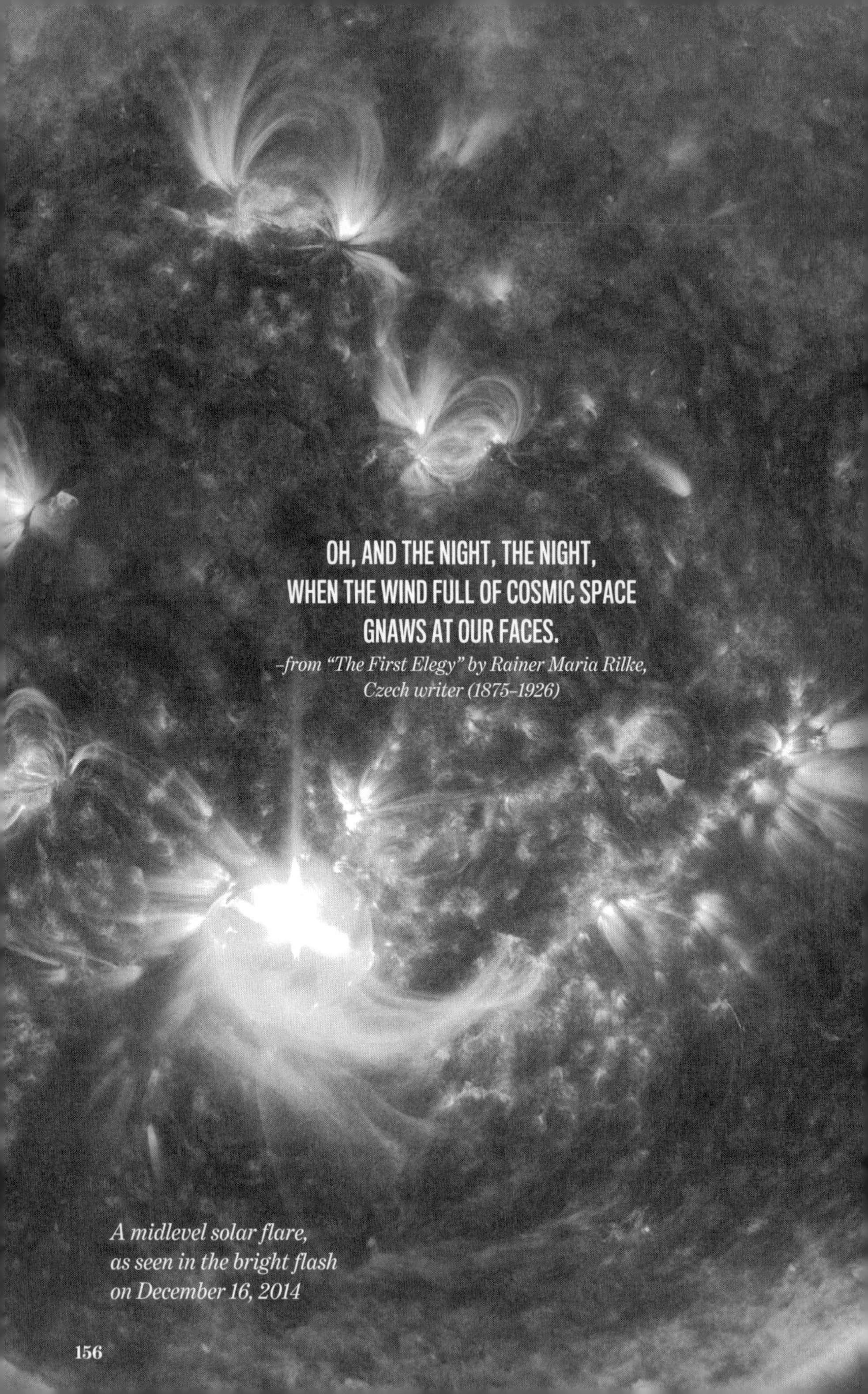

OH, AND THE NIGHT, THE NIGHT,
WHEN THE WIND FULL OF COSMIC SPACE
GNAWS AT OUR FACES.
–from "The First Elegy" by Rainer Maria Rilke,
Czech writer (1875–1926)

A midlevel solar flare,
as seen in the bright flash
on December 16, 2014

THE DAY THE SUN
EXPLODED

BY BOB BERMAN

YES, IT COULD HAPPEN AGAIN!

In the mid–19th century, the scientific community was puzzled and fascinated by sunspots—dark marks on the solar surface that came and went in roughly 11-year cycles. None of these experts had any idea what they were, how they moved across the Sun, or if they affected Earth. One of them, 33-year-old British astronomer Richard Carrington, was obsessed by solar activity. Through his 4-inch refracting telescope, he observed the spots on every clear day.

The days leading into September 1859 had seen unusually intense solar storms, and scientists were abuzz. Suddenly, at 11:18 A.M. on September 1,

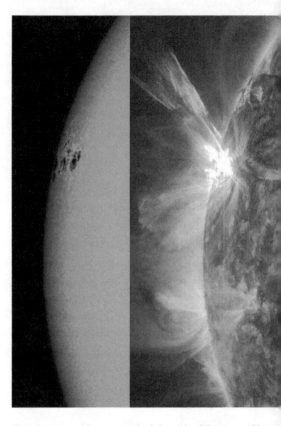

A FLARE'S FULL EFFECTS

A very strong solar storm creates high-energy electromagnetic waves and extreme X- and ultraviolet rays that travel toward Earth at light speed. These ionize, or break apart, atoms in our atmosphere. Such solar violence often then unleashes a radiation storm that is a potential danger to airline passengers and an extreme (even lethal) hazard to astronauts. This energy could travel to ground level, where it would zap everything with radiation. A solar explosion also causes a geomagnetic storm. This could cause electric grid collapses and power blackouts; send currents of hundreds of amps along railroads, wires, and oil and gas pipelines; damage transformers; destroy radio communications; knock out satellites; and disrupt the GPS system.

Carrington was rewarded for his diligence: To his amazement, a large sunspot cluster near the top of the Sun grew strangely dazzling. Despite a protective eye filter, he could barely watch. The flare became so luminous that it doubled the brightness of the Sun. He knew that this was no optical illusion, and his observation was soon confirmed by another British observer, Richard Hodgson.

Carrington was the first known witness to a solar flare, a violent—and as yet unmatched—solar phenomenon of the sort that makes solar researchers nervous even now, 160 years later.

As Carrington and Hodgson watched the flare, instruments at England's King's (Kew)

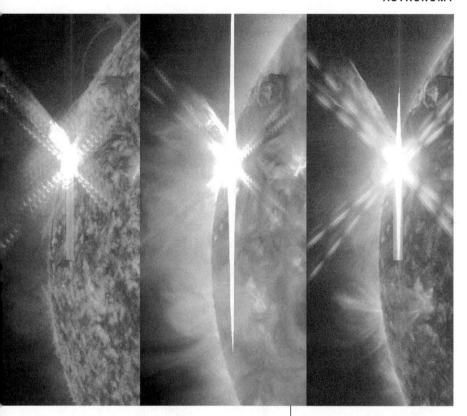

Observatory recorded a disturbance in Earth's magnetic field. Would this be the long-sought evidence that events on the Sun affect our planet?

The answer arrived that night.

Brilliant auroras in vivid deep reds (not the ordinary green hues) lit up the skies around the globe, even over regions as far south as the Caribbean. These twisted displays alarmed millions of people who had never seen or imagined that the heavens could possibly contort in this way. So bright were these illuminations over the U.S. West that some people assumed that day had dawned—so they got up and made breakfast. In New York City, gawkers crowded rooftops and sidewalks.

The light shows were breathtaking, but other effects were literally shocking. Supercharged by

NASA's Solar Dynamics Observatory captured these images of a significant solar flare on May 5, 2015. Each image shows a different wavelength of extreme ultraviolet light that highlights a different temperature of material on the Sun. By comparing different images, scientists can better understand the movement of solar matter and energy during a flare.

OUR SOLAR SENTRIES

Currently, an armada of specialized satellites keeps watch on the Sun:

• The Geostationary Operational Environmental Satellite (GOES) system stares at the Sun and Earth simultaneously from Earth orbit.

• The Solar and Heliospheric Observatory (SOHO) uses a coronagraph to observe solar flares and coronal mass ejections (CMEs)—large expulsions of magnetic field and plasma—and usually provides 2 to 4 days' warning.

• The Deep Space Climate Observatory (DSCOVR) is parked at Lagrangian Point L1 (where the Sun's gravity balances that of Earth) and measures the density and magnetic polarity of the solar wind heading to Earth; it gives 15- to 60-minute warnings.

• The Solar TErrestrial RElations Observatory (STEREO) duo observes flares, CMEs, and solar wind streams and can peer behind the Sun to see coming storms.

• The Solar Dynamic Observatory (SDO) monitors the Sun's magnetism, flares, surface pulses, and extreme UV, transmitting high-def images on 10 wavelengths.

solar emissions, the current-carrying telegraph wires that crisscrossed the United States and Europe started sizzling and popping, emitting showering sparks. For 5 minutes, the impossibly high current traveled into populated areas. Sparking equipment shocked telegraph operators, who leaped from their seats. Some did not move fast enough and were found unconscious on the floor.

A decade passed before any astronomer saw another flare, but it would be over a half-century before the world again felt the effects.

The second worst geomagnetic storm in recorded history began at 7:04 A.M. on May 13, 1921. According to *The New York Times,* all of the signal and switching mechanisms of the New York Central Railroad were knocked out of operation. A fire raged in the control tower at New York City's 57th Street and Park Avenue, while flames in the Central New England Railroad station destroyed that entire building. Telegraph operations throughout the country came to a standstill due to damaged equipment and blown fuses.

Another flare occurred on March 13, 1989. At 2:44 A.M., Sun-induced surges began wreaking havoc on Quebec's electrical power grid, and within a minute, the province and its 6 million people were in darkness. And cold. Over a half-million Quebecois depended on electricity for heat. In Montreal, the Metro came to a halt, and, with airport radar out of service, planes at the city's main airport were grounded. Meanwhile, as U.S. electric grids experienced shutdowns and voltage swings at major substations, the country managed—just barely—to avoid cascading blackouts.

The next solar storm occurred from October 19 through November 7, 2003. While it was a solar burp compared with the Carrington event, the National Oceanographic and Atmospheric

Administration (NOAA) reported the second fastest known journey of solar material to Earth; it arrived in half the normal 3 to 4 days' travel time. The storm's effects ranged from a blackout in northern Europe to rerouted airlines (to avoid high radiation levels) and damaged spacecraft—notably, the loss of the $640 million ADEOS-II satellite, which was on a mission to study climate change.

Coronal mass ejections (CMEs) are thought to be triggered by the destabilization of a series of magnetic loops (below) known as a flux rope.

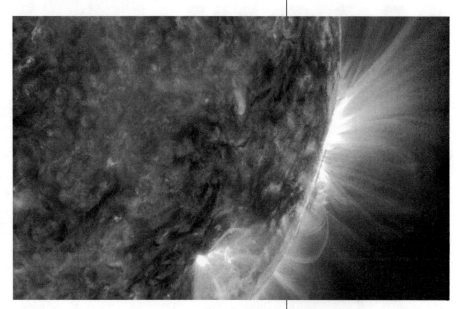

As advances in technology accelerate, so does the scale of damage that a solar flare could inflict. In May 2008, a team of space weather experts estimated that a "low-frequency/high-consequence event" would produce damage of $1 trillion to $2 trillion during the first year and that recovery would take 4 to 10 years. However, we can now see the threat as it's happening (see "Our Solar Sentries"), and the potential exists to issue warnings.

Maybe the next "big one" won't happen for another century. Let's hope that it doesn't happen at all. ■

LISTEN UP!
Be astounded! Explore the "Astonishing Universe," Bob Berman and Jim Metzger's podcast, at Almanac.ca/ Podcast.

Bob Berman is the Almanac's astronomy editor.

MUST BE A
FULL
MOON!

by Tim Clark

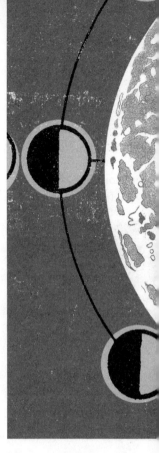

Doctors, nurses, EMTs, police officers, and elementary school teachers generally agree that full Moons will bring crazier behavior. They are not dissuaded from this belief by the complete absence of statistical proof.

Hundreds of studies have failed to turn up evidence of "the lunar effect," as some call it. Those few studies that seem to show a connection are usually disproved by attempts to confirm them. Or other studies contradict them.

For example, one study says that more animal bites (from cats, rats, dogs, horses) occur at the full Moon—but another says that there's no increase in dog bites. One shows an increase in crime, but others find no increase in arrests, calls for police assistance, prison assaults, batteries, homicides, or acting out in mental hospitals. In fact, admissions for psychosis are lowest during the full Moon, and psychiatric emergency room visits decline. Calls to suicide prevention hotlines peak at the new Moon.

Yet 43 percent of health care professionals believe in the lunar effect, as do 81 percent of mental health care specialists. What's going on?

One explanation might be what psychologists call "confirmation bias"—people are more likely to notice things that confirm a preexisting belief. So you're working in an emergency room, and something weird happens on the full Moon, and your older and wiser colleagues nod and say, "Must be a full Moon." That's what they heard from their elders when they were new at the job, too. (Psychologists

Illustration: Tim Robinson

81 PERCENT of mental health care specialists believe in the lunar effect.

also have a name for that: "communal reinforcement.")

But if something weird happens at a different phase of the lunar cycle, nobody says, "Must be the first quarter Moon!" And when nothing unusual happens on the full Moon, nobody says anything.

What do we call widespread beliefs that are unsupported by fact? Folklore. Maria Leach, editor of the *Funk & Wagnalls*

Standard Dictionary of Folklore, Mythology, and Legend (Harper & Row, 1984), defined it as "the inextinguishable hope that all that is wrong in the world can somehow be put right."

So, how does a belief that strange things happen on the full Moon help us to feel safer? The full Moon occurs only once every 29.5 days; this means that the other 4 weeks of the lunar month should

be less dangerous and unpredictable.

Therefore, this folk belief suggests that our fears about everything from increased bleeding to werewolves should be limited to only the 13 actual full Moon days that occur each year.

Come to think of it, maybe that's why the number 13 worries people! ■

Tim Clark studied folklore at Harvard University.

THE BEES' LIFE IS LIKE A MAGIC WELL:
THE MORE YOU DRAW FROM IT, THE MORE IT FILLS WITH WATER.
–Karl von Frisch, Austrian ethologist (1886–1982)

TELLING THE BEES
A SWARM OF FACTS, FOLKLORE, AND TRADITIONS

BY TIM CLARK

For thousands of years, human beings have shared a special bond with bees. Bees are not truly domesticated; their relationship with humans is an equal partnership. In Central Europe, beekeepers gave their bees written contracts, promising to provide shelter and care in return for wax and honey.

The orderliness and industry of honeybees and their loyalty to their queen are a timeless metaphor. In ancient Egypt, the hieroglyph that represented a king was a bee. When Napoleon Bonaparte made himself emperor, he wore a sumptuous gown decorated with golden bees. Even today, a beehive adorns the state flag of Utah, along with the motto "Industry." Indeed, the bee has given its name to occasions of collective labor, such as a sewing bee.

Bees were symbolic of wisdom and morality. Muslims believe that the bee is the only animal that left the Garden of Eden unchanged and the only animal that goes to heaven. The Germans believed that bees were created by God to provide wax for church candles, and the Bretons said that they were the transformed tears of Christ. In India, the three Hindu gods Indra, Krishna, and Vishnu were called "the nectar-born," and Kama, a love goddess, had a bowstring made of bees.

The Greeks and Romans thought that bees sucked their young out of flowers. In fact, queen bees are impregnated by drones in the so-called "mating flight," far from the hive. But no one understood this until the late 19th century. Until then, bees represented chastity and were a symbol of Artemis, the Greek goddess of virginity. Beekeepers had to abstain from sex during certain ritual periods, and young women would parade their sweethearts before the hives, believing that bees would sting a faithless lover. Valentine is not only the patron saint of lovers, but of beekeepers as well.

In Greek mythology, two daughters of the king of Crete, Melissa and Amalthea, protected the infant Zeus, and the grateful god turned them into bees. Greeks also believed that if a bee landed on a baby's lips, the child would grow up to be an eloquent speaker. The philosopher Plato, the dramatist Sophocles, and the historian Xenophon were said to have received the gift, and each was nicknamed "The Athenian Bee."

A vast collection of folklore relates to bees. A bee flying into a house means that a stranger is coming. If the bee flies in and out of the house, it's good luck, but it mustn't be shooed out, and if the bee dies in the house, bad luck will follow. If a swarm comes to your home without your knowledge, disaster will follow. The Roman general Scipio once canceled an attack because a swarm landed in his camp.

Bees can even predict the weather, it is said. Unusually large stores of honey in the fall mean a hard winter is coming.

Some of the most interesting folklore about bees involves human–bee communication. Bees were said to hum hymns on Christmas Eve, and beekeepers sang to their bees to prevent them from swarming. Swearing or quarreling in front of bees was strictly forbidden, lest they become upset and leave.

It was thought that the public exchange of money for bees was offensive to them, so barter was the preferred method of acquiring a swarm. If money must be used, the buyer should leave it on a stone in an agreed-upon place for the seller to collect later, and the exchange should never take place on a Friday.

The most touching custom was to tell the bees of any significant events in the beekeeper's life. Bees were often invited to weddings, for example, and in Brittany and parts of England, betrothals were announced to the bees. The new couple would introduce themselves to the gaily-decorated hives, and pieces of wedding cake would be left there as gifts for the bees.

It was critical to tell the bees of a death in the beekeeper's family. Many tales have been told of colonies leaving the farm or dying off if they were not told, especially when the beekeeper himself or herself died. A family member (some stories specify the youngest child or the oldest female relation) had to gently knock on the hive and announce, "The Master is dead." Then she or he would beg the bees not to leave the farm. Often the hives were decorated with black crepe for the funeral.

John Greenleaf Whittier's 1858 poem "Telling the Bees" relates such a story, and in 1906, Rudyard Kipling's "The Bee-Boy's Song" gave the bees themselves a voice:

Bees! Bees! Hark to your bees!
Hide from your neighbors as much as
*   you please,*
But all that has happened, to us you
*   must tell,*
Or else we will give you no honey to sell!

An ancient custom of no modern consequence? Perhaps. But following the death of England's King George VI in 1952, thousands of British beekeepers rushed outside to tell the bees. ∎

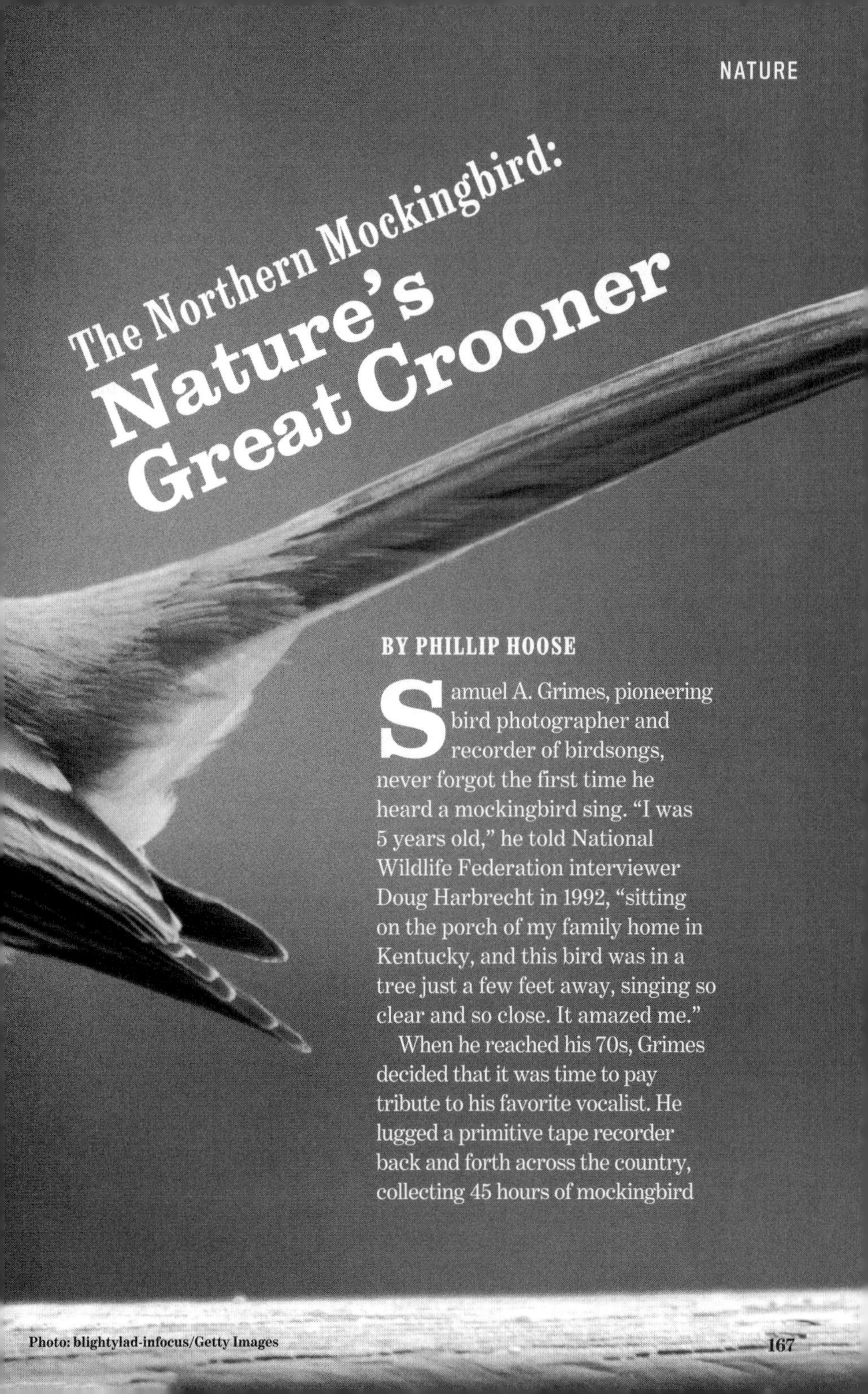

The Northern Mockingbird: Nature's Great Crooner

BY PHILLIP HOOSE

Samuel A. Grimes, pioneering bird photographer and recorder of birdsongs, never forgot the first time he heard a mockingbird sing. "I was 5 years old," he told National Wildlife Federation interviewer Doug Harbrecht in 1992, "sitting on the porch of my family home in Kentucky, and this bird was in a tree just a few feet away, singing so clear and so close. It amazed me."

When he reached his 70s, Grimes decided that it was time to pay tribute to his favorite vocalist. He lugged a primitive tape recorder back and forth across the country, collecting 45 hours of mockingbird

Photo: blightylad-infocus/Getty Images

song onto 2 miles of tape. The result was "The Vocally Versatile Mockingbird," a 1979 release of the golden songs of *Mimus polyglottos,* the northern mockingbird's Latin name, which translates to "many-tongued mimic."

As Grimes knew, the northern mockingbird is one of the truly great singers in the animal kingdom. Parrots can be taught to mimic, but only in captivity. The mockingbird sings its famous song of varied, repeated phrases all day during nesting season (and often all night as well). The mocker begins learning songs in early youth and adds as many as 200 tunes throughout its life. Many are imitations of other birds' songs. While other songbirds sing from leafy hideouts, mockingbirds belt out their playlists from wires, towers, cactus tops, telephone poles, and rooftops. They dive-bomb cats, dogs, and even humans that stray too close to their nests.

Mockingbirds imitate human sounds, too, notably laughter, as well as inanimate objects, including sirens, musical instruments, rusty gates, cell phones, doorbells, and the whirrs, dings, and clangs of almost any home appliance. During his tape-recording odyssey, Grimes came across one mockingbird near Miami that expertly imitated an alarm clock, awakening nearby residents every morning. A Pennsylvania woman wrote of a mockingbird that picked up the sound of her telephone: "A lot of times, we would run inside to answer the phone and realize that it was that crazy bird!"

How many songs can a mockingbird sing? Author and

The northern mockingbird is one of the truly great singers in the animal kingdom.

birdsong expert Donald Kroodsma recorded the songs of one Florida mockingbird—probably a bachelor crooning for a mate—that sang all night long. In one stretch, it sang an amazing 465 songs in 26 minutes' time, and 93 of the songs were different from one another.

Mockingbirds nearly vanished from parts of the U.S. East Coast.

What is the advantage of knowing and performing hundreds of songs? Ask any rock star.

Research shows that as a male mockingbird expands his playlist, he becomes increasingly attractive to females. A great set list, which takes years to amass, shows that the singer is a good catch. In essence, the veteran crooner proclaims, "I've been around. We both know that life is tough in the wild. But I'm a survivor. I've already established a territory with plenty of food. Why not throw in with me? You could do worse." (A great concert sometimes triggers the female's reproductive system. Female mockers sing, too, but not during breeding season.)

Mockingbirds were captured and sold as caged pets like parakeets from the late 1700s to the early 1900s. The best singers sold for as much as $50. So many mockingbirds were snatched and caged that the birds nearly vanished from parts of the U.S. East Coast. The mockingbird's population has rebuilt steadily since receiving protection under the Migratory Bird Treaty Act of 1918.

Mockers have maintained their population and expanded their range by learning to coexist with humans and eating a varied diet of insects and cultivated fruit. Mockingbirds often run after insects on open lawns, sprinting a few steps and then stopping suddenly to lift up their wings and flash white patches downward, which startles insect prey to the surface. Some mockingbirds migrate south in the winter, but usually not far. Most adjust their diets, accept the hardship, and tough it out, occasionally erupting into song on bright, warm winter days. *(continued)*

A mockingbird, defending its territory, chases off the much larger osprey from its perch.

How Well Do You Know the Mockingbird?

- Mockingbirds have impressed and fascinated humans for centuries. A tribe of Algonquins called the mockingbird *cencontlatolly,* or "400 tongues." The Biloxi Native Americans believed that the bird "mocked one's words," while the Choctaws referred to it as the bird "that speaks a foreign tongue."

- In 1772, Thomas Jefferson bought a mockingbird from a slave of his father-in-law, John Wayles. Won over by the bird's intelligence and charm, Jefferson bought three more mockingbirds and took his favorite, named Dick, with him to the White House in 1801. (Dick is commonly believed to have been the first pet to live there.) According to Jefferson's friend and early American historian Margaret Bayard Smith, Jefferson routinely kept Dick's cage door open. The presidential mockingbird spent its days whizzing around Jefferson's study, perching on one object or another to "regale him with its sweetest notes." Dick sat on Jefferson's shoulder while he worked and sometimes took its food from Jefferson's lips. At naptime, Dick would hop up the stairs behind Jefferson and then perch on a couch and sing him to sleep. "How he loved the bird," Smith observed. Jefferson wrote of the mocker: "Learn all the children to venerate it as a superior being in the form of a bird, or as a being which will haunt them if any harm is done to itself or its eggs."

- Mockingbirds have inspired songs, lullabies, paintings, poetry, and literature. In 1827, celebrated

Photo: Lorraine Hudgins/Getty Images

The *EASY DR®* Way to *TRIM and MOW!*

The ORIGINAL Trimmer on Wheels!

Starting at just $349⁹⁹

The DR® TRIMMER MOWER gives you 5X the power and NONE of the backstrain of handheld trimmers!

TRIMS & MOWS thick grass and weeds without bogging down—the only trimmer guaranteed not to wrap!

ROLLS LIGHT AS A FEATHER on big, easy-rolling wheels!

THICKEST, LONGEST-LASTING cutting cord (up to 225 mil) takes seconds to change.

NEW TOW-BEHIND MODELS FOR TRACTORS AND ATVS!

19028B © 2018

DRtrimmers.com

World's Most Powerful Leaf Vacuum ...at a New LOW PRICE!

Now Starting at Just $999⁹⁹ with FREE SHIPPING

DR® LEAF VACUUMS have proven in laboratory testing to achieve the most vacuum power vs. competitors. And now, our *All-New PILOT Model* combines this same amazing yard clean-up power with an equally amazing new price!

☑ **Rated #1 in Vacuum Power**
☑ **Now at the Lowest Price Ever**
☑ **Converts to an All-Purpose Trailer**
☑ **Stores Flat in Minutes**

19028A © 2018

DRleafvac.com

FREE SHIPPING
6 MONTH TRIAL
SOME LIMITATIONS APPLY
Call or go online for details.

Call for a FREE DVD and Catalog!
Includes product specifications and factory-direct offers.

TOLL FREE 800-731-0493

PROFESSIONAL POWER
DR
DONE RIGHT

bird artist John James Audubon portrayed the mockingbird through a treetop battle scene that aroused great controversy. In the image, a rattlesnake, fangs bared, has slithered up a tree to invade a mockingbird's nest as four birds mount a defense. The painting was blasted by naturalists who asserted that rattlesnakes couldn't climb trees. Audubon huffed that he drew the birds just as he had observed them in the wild.

• The immortal lullaby "Hush, Little Baby,"

"Hush, Little Baby."

• "Listen to the Mockingbird" (1855) was one of the most popular songs of all time, telling the story of a young man who dreams of his dead sweetheart as a mockingbird sings over her grave. Through the years, its sheet music has sold more than 20 million copies. Union soldiers marched to it during the Civil War, and Abraham Lincoln proclaimed it "as sincere as the laughter of a little girl at play."

• Mockingbirds have continued to enchant and inspire. Slim Whitman's

• The most famous portrait, and the best case for the mockingbird, comes from a literary classic. "Mockingbirds don't do one thing but make music for us to enjoy," says Miss Maudie Atkinson famously in Harper Lee's classic, *To Kill a Mockingbird*. "They don't eat up people's gardens, don't nest in corncribs, they don't do one thing but sing their hearts out."

• *Mama's Going to Buy You a Mockingbird* (1984) is a famous book by renowned Canadian children's

Mockingbirds have inspired songs, lullabies, paintings, poetry, and literature.

whose author is unknown, was probably written during the years when mockingbirds were sold as caged birds. It begins with a famous proposition: "Hush, little baby, don't say a word, / Papa's gonna buy you a mockingbird." Inez and Charlie Foxx, James Taylor, Carly Simon, and Eminem are among the many recording artists who have made their own versions of

waltz "Mockingbird Hill" rocketed to the top of the pop music charts in 1951.

• "The Mocking Bird" (1952) was the first single recorded by famed Canadian singing group The Four Lads.

• Mockers are even present in the dystopian future. The Mockingjay—admittedly a hybrid—is the proud symbol of rebellion worn by Katniss Everdeen in *The Hunger Games*.

author Jean Little (b. 1932) that poignantly touches on death and dying, love, family, friendship, and hope. ∎

Phillip Hoose is a graduate of the Yale School of Forestry and Environmental Sciences and was a staff member of The Nature Conservancy for 37 years. He is the author of 12 books, including National Book Award–winning *Claudette Colvin: Twice Toward Justice* (Farrar, Straus, and Giroux, 2009).

Prepare Your Garden the EASY WAY!

HUGE TILLER SALE!
Starting at just $199⁹⁹

Walk-Behind

Tow-Behind   PTO

NEW Top-of-the-Line DR® ROTOTILLER!

DUAL ROTATING TINES on our NEW top end walk-behind model let you choose forward rotation for cultivating or counter-rotation for deep soil tilling or sod busting.

ONE-HAND OPERATION! Self-propulsion lets you walk to one side while you easily steer with one hand, leaving no footprints in the freshly tilled bed!

8 TILLER MODELS! No matter how big or small the job, we've got one for you!

19029A © 2018

DRrototiller.com

All New DR® CHIPPERS
Larger Capacity, Lower Prices!

LOWEST PRICES EVER!
Starting at just $699⁹⁹
PTO MODELS TOO!

- **Chip big branches** up to 5.75" thick!
- **Self-feeding** models available. No more force-feeding!
- **Powerful engines** spin big flywheels (up to 62 lbs.), generating massive chipping force!
- **Models that shred** yard and garden waste as well as CHIP branches.

19029B © 2018

DRchipper.com

America's ORIGINAL
Walk-Behind Brush Mower!

USA ENGINEERED & BUILT*

*Assembled in the USA using domestic and foreign parts.

The DR® Field & Brush Mower just got even better—

FASTER. Up to 20 HP and 34"-wide cut for faster mowing!

EASIER. New power steering for turn-on-a-dime ease!

LOWER PRICES. Reduced by up to $500!

NEW CHOICES: including PTO and tow-behind models for tractors and ATVs.

Now Starting at $1499⁹⁹

19029C © 2018

DRfieldbrush.com

FREE SHIPPING
6 MONTH TRIAL
SOME LIMITATIONS APPLY
Call or go online for details.

Call for a FREE DVD and Catalog!
Includes product specifications and factory-direct offers.

TOLL FREE **800-731-0493**

PROFESSIONAL POWER
DR
DONE RIGHT

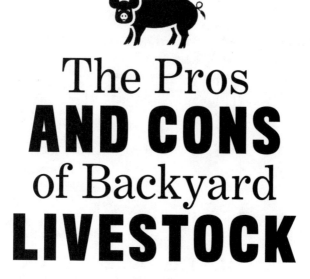

The Pros
AND CONS
of Backyard
LIVESTOCK

BY JACK SAVAGE

WHO AMONG US DOESN'T ASPIRE TO SELF-sufficiency? Equipped with only a little land and less knowledge, we think about getting some chickens for the backyard. And as long as we're feeding the chickens, why not raise a pig? Or a goat? Maybe even a cow? How about a horse?

The desire for healthy, affordable food and a connection to animals has driven a backyard livestock boom. Knowing the pros and cons of common farm animals can help you to make a good choice—or send you to the nearest market, happy to empty your wallet.

CHICKENS

THE domestic chicken can be traced back some 10,000 years. Today, the world has three times as many chickens as human beings, but you may not recognize all of them: In suburbs where they are prohibited by zoning, people have been known to put their chickens in dog costumes.

PROS

EGGS, OF COURSE.

IF you get one of the smaller (little) breeds, you will know before everyone else when the sky is falling.

FRESH meat. Yes, this means slaughtering the chicken.

EFFICIENCY. You can keep a few chickens in far less space than a goat or pig or cow. And on average it takes only 2 pounds of feed to produce 1 pound of chicken meat.

CONS

IF you become a true chicken person, you will spend all your time talking about chickens. Occasionally, you will cluck.

PREDATORS. Foxes, coyotes, and weasels love chickens. For dinner. Keeping your brood safe can be a challenge.

NO MATTER HOW HARD YOU TRY, YOU CAN NOT MILK A CHICKEN.

(continued)

Illustrations: Getty Images

HORSES are majestic, intelligent herd animals that like open space, so make sure that you have enough of it to keep your horse content. Note that you'll be feeding your horse, but the horse will not be feeding you. At least not nutritionally. Spiritually, however, the connection to a horse can be strong and meaningful.

PROS

YOU can ride a horse. Saddling up a chicken is generally frowned upon and your boots drag.

WITH A HORSE AND A COW, YOU CAN BE A COWBOY.

PEOPLE stop by, and from them you will learn a great lesson: that the best kind of horse is the one your friend owns.

CONS

HORSES are large (on average, 1,000-plus pounds), powerful, and genetically predisposed to believe that the grass is greener on the other side of the fence. If you keep a horse, then "fixing fence" will be your hobby.

IF you are not in sync with your horse or are not an experienced rider, your horse will have final say over who rides whom.

CHECK-WRITING won't stop with the hay guy, the vet, or the tack shop staff. You'll be a regular at the truck-and-trailer dealership and the permit office for that barn or run-in shed.

 HORSES

GOATS

GOATS are highly social—curious, interactive, and smart. You can read to a goat, and it will listen, especially if it's a doe. Goats are ruminants, which means that a chamber in their stomach called the rumen ferments the plant-based food that they eat. (Contrary to legend, they do not eat tin cans.) Rumination involves the goat chewing its cud, which is regurgitated food.

PROS

BABY goats are hilarious. They love to hop on top of sheep and adult goats.

YOU can halter a goat for handling and showing. They'll go where you want, if you convince them that it was their idea.

GOATS CAN PROVIDE YOU WITH MOHAIR, MILK, CHEESE, AND MEAT.

CONS

TO make that homegrown Greek salad with feta cheese, you may need goat's milk. Which means you'll need to breed the goat. Once she's lactating, you'll need to milk her. And keep milking her.

IF you have an intact boy goat, or billy, you will know it. So will your downwind neighbors. And everyone you meet at the store if you wear your barn clothes. Billy thinks that this is awesome and, occasionally, so does the nanny goat.

GOATS' feet usually have to be trimmed, and sometimes the horns, too. Good luck!
(continued)

LET'S acknowledge that pigs are the most delicious of livestock. Plus, they are cute when they're young and not as filthy as their reputation suggests, and they put on weight fast.

 # PIGS

PROS

BACON. HAM. SAUSAGE. PORK ROAST. DID WE MENTION BACON?

YOU can raise a pig in a year, then send it off to the freezer. If the experience was a good one, you can start over.

WHEN your backyard pig escapes (and it will), you get to watch the local constabulary try to catch it. Capture that on video, and it'll go viral.

PORK fat is rendered into lard. For traditional (if short-lived) cooks, lard makes almost everything better.

CONS

PIGS can have two litters a year. If you're not careful, you can find yourself overrun.

PIGS grow fast, get big (depending on the breed), and can be destructive. Did you want your backyard excavated?

PIGS sunburn easily, and they never remember to put on sunscreen. They'll need shade.

BUTCHERING a pig is serious business. Rashers and ribs don't come vacuum-packed inside the pig.

Illustrations: Getty Images

COWS

HAVING a cow makes you feel like a real farmer. And, as any elephant farmer will tell you, cows are a lot easier to handle and clean up after than elephants. Cows, too, like goats, are ruminants and thus are prone to ruminating about questions such as "What kind of cow is God?" and "Why would He allow a hamburger to be called a 'Happy Meal'?" Cows don't often come up with answers. But you might.

PROS

MILK. Unadulterated milk for you, your family, and your neighbors. And cheese.

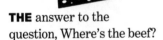

THE answer to the question, Where's the beef?

IF you don't mind "harvesting" the manure, you can sell it. (You'll make more that way than selling the milk.)

CONS

BEFORE you get a dairy cow, talk to a dairy farmer. It won't be difficult, as they won't be on vacation. He or she will tell you how to make a small fortune (from a large one).

GET to know your large-animal veterinarian, if you can find one. Give him or her all your money. You will understand immediately what it takes to keep a cow healthy.

CONVERTING your backyard into a barnyard can make you feel like you have the working farm you've always wanted. But it's more responsibility, not less, and your animals will let you know when you're late with their dinner. You're going to love it! ■

Jack Savage is a former editor of *New Hampshire Profiles* and was a founder of the New Hampshire Writers' Project.

Photo: H. Armstrong Roberts/Getty Images

TAKE TWO
COCKER SPANIELS
AND CALL ME IN
THE MORNING

WHY A DOG MAY BE
THE BEST MEDICINE

BY SUSAN PEERY

PETTING, SCRATCHING, AND CUDDLING A DOG COULD BE AS SOOTHING TO THE MIND AND HEART AS DEEP MEDITATION AND ALMOST AS GOOD FOR THE SOUL AS PRAYER.

–Dean Koontz, American writer (b. 1945)

There are a lot of reasons why you might not want to live with a dog: muddy pawprints on your couch, tumbling tumbleweeds of dog hair on the floor, dog breath in your face. But what if you knew that the dirt, the hair, the very breath of the dog would improve your health?

Scientists have taken an intense interest recently in the gut microbiome—yours and your dog's. The gut microbiome refers to the billions of bacteria, viruses, and other tiny microorganisms that inhabit our innards. A few may be associated with disease, but most are needed to help us ward off infections and malfunctions. Although there is still much to be learned, researchers are certain of one thing: The more diversity in the microbiome, the better.

The discussion started in 1989, when epidemiologist David Strachan at the University of London introduced a theory called the "hygiene hypothesis." Dr. Strachan reasoned that the large increase in allergies and other autoimmune disorders in developed countries during the past century may have been an unintended consequence of cleaner environments, less contact with the great outdoors, and thereby decreased exposure to a variety of microorganisms—especially very early in life, when a baby's immune system is still developing. Had we become too clean? Too scrubbed and disinfected?

As other researchers jumped in, studying the development of the immune system and its relationship to the gut microbiome, studies began to show that exposure to a little dirt, especially in early childhood, can be beneficial and may even help to ward off disease.

This is where dogs come wagging into the picture, along with their ubiquitous fur and saliva. Researchers have documented a lower incidence of asthma among children who grew up with dogs. Scientists suspect that because people and dogs have coexisted for millennia, there's been a lot of trading of human and canine microbiomes, with mutual dependence and evolution. "All of the people alive today probably had ancestors who lived in tribes that hunted with dogs," says Dr. Jack Gilbert, director of the Microbiome Center at the University of Chicago.

Although research into the details of this transference between dogs and humans is still in the early stages, some

scientists think that the family pet, with its diverse microbiome, can convey benefits even beyond biodiversity and a reduced likelihood of allergies.

At the University of Alberta in Edmonton, Dr. Anita Kozyrskyj, a pediatric epidemiologist and leading researcher on gut microbes, thinks that pets—especially dogs—also might lower the risk of obesity. Dr. Kozyrskyj and her team have identified two different bacteria, *Ruminococcus* and *Oscillospira,* that have been linked to reduced risk of childhood allergies and obesity, respectively, and are doubly abundant in the gut microbiome of small babies who live in households with pets. The researchers are partway into a long-term investigation (the Canadian Healthy Infant Longitudinal Development, or CHILD, cohort study) to try to pinpoint what is going on.

It may be that it is mostly small children who benefit from a wet kiss from a furry friend, although studies now in the works may show a broader benefit. Or perhaps drug companies will develop a "dog pill" that will introduce those special doggy microbes without the telltale pawprints on the couch. But will a pill keep you warm on a three-dog night? Cue the cocker spaniels! Bring on the beagles!

DOGS ARE NOT OUR WHOLE LIFE, BUT THEY MAKE OUR LIVES WHOLE.
–Roger A. Caras, American photographer and writer (1928–2001)

HOW TO KEEP ROVER
(AND HIS MICROBIOME) HEALTHY

BEFORE YOU CALL THE VET, KEEP CALM AND TRY A HOME REMEDY FOR SOME COMMON CANINE CHALLENGES.

• For doggy breath: You can remove tartar (a source of bad breath) from your dog's teeth with a washcloth dipped in pet—not human!—toothpaste. Feed your dog something dry and crunchy (kibble, hard dog biscuits) every day to help scour off the tartar. Some dogs enjoy eating raw carrots and even parsley, both of which help to freshen the breath.

• For upset stomach: As long as your dog has no other alarming symptoms, withhold food and water for 12 hours, then try offering one or two ice cubes. Proceed with caution: Offer a bland diet of cooked white rice; plain skinless, boneless chicken; and plain yogurt in small amounts for 2 to 3 days, until your dog is holding down its food.

• For diarrhea: As long as the stools do not contain blood or worms and the dog has a decent appetite, make small meals of cooked white rice or potatoes and a small amount of nongreasy meat. Your dog should get better in 2 to 3 days.

• For when your dog rolls in turkey poop or something even more disgusting: Using a hose, spray off as much as you can. Then reach for a bottle of Nature's Miracle spray and rub it into the dog's coat with an old towel. Rinse and repeat. Nature's Miracle has enzymes that neutralize organic odors.

• For when your dog has been sprayed by a skunk: Forget dousing with tomato juice (it just makes a huge mess). Instead, stir together 1 quart hydrogen peroxide, ¼ cup baking soda, and 1 teaspoon dishwashing liquid. Wear rubber gloves and lather this mixture into the dog's fur (keep out of its eyes). Rinse with water. Use the tomato juice to make yourself a well-deserved Bloody Mary.

• For fleas: A daily supplement of brewer's yeast may deter the little critters.

• For ticks: Given the spread of ticks and rise of Lyme disease, which can cripple a dog, this might be one time to get your vet's best advice. New chewable tick medications last up to 3 months per dose. For maximum protection, check your dog (and humans!) nightly during the height of tick season, usually spring and fall. ■

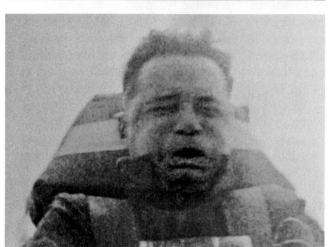

The Fastest Man's Last

. . . AND HOW IT LED TO

BY TIM CLARK

Bruises. Cracked ribs. Broken wrists. Bleeding blisters caused by high-speed sand abrasion. Concussions. Retinal hemorrhages and temporary blindness. The injuries suffered by John Paul Stapp in the late 1940s and early '50s sound like those from a series of high-speed, head-on auto crashes.

Which, in a way, they were. In the interest of science—specifically to study the effects of extreme deceleration on the human body—Stapp strapped himself into rocket-propelled sleds and rode the flame-belching vehicles down a railroad track at speeds of hundreds of miles per hour into braking devices that slammed him to a dead stop in less

Photo montage: NASA/Science Photo Library

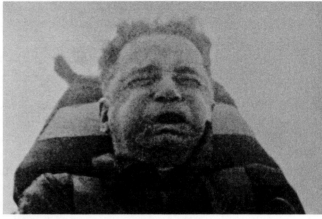

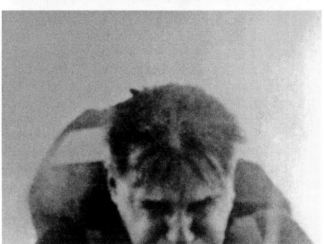

Death-Defying Ride

SEAT BELTS IN CARS

than 2 seconds. He did this 29 times!

The most extreme such experiment, which took place 65 years ago, was the equivalent of a car hitting a brick wall at 120 miles per hour.

Stapp was born in 1910 in Brazil, the son of two Baptist missionaries. A U.S. Army Air Corps flight surgeon during World War II, he took an immediate

Above: John Stapp strapped in a sled seat during high G-force acceleration and deceleration testing. Stapp reached 632 miles per hour in 5 seconds before being brought back to rest in just over a second with a force of over 40 Gs. Despite initial blindness and collapsed lungs, he quickly recovered, proving that it was possible to survive ejection from a supersonic aircraft.

Of the *Sonic Wind* ride, Stapp once remarked,
"I felt like a fly on the nose of a bullet."

interest in the challenge of keeping pilots alive while flying at (and parachuting from) extreme altitudes. This commitment ultimately led him to Holloman Air Force Base in New Mexico, in 1953, to test the limits of how much deceleration a human body could stand.

At this time, the generally accepted deceleration limit was 18 Gs, or 18 times the force of gravity at sea level. Stopping at that speed, some experts believed, would break all of the bones in a human body. By comparison, a passenger in a car making an emergency stop feels 2 Gs. (Normal life is 1 G.) Some amusement parks have rides that subject thrillseekers to 4.5 Gs. Fighter pilots and astronauts train on centrifuges that press them into their seats at up to 15 Gs.

John Stapp on board the Sonic Wind

Stapp believed that humans could withstand far more Gs. He proved it on his record-setting "Big Run" of December 10, 1954, when he mounted a rocket sled named *Sonic Wind* and, in 5 seconds, accelerated from zero to 632 mph—close to the speed of sound and literally faster than a .45 caliber bullet. Then a series of water brakes decelerated him back to zero in 1.4 seconds, delivering a 46.2 G wallop. Of the *Sonic Wind* ride, Stapp once remarked, "I felt like a fly on the nose of a bullet."

The event set a world land-speed record, making 44-year-old Stapp the Fastest Man on Earth—and one in great discomfort.

His eyes filled with blood and he experienced pain that he compared to having teeth extracted without anesthesia, yet he insisted on walking away from the sled. He was able to stagger a few steps, with assistance, before accepting a stretcher ride. Blind at first, he was able to see shapes after 4 hours and could identify friends and colleagues the next day.

The eye doctor who cared for him at that time reported, "One might possibly expect, after 29 experiments, brain damage such as is found in a 'punch drunk' pugilist. The contrary is the case, as anyone can testify after a few minutes' conversation with Colonel Stapp." In fact, a day later he was talking excitedly about trying for a 1,000-mph run.

It would never happen. His Air Force

superiors made it clear that Stapp was far too valuable a public relations bonanza to be risked. His next run was into the history books.

A painting of his helmeted head atop *Sonic Wind* appeared on the cover of *Time* magazine in September 1955. He was lured to Hollywood to be on the popular TV show *This Is Your Life*. He won medals from the Air Force and various civilian groups.

Decades later, he would be inducted into both the Aviation and Space Halls of Fame. In 1991, he received the National Medal of Technology. There was even a feature film about him called *On the Threshold of Space,* which Stapp described to a friend as "perhaps the worst movie ever made."

F. Scott Fitzgerald once wrote, "There are no second acts in American lives." Stapp's second act was less famous than his first, but it was far more significant.

I n the course of his studies of aircraft safety, Stapp had discovered that the Air Force was losing more trained pilots to auto accidents than plane crashes. Only days after the "Big Run," he had received a letter from an engineer studying the design of seat belts, which were not at that time required in American cars. The contact resulted in the first Automotive Crash Research Field Demonstration and Conference, a gathering of military, civilian, and academic authorities, along

Cover of Time *magazine, 1955*

with representatives from all of the major automakers, at Holloman AFB in 1955. The annual conference continues to this day, now known as the Stapp Car Crash Conference. It has inspired innovations such as three-point seat belts and air bags, saving millions of lives. When President Lyndon Johnson signed the 1966 law requiring automobile seat belts, Stapp was standing at his shoulder.

Stapp continued his research until he retired from the Air Force in 1970. He continued to work to improve the safety of automobiles until his death at age 89.

Think of John Stapp the next time you buckle up. ■

The Stapp Car Crash Conference has inspired innovations such as three-point seat belts and air bags, saving millions of lives.

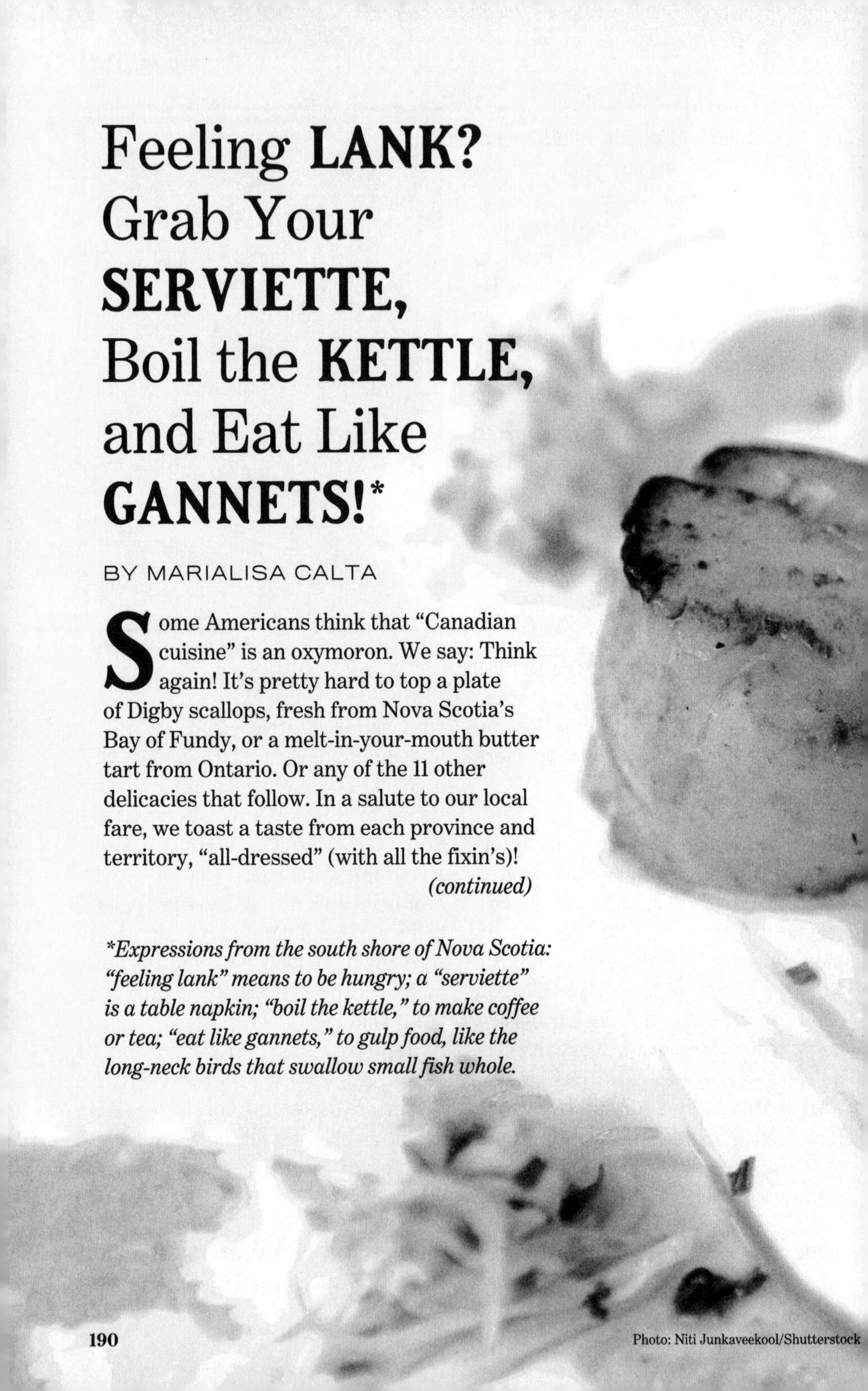

Feeling **LANK?** Grab Your **SERVIETTE,** Boil the **KETTLE,** and Eat Like **GANNETS!***

BY MARIALISA CALTA

Some Americans think that "Canadian cuisine" is an oxymoron. We say: Think again! It's pretty hard to top a plate of Digby scallops, fresh from Nova Scotia's Bay of Fundy, or a melt-in-your-mouth butter tart from Ontario. Or any of the 11 other delicacies that follow. In a salute to our local fare, we toast a taste from each province and territory, "all-dressed" (with all the fixin's)!

(continued)

**Expressions from the south shore of Nova Scotia: "feeling lank" means to be hungry; a "serviette" is a table napkin; "boil the kettle," to make coffee or tea; "eat like gannets," to gulp food, like the long-neck birds that swallow small fish whole.*

Photo: Niti Junkaveekool/Shutterstock

DIGBY SCALLOPS
SEE PAGE 193.

ALBERTA:
STAMPEDE FEED

Where else but at the legendary Calgary Stampede can you sample a $100 "Dragon Dog" (includes lobster tail, truffles, and century-old cognac) and chase it with a PB&J kabob with Reese's in the middle or a glazed donut grilled cheese? There's deep-fried everything: Oreos, Twix bars, lobster corn dogs, and more, including churros from Calgary's own "Indi-Mexi" Naaco Truck (Naan + Taco = Naaco). More than a million visitors attend the event, says midway manager James Radke, and most of them dig in. "We have 355 days a year to worry about what we eat," he says. "The 10 days of Stampede are for having fun."

BRITISH COLUMBIA:
BEST BARS, BAR NONE

There are heretics who say that the Nanaimo Bar might have originated in London or New York, but we're giving the "Harbor City" on Vancouver Island bragging rights to the no-bake confection that bears its name. It's composed of three layers: chocolate-flavor crumbs; buttercream icing; and chocolate topping. Variations include mint, peanut butter, coconut, bacon, gluten-free, vegan, and deep-fried. Sample them on the Nanaimo Trail.

MANITOBA:
THE BUCKWHEAT BELT

It's likely that many of us don't realize that Manitoba is "The Buckwheat Capital of Canada," but in fact this province produces 70 percent of the country's crop. While most of it is exported to Japan (think soba noodles) and the U.S. (think "gluten-free health

food"), this nongrain (it's actually a fruit!) is also popular with Manitoba's Ukrainian community. Valerie Charkewycz of Estellia's Ukrainian Comfort Food in Dugald says that buckwheat groats, or *kasha*, can be fried with onions, baked and eaten with milk, or stuffed into cabbage rolls. *Tse duzhe smachno!* (It's very delicious!)

NEW BRUNSWICK:
DULSE IS THE WORD
Straight from the sea to the plate comes the seaweed known as dulse, one of the main harvests of Grand Manan Island, off New Brunswick's coast. Prized as an excellent source of protein, iron, iodine, zinc, copper, and antioxidants, dulse is eaten by aficionados straight from the sea, raw or cooked, and also enjoyed dried, whole or flaked. It can be added to stews, omelets, salads, and soups. Grand Manan parents find it handy to pacify teething babies: The children are given a strip of raw dulse to chew.

NEWFOUNDLAND AND LABRADOR:
COD GOT YOUR TONGUE?
Once a staple, now a prized (and pricey) "localvore" delicacy, cod tongue is actually a gelatinous piece from the cod's throat. Restaurants serve them, often as an appetizer: lightly battered and fried, topped with everything from the traditional scrunchions (crispy pieces of salt pork) to fruit salsa and aioli. Wash 'em down with a bit of Screech (originally moonshine, but

now also a brand of rum), and you've got yourself a true Newfoundland meal. When in St. John's, stop in at the historic Belbin's Grocery or the enormous Bidgood's, both known for their selection of local ingredients.

NORTHWEST TERRITORIES:
MANIC FOR BANNOCK
"Don't panic, eat bannock" reads a t-shirt sold in Yellowknife. And eat bannock they do. These ubiquitous biscuits are traditionally cooked over a campfire, wrapped around a stick or in a skillet. "It is necessary to shift the bannock around while it is baking," wrote Jake Woolgar, a Canadian Ranger and WWII pilot. "This is done by twitching the wrist while holding the pan steady.... With a little practice, one becomes quite efficient." Home cooks tend to use the oven, as do restaurants like the famed Wildcat Café, a Yellowknife landmark run seasonally from an old, mining camp–style, log cabin.

NOVA SCOTIA:
DIG THOSE SCALLOPS
The outline of this province is shaped like a lobster claw, but its star seafood

attraction is arguably the Digby scallop. Harvested by one of the world's most storied fleets of trawlers, these succulent mollusks benefit from the dynamic action of the famed Bay of Fundy, whose dramatic tides bring in the fresh nutrients and oxygen that give the scallops their signature sweetness and plumpness.

NUNAVUT:
WE ALL SCREAM FOR ALU
No feast in our newest territory is complete without what in local Inuktitut is called *alu,* a dessert of chopped caribou fat, berries, oil, and water, all whipped together until fluffy. This homemade treat, which is sometimes sweetened and chilled, is often compared to ice cream. It can complement a feast of "country food"—frozen caribou, char, muktaq (narwhal skin), iqunaq (fermented meat), and seal—components of the traditional diet in which the vitamins and omega-3s of the wild game made up for the lack of available vegetables and the protein and fat were guaranteed to keep you warm.

ONTARIO:
YOU HAD ME AT "BUTTER"
Butter tarts are a Canadian favorite claimed by Ontario as a native treat; the earliest recipe dates back to a 1900 cookbook from the city of Barrie. Traditionalists argue for raisins-only in the butter-sugar filling, but pecans are a frequent addition. At the Best Butter Tart Festival in Midland, however, combinations have included cherry-almond, Nutella-raspberry, and

peanut butter–banana–bacon. Also, enjoy the great variety of butter tarts offered by vendors along the Butter Tart Trail in North Wellington and the Kawarthas Northumberland Butter Tart Tour. Butter get a move on.

PRINCE EDWARD ISLAND:
TERRIFIC TATERS
They don't call it "Spud Isle" for nothing. PEI, our smallest province, is also a potato paradise. Red, sandy, iron-rich soil is one of the secrets to spud success, as is the ocean, which acts as a barrier against air- and insect-borne diseases. Most of the tasty tubers are grown on family farms—and have been since the 18th century. Potato farming brings in more than a billion dollars to the island's economy. No small potatoes. You can find PEI seed and table potatoes worldwide.

QUEBEC:
OKA, OKAY!
In the beginning, there was cheddar, the "official" cheese of Quebec as decreed by the British after the Conquest of 1760. In 1893, a monk,

sent to the Oka Abbey in hope of saving the financially troubled monastery with the Port-du-Salut recipe from the mother abbey in France, tweaked it here and there and Oka—a washed-rind, semisoft, cow's milk cheese with a buttery, nutty flavor—was born. Since 1981, Oka, still aged in the abbey's cellars, has been made by Agropur, a large, Quebec-based, dairy cooperative. And Quebec is now home to more than 300 artisan cheeses.

SASKATCHEWAN:
CUTTING THE MUSTARD

Fun fact: Saskatchewan mustard producers are the largest exporters of mustard seed in the world. But with all of this exported seed, there are precious few producers of the condiment itself: Gravelbourg Mustard is one, offering six flavors, including a "Saskatoon-Style" condiment that contains local saskatoon berries. As the "eat local" movement grows, so does the use of local mustard in chefs' dishes. Greg Hanwell, cochair of the annual Mustard Festival in Regina, says that mustard is included in several offerings at Beer Bros. Gastropub, one of his two restaurants.

YUKON:
SOURDOUGH SAM(PLING)

In 1896, the discovery of gold in a tributary of the Klondike River propelled prospectors from San Francisco to the Yukon Territory. Miners, aware that yeast and other conventional leavenings were less reliable in extreme weather, brought with them their sourdough starters, keeping them close to their bodies in pouches to prevent freezing. (Hence the nickname "sourdough" for an old-timer.) Today, Yukon sourdough, considered a moderately sour starter compared to starters from Italy (more sour) or France (mild), is still popular in homes, bakeries, and restaurants and made into breads, flapjacks, even crepes. "Bard of the Yukon" Robert Service gave the nod to this bread in his collection *Songs of a Sourdough*. ∎

Marialisa Calta is a syndicated food columnist from Vermont.

Photo, bottom right: Phil Mythen/Shutterstock

How to Make Sausage at Home

BY SUSAN PEERY

Home sausage-making is enjoying a revival. It's as easy as making meat loaf, and anyone can do it with minimal equipment. If you don't want to stuff your sausage mixture into casings, you can make patties or rolls. Either way, once you learn the basics of making fresh sausage, you can personalize these recipes and create your own.

THE EQUIPMENT

- Meat grinder or heavy-duty food processor with coarse and fine grinding disks
- For links, a sausage stuffer or funnel attachment for pushing the mixture into casings
- Natural or other casings (available from sausage-supply houses, meatpacking companies, ethnic groceries, or butchers)

THE STEPS

1. Rinse, flush out, and soak natural casings (if using) in water for 30 minutes.

2. Cut meat and fat into 1-inch cubes. Freeze for 30 minutes to make it easier to grind.

3. Grind meat and fat together, using the proper disk (see individual recipes, page 198).

4. Add seasonings and other ingredients, knead by hand, and grind the entire mixture a second time.

5. Fry a small portion, taste, and adjust the seasonings if necessary.

6. To stuff the casings: Gather the casing over the end of the funnel. Tie a knot in the free end. Feed the mixture through the funnel, gently pushing it into the casing and filling it evenly.

7. Inspect your sausage and prick any air bubbles with a pin.

8. Begin at the tied end: Twist off the links, twisting two or three times every 3 inches or at the desired length. Cut links apart with a sharp knife.

9. Cover and refrigerate the sausage for at least 2 hours, or as directed, to meld the flavors and firm the texture. Use within 3 days, or freeze.

10. Panfry, poach, roast, or grill until golden, to an internal temperature of 160°F on a meat thermometer.   *(continued)*

Adapted from *Home Sausage Making* (Storey Publishing, 2003), by Susan Mahnke Peery and Charles G. Reavis; used with permission.

Everything has an end, except a sausage, which has two.
–Danish proverb

CONSIDERING CURING?
Cured sausages (such as pepperoni and salami) require the addition of sodium nitrite or nitrate, which must be handled with caution. If you attempt one of these, use a commercial premixed cure at the levels recommended.

PORK
Luganega

These are a delicious companion to tomato sauces or risotto.

4 feet medium hog casing
3½ pounds lean pork butt
½ pound pork fat
1½ teaspoons kosher or coarse salt
1 teaspoon grated lemon zest
1 teaspoon grated orange zest
1 teaspoon freshly ground black pepper
1 teaspoon ground coriander
½ teaspoon ground nutmeg
2 cloves garlic, minced
½ cup dry vermouth
1 cup freshly grated Parmesan cheese

Prepare casing, then meat and fat (steps 1, 2). Grind, using the fine disk (step 3). Separately, combine remaining ingredients, except cheese. Mix well. Add meat and cheese and knead by hand. Stuff casing, twisting off 8-inch links (steps 6, 7, 8). Proceed with steps 9 and 10.

Makes 4 pounds.

Pork and Apple Sausage

Moist, savory, and sweetened with reduced apple cider

2½ feet medium hog casing
2¾ pounds lean pork butt or shoulder
¼ pound pork fat
1 cup apple cider
1 tablespoon olive oil
2 small leeks, cleaned and chopped
    (white part only)
1 tart apple, peeled, cored, and chopped
2 tablespoons chopped fresh parsley
2 tablespoons chopped fresh rosemary
    leaves
1 tablespoon kosher or coarse salt

1 teaspoon grated lemon zest
½ teaspoon freshly ground black pepper

Prepare casing, then meat and fat (steps 1, 2). Separately, simmer cider, uncovered, until it is reduced to ¼ cup syrupy liquid. Set aside. Heat oil in a skillet. Cook leeks and apple over moderate heat for 3 to 5 minutes, or until apple is golden. Grind meat and fat, using the fine disk (step 3). Transfer to a bowl and add remaining ingredients. Mix to combine. Freeze for 30 minutes.

Grind mixture again. Combine meat mixture with leeks, apples, and cider. Knead by hand. Stuff casing, twisting off 4-inch links (steps 6, 7, 8). Proceed with steps 9 and 10.

Makes 3 pounds.

BEEF
Garlic-Mustard Beef Sausage

For best flavor, grill or roast.

4 feet medium hog casing
2 pounds blade-cut boneless chuck
    with 25 percent fat
5 cloves garlic, minced
1 tablespoon yellow mustard seed
1 tablespoon minced fresh rosemary leaves
1 tablespoon Dijon-style mustard
2 teaspoons kosher or coarse salt
1 teaspoon freshly ground black pepper
1 teaspoon sugar
½ teaspoon crushed red pepper flakes
    (optional)

Prepare casing, then meat and fat (steps 1, 2). Combine meat, fat, garlic, mustard seed, and rosemary. Grind mixture, using the coarse disk (step 3). Transfer to a bowl, add remaining ingredients, and knead by hand. Stuff the casing, twisting off 4-inch links (steps 6, 7, 8). Proceed with steps 9 and 10.

Makes 2 pounds.

LAMB
Lamb, Ginger, and Fruit Sausage

Crystallized ginger and dried apricots add bite and texture.

4 feet sheep or small hog casing
2½ pounds lean lamb
½ pound lamb fat
2 tablespoons lemon juice or white wine
2 tablespoons finely chopped dried apricots
1 tablespoon finely chopped crystallized ginger
1 tablespoon kosher or coarse salt
1 teaspoon freshly ground black pepper

Prepare casing, then meat and fat (steps 1, 2). Transfer to a bowl, add remaining ingredients, and knead by hand. Freeze for 30 minutes.

Grind mixture, using the fine disk (step 3). Stuff casing, twisting off 3-inch links (steps 6, 7, 8). Proceed with steps 9 and 10.

Makes 3 pounds.

POULTRY
Chicken Sausage With Chardonnay and Apples

Delicious as an entrée or sliced and served warm with cheese and crackers

2 feet small hog or sheep casing
2 pounds boneless chicken thighs with skin
1 tart apple, peeled, cored, and chopped
¼ cup Chardonnay
2 tablespoons minced onion

2 teaspoons kosher or coarse salt
1 teaspoon ground ginger
½ teaspoon freshly ground black pepper

Prepare casing (step 1). Grind chicken and skin, using the fine disk (step 3). Transfer to a bowl, add remaining ingredients, and knead by hand. Grind mixture again. Stuff casing, twisting off 3-inch links (steps 6, 7, 8). Proceed with steps 9 and 10.

Makes 2 pounds.

Southwestern Turkey Sausage

Perfect in a fajita or black bean stew. Wear rubber gloves to handle the chiles and roast them to intensify their rich flavor.

3 feet medium hog casing
3 pounds turkey meat with skin, cut into cubes
¼ cup chopped fresh cilantro
1 Anaheim chile, roasted, seeded, and chopped
1 jalapeño chile, roasted, seeded, and chopped
2 tablespoons red-wine vinegar
2 tablespoons chili powder
1 tablespoon kosher or coarse salt
1 tablespoon lime juice
2 teaspoons minced garlic
2 teaspoons ground cumin
1 teaspoon freshly ground black pepper

Prepare casing (step 1). Grind meat, using the coarse disk (step 3). Transfer to a bowl, add remaining ingredients, mix to blend. Chill for 1 hour.

Grind mixture again. Stuff casing, twisting off 4-inch links (steps 6, 7, 8). Proceed with steps 9 and 10.

Makes 3 pounds. ∎

Pickling continued from page 54

Crispy Pickled Asparagus

Test your spears: Snap one in half. If it breaks cleanly without any strings, it is fresh and will stay crispy when pickled.

5 pounds asparagus, washed
5 large cloves garlic
5 small hot peppers
2½ cups distilled white vinegar
⅓ cup pickling salt
1 teaspoon dill seed

1. Trim asparagus stems so that spears fit into jars with about ½-inch of headspace (area under the jar lid). Put a garlic clove and hot pepper into each jar. Tightly pack asparagus in jars, with tips up.

2. In a pot, combine vinegar, salt, dill seed, and 2½ cups of water. Bring to a boil. Pour hot liquid over spears, leaving ½-inch of headspace. Seal and process in a boiling-water bath for 10 minutes. Set aside to cool, then store in a dark place. For best flavor, wait 3 to 5 days before eating.

Makes five 12-ounce jars.

Variation: Instead of hot peppers, use 1 teaspoon mustard seed in each jar.

Serving suggestion: Wrap thin slices of ham (e.g., prosciutto) around pickled asparagus spears.

Swedish Pickled Beets

Beet colors range from deep red to yellow and orange—so mix them up.

2 cups cooked, peeled, and sliced beets
½ cup distilled white vinegar
½ cup sugar
1 teaspoon pickling salt
1 teaspoon caraway seed

1. Place beets in a glass bowl.

2. In a pot, combine vinegar, sugar, salt, caraway seed, and ½ cup of water. Bring to a boil. Reduce heat and simmer for about 5 minutes to dissolve sugar.

3. Pour hot vinegar mixture over the beets, cover, and chill for at least 2 hours before serving. Eat beets within a couple of weeks.

Makes 4 to 6 servings.

Variation: Instead of caraway seed, use a cinnamon stick, broken into pieces; a couple of whole cloves; and a few whole allspice buds.

Serving suggestion: Add chopped pickled beets and feta cheese to a mixed greens salad.

Pickled Corn Relish

The freshest kernels should be full and milky. Check by puncturing one with your finger.

12 ears sweet corn
2 onions, finely chopped
2 green peppers, seeded and finely chopped
1 red pepper, seeded and finely chopped

1 cup finely chopped green cabbage
2 cups distilled white vinegar
1 cup sugar
2 tablespoons pickling salt
1½ tablespoons ground mustard
¼ teaspoon freshly ground black pepper

1. Cut corn kernels from cobs but do not scrape them. Transfer kernels to a pot and add remaining ingredients. Simmer over low heat for 15 minutes, stirring occasionally. Pour into sterilized jars, leaving ½-inch of headspace. Seal and process in a boiling-water bath for 15 minutes. Set aside to cool, then store in a dark place.

Makes about five ½-pint jars.

Variation: Instead of 1 cup cabbage, use 1 cup finely chopped tomatoes.

Serving suggestion: Fold corn relish into a cheese omelet or use on hamburgers and hot dogs.

Kosher-Style Dill Pickles

Cucumber pickles may shrivel after processing but will later plump in the sealed jars.

1 small bunch fresh dill or 1 teaspoon dried dill
2 cloves garlic, blanched and sliced
1 tablespoon mustard seed
30 to 36 pickling cucumbers (3 to 4 inches long), washed
3 cups distilled white vinegar
6 tablespoons pickling salt

1. In each sterilized jar, place a layer of dill, 1 clove of garlic, and ½ tablespoon of mustard seed. Pack cucumbers into each jar until half-full, add more dill, and fill with remaining cucumbers.

2. In a pot, combine vinegar, salt, and 3 cups of water and bring to a boil. Pour hot liquid over cucumbers, leaving ½-inch of headspace. Seal and process in a boiling-water bath for 15 minutes.

Makes two 1-quart jars.

Variation: Instead of mustard seed, use ½ tablespoon coriander seed or black peppercorns.

Serving suggestion: Add dill pickle chips to grilled cheese sandwiches or chop and add to pasta salad.

Recipe Contest continued from page 60

Chunky Orange Salsa
for Orange-Glazed Grilled Chicken

1 cup coarsely chopped Granny Smith apple
1 cup coarsely chopped mandarin orange
½ cup coarsely chopped red onion
½ cup coarsely chopped green bell pepper
½ cup coarsely chopped Roma tomato
1 tablespoon finely chopped jalapeño (optional)
¼ teaspoon finely chopped cilantro
juice of 1 lime

1. In a bowl, combine apples, oranges, onions, peppers, tomatoes, jalapeños (if using), and cilantro. Add lime juice and stir to incorporate.

Makes 4 servings.

–Andrea Winget, Minden, Louisiana ∎

A WING

AND A

PRAYER

FOR HOCKEY LEFT WINGER AND PRIEST LES COSTELLO, "CROSS-CHECKING" WAS A WAY OF LIFE, NOT A PENALTY.

BY VICTOR M. PARACHIN • ILLUSTRATION BY TIM ROBINSON

HIS HEART OF GOLD WAS PART OF HIS HERITAGE.

Les John Thomas Costello was born to immigrant parents in South Porcupine (part of Timmons), Ontario, on February 16, 1928. His father, like most men in the community, worked in the gold mines.

ON THE ICE, COSTELLO WAS A CONTENDER.

An exceptionally skilled youth hockey player, he was invited to play for St. Michael's College School, a Catholic secondary school in Toronto. There he helped the team, St. Michael's Majors, win the Memorial Cup two times (1945 and '47). Following graduation, he joined the

Toronto Maple Leafs' farm team, the Pittsburgh Hornets. The Leafs called him up at the end of the season to skate in the 1948 playoffs. His two goals and two assists, as a left wing, earned his name a place on the Stanley Cup and him a spot on the roster for the following season. Partway through that season, he was sent back to the Hornets, only to be called back in 1950, when the Leafs were again vying for the Cup.

COSTELLO, OR "COSSIE," AS HE WAS KNOWN, LEFT HOCKEY AT THE TOP OF HIS GAME TO PURSUE A HIGHER CALLING.

He found the pro sports experience unsatisfying, and especially the hours off the ice. In a *Liberty* magazine interview in 1950, he said, "Days at the movies, nights at the hockey rink. I thought that there must be a better way to end my life." He began studies to become a Catholic priest at St. Augustine's Seminary in Toronto and was ordained 7 years later, becoming the only professional hockey player to become a priest.

COSTELLO OPENED HIS DOORS TO THE POOR, NEEDY, AND DESTITUTE IN NORTHERN ONTARIO.

His residence became a donation center, with food, clothing, furniture, and appliances coming and going. It has been said that the area in front of his church looked like a perpetual yard sale. Among those he helped were Sharon and Jerry Twain, parents of singer and songwriter Shania.

IN 1962, COSTELLO RETURNED TO HOCKEY.

He skated almost daily at a local rink, which inspired him with a way to fund charities. He and a friend named Brian McKee formed a team of Catholic priests from all over Canada and dubbed them the Flying Fathers. Their first game was so entertaining that they received invitations to tour and play exhibition games with local teams all over North America. In 1970, they toured Europe and even met Pope Paul VI, to whom Costello gave a hockey stick.

UNDER COSTELLO, THE FLYING FATHERS TURNED THEIR SLAP SHOTS INTO SLAPSTICK.

They played for laughs; one goal was to make sure that the audience had fun, and the Fathers ensured this by throwing pies in refs' faces, having a clown on the team, and hosting special appearances on the ice by "Sister Mary Shooter"—dressed in a habit and veil (played by Costello in costume).

THE FLYING FATHERS SUCCEEDED ON MORE THAN A WING AND A PRAYER.

In interviews, Costello remarked that the team flooded the rink with holy water before a game, heard confessions behind the net ("good for 5 years or 50,000 sins, whichever came first"), and won so many games because "we cheat." The team didn't practice. "We don't have to," he said. "We've got God on our side." Their 20-year record was 900 wins, 6 losses, 1 tie—and more than $4 million for charity.

COSTELLO LOVED TO HUNT AND FISH.

One freezing-cold day in early May 1979, he struck out alone. He shot a partridge and collected it, but then slipped on a beaver dam and lost a boot in the muskeg. Although he shoved his bare foot into the still-warm bird, he rapidly lost body heat and became disoriented. As night fell, he took refuge under a tree, ate portions of the partridge, and prayed. In the morning, he heard a gunshot, responded with his own, and was soon located. Later, doctors had to amputate seven frostbitten toes. To recover his sense of balance, Costello stuffed socks into the toes of his skates. In the early morning, alone in the arena, he would practice skating.

OCCASIONALLY, WHILE SKATING, COSTELLO WOULD FAKE AN INJURY and

be carried out on a stretcher as funeral music echoed through the arena. One time, in 2002, he wasn't faking: During a pregame warm-up, a puck got caught in his skates and he fell on the ice, hitting his helmetless head. He sat out the next night's game and then was taken to the hospital. He went into a coma on December 4 and died on December 10, at age 74. Some 2,200 people attended his funeral, which was held at the ice skating rink.

A COLORFUL CHARACTER, COSTELLO SEEMED NEVER TO BE AT A LOSS FOR WORDS.

His favorite saying defined him: "God loves the rebel." Seeing him in his coffin at his funeral, a priest remarked, "God bless; it's the first time I've seen him quiet." ■

Victor M. Parachin is a graduate of the University of Toronto and an ordained minister.

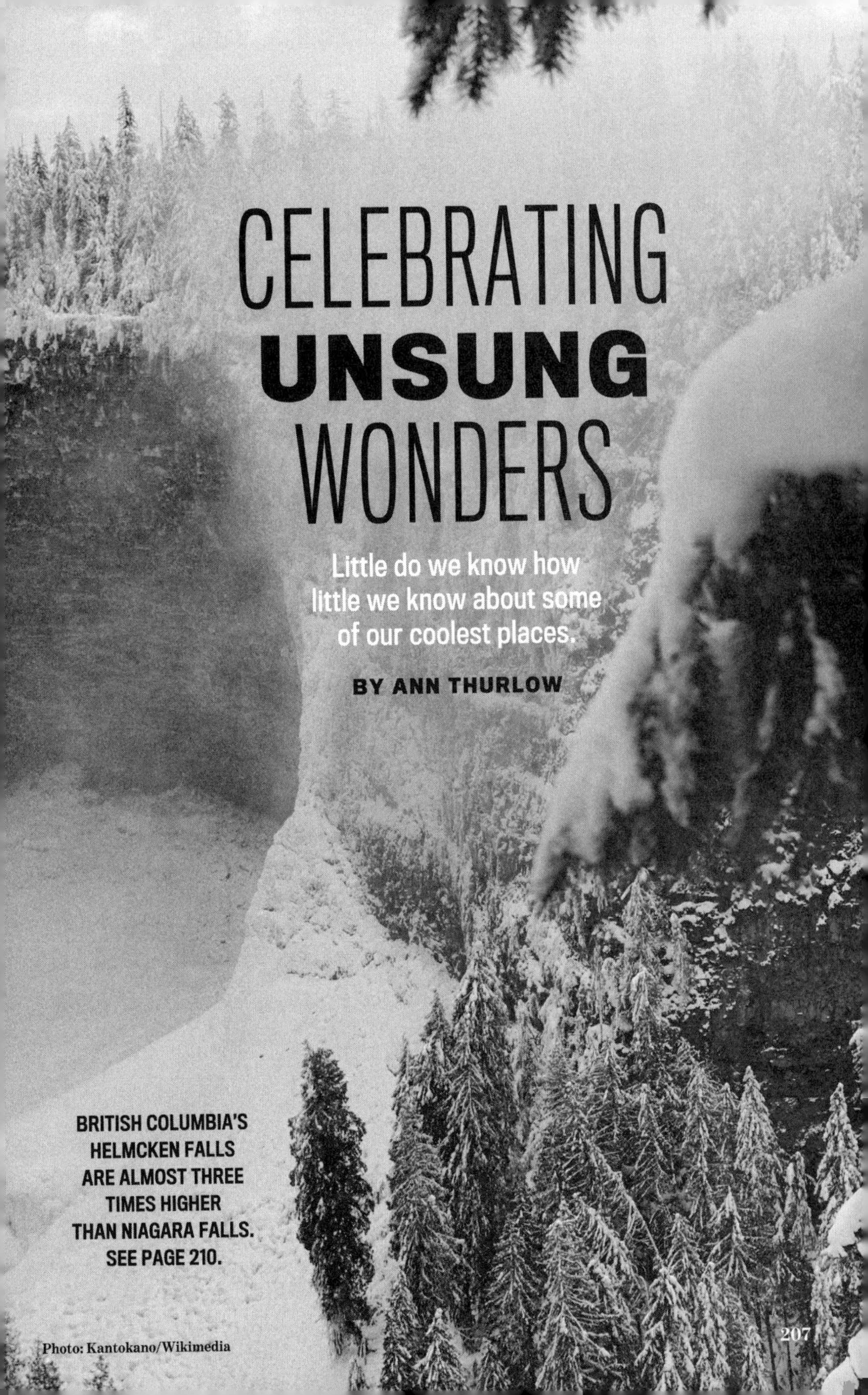

CELEBRATING **UNSUNG** WONDERS

Little do we know how little we know about some of our coolest places.

BY ANN THURLOW

BRITISH COLUMBIA'S HELMCKEN FALLS ARE ALMOST THREE TIMES HIGHER THAN NIAGARA FALLS. **SEE PAGE 210.**

Photo: Kantokano/Wikimedia

CASTLE KILBRIDE

O Canada! Home of the splendid and the great: Niagara Falls, the Rocky Mountains, Anne of Green Gables, the Gopher Hole Museum . . .

Wait. What?

That's right. Torrington, **ALBERTA**, is home to a museum that features dioramas of costumed, stuffed gophers doing things like curling, going to the hairdresser, picking up the mail, getting married, playing in the snow. You want jaw-dropping? Skip the mountains; head to Torrington.

Canada is chock-full of equally amazing but, sadly, often little-known wonders.

Castle Kilbride in Baden, **ONTARIO**, boasts the very finest example of trompe l'oeil painting in the entire country. "Trompe l'oeil" means "fool the eye." The vase of flowers in front of that wall? It's not; it's painted on it.

CARCROSS DESERT

Photos, from top: The Giant Vermin/Wikimedia; nickjene/Getty Images

Ditto for that statue on display. If this doesn't move you, the castle also features what is arguably the country's most solid and impressive double-occupancy outhouse. And in case you're wondering, it's brick.

The world's smallest desert? It's in Carcross, **YUKON**. Okay, so—strictly speaking—it's a sand dune. But it's called a desert on a sign by the side of the road. The 642 acres of sand are continuously replenished by small storms stirred up by a nearby lake. And the footsteps of would-be Lawrences of Arabia keep the vegetation to a minimum, although at just 6 degrees south of the Arctic Circle, they are more likely to be crossed by a bear than a camel.

Gegenwalle! Qiviut! We've got 'em both.

Gegenwalle are small series of concentric counter ridges of sand, the only North American examples of which are at the national park in Greenwich, **PRINCE EDWARD ISLAND**. They're formed by the wind at the base of the park's rare, spectacular, parabolic dunes. And they're on the move. At the edge of this formation are ghostly skeletons of trees that have been consumed by the shifting sands.

Eight times warmer than wool and softer and more luxurious than cashmere, qiviut is the fine undercoat of the musk ox. You'll find a lot of them in **NUNAVUT**. When the musk ox sheds its wool, it is collected and spun into highly prized and very expensive fiber. In what might be a total surprise to the humble musk ox, a qiviut sweater can set you back at least $600.

When you think **MANITOBA**, you think landlocked prairie. But it's actually a maritime province with 400 miles of

NUNAVUT MUSK OX

coastline. Sadly for swimmers, it's all on Hudson's Bay. If a frigid plunge doesn't suit you, how about a dip in Lake Winnipeg, the 10th largest freshwater lake in the world? At 9,465 square miles, it's not a Great Lake. But it's a pretty darn good one.

Then there's Old Sow, the largest tidal whirlpool in the Western Hemisphere. Located just off Deer Island, **NEW BRUNSWICK**, the big sucker roils up the waters around 7 miles away. When active, one of the vortexes that makes up Old Sow is about 250 feet in diameter. You can hop a boat and ride the wave, listening to the odd sucking sound that gives the Old Sow its name.

Forget Niagara Falls. Helmcken Falls in **BRITISH COLUMBIA**'s Wells Grey Provincial Park drops 462 feet—nearly three times the drop of that little squirt in Ontario. The park also features Murtle Lake, the largest canoe-only lake in North America.

Where else but in Canada are you going to see a sport called the blanket toss? Here's how it works: Several strong people hold a tarp. One person gets in the center and is tossed into the air. Heights for a good team can reach 32 feet. This used to be a method for spotting game on the flat arctic tundra. Now, people in the **NORTHWEST TERRITORIES** do it for sport, even having demonstrated their prowess at the Vancouver Olympics.

Canadians love their drive-thrus, and they love their perogies. In Saskatoon, **SASKATCHEWAN**, you can find both. At Baba's Homestyle Perogies, there's no need to even leave your car for a taste of this traditional prairie treat. And if you ask for a "double double," you'll probably get cabbage rolls with your perogies.

By now, you may be thinking, "Wow, I'd have to go to the four corners of the Earth to see so much greatness!" Relax. One of the four corners of the Earth is right here. According to the Flat Earth Society, Brimstone Head on Fogo Island in **NEWFOUNDLAND/LABRADOR** is one of our planet's four corners.

Ann Thurlow is a writer and editor in Charlottetown, Prince Edward Island. She believes that her sweet potato pie may qualify as one of Canada's unsung wonders.

LAKE WINNIPEG

VEGREVILLE, ALBERTA

NACKAWIC, NEW BRUNSWICK

WAWA, ONTARIO

TRANS-CANADA

BIG DEALS

• Vegreville, Alberta, has the world's largest Easter Egg. The 31-foot-high sculpture celebrates the city's Ukrainians and their egg-decorating skills.

• Nackawic, New Brunswick, boasts the world's biggest axe. This 49-foot-long chopper commemorates the town's designation as the Forestry Capital of Canada.

• The Anna Swan Museum in Tatamagouche, Nova Scotia, celebrates the life of the giantress, who grew to be 7 feet 11 inches tall. Born in 1846, she worked at P. T. Barnum's American Museum and married the man of her dreams, Martin Van Buren Bates, who topped out at a mere 7 feet 9 inches.

• Take a gander at this! Wawa, Ontario, lays claim to Canada's largest sculpture of a goose, 28 feet high.

• And how do you get to all these wonderful places? On one of the longest national highways in the world, of course—the mighty (and 4,860-mile-long) Trans-Canada. ■

Photos, clockwise from top left: Myke2020/Wikimedia; Wikimedia; PavelS/Getty Images; P199/Wikimedia

HOW WE PREDICT THE WEATHER

We derive our weather forecasts from a secret formula that was devised by the founder of this Almanac, Robert B. Thomas, in 1792. Thomas believed that weather on Earth was influenced by sunspots, which are magnetic storms on the surface of the Sun.

Over the years, we have refined and enhanced this formula with state-of-the-art technology and modern scientific calculations. We employ three scientific disciplines to make our long-range predictions: solar science, the study of sunspots and other solar activity; climatology, the study of prevailing weather patterns; and meteorology, the study of the atmosphere. We predict weather trends and events by comparing solar patterns and historical weather conditions with current solar activity.

Our forecasts emphasize temperature and precipitation deviations from averages, or normals. These are based on 30-year statistical averages prepared by government meteorological agencies and updated every 10 years. The most-recent tabulations span the period 1981 through 2010.

The borders of the provincial weather regions (page 214) are based primarily on climatology and the movement of weather systems. For example, while both Ottawa and Toronto are in Ontario, we place Ottawa in Region 2 rather than Region 3 (Toronto) because its weather trends more closely resemble those of other locales in Region 2.

We believe that nothing in the universe happens haphazardly, that there is a cause-and-effect pattern to all phenomena.

However, although neither we nor any other forecasters have as yet gained sufficient insight into the mysteries of the universe to predict the weather with total accuracy, our results are almost always very close to our traditional claim of 80%.

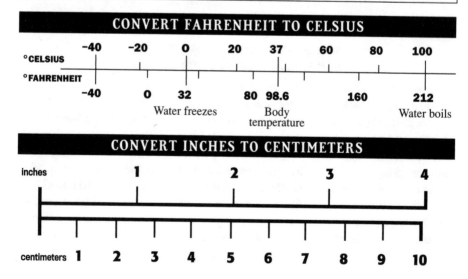

CONVERT FAHRENHEIT TO CELSIUS

°CELSIUS	-40	-20	0	20	37	60	80	100

°FAHRENHEIT	-40	0	32	80	98.6	160	212

Water freezes   Body temperature   Water boils

CONVERT INCHES TO CENTIMETERS

inches	1	2	3	4

centimeters	1	2	3	4	5	6	7	8	9	10

WEATHER REGIONS

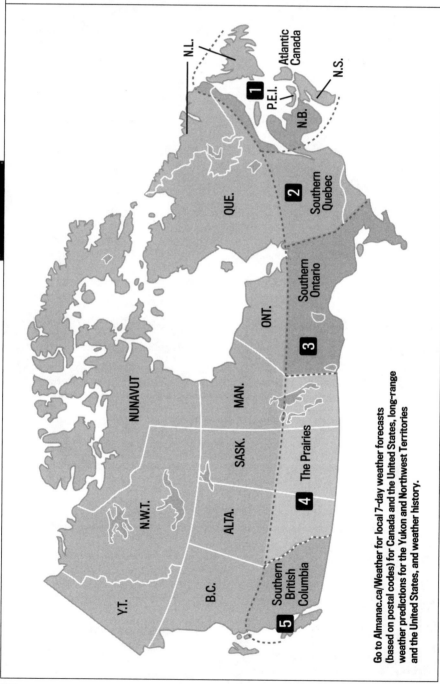

N.L.

Atlantic Canada

N.S.

P.E.I.

N.B.

1

QUE.

Southern Quebec

2

Southern Ontario

ONT.

3

NUNAVUT

MAN.

The Prairies

SASK.

4

N.W.T.

ALTA.

Southern British Columbia

B.C.

5

Y.T.

Go to Almanac.ca/Weather for local 7-day weather forecasts (based on postal codes) for Canada and the United States, long-range weather predictions for the Yukon and Northwest Territories and the United States, and weather history.

WEATHER

ATLANTIC CANADA

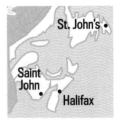

SUMMARY: Winter temperatures will be above normal, on average, with the coldest periods in late December, early to mid-January, and early to mid-February. Precipitation will be below normal in the northeast and above normal in the southwest. Snowfall will be above normal generally, with the snowiest periods in mid- and late January, mid-February, and early March. **April** and **May** will be cooler and slightly drier than normal. **Summer** will be slightly cooler and drier than normal, with the hottest periods in early to mid-July and mid-August. Watch for a tropical storm threat in late August. **September** and **October** will be rainier and slightly cooler than normal.

WEATHER

NOV. 2018: Temp. 3°C (avg.); precip. 90mm (50mm below avg.). 1–3 Rainy, cold. 4–8 Showers, cool. 9–17 Periods of rain and snow, cool. 18–21 Snow, then flurries, cold. 22–30 Rainy periods, mild.

DEC. 2018: Temp. 1°C (4° above avg.); precip. 130mm (70mm below avg. northeast, 70mm above southwest). 1–6 Rainy periods, mild. 7–16 Showers north, rainy periods south; mild. 17–24 Snow, then rainy periods; cold, then mild. 25–31 Snow showers, turning cold.

JAN. 2019: Temp. –7°C (1° below avg.); precip. 90mm (30mm below avg.). 1–4 Snow showers, cold. 5–11 Snow, then flurries, very cold. 12–14 Snowstorm. 15–18 Periods of rain and snow, mild. 19–23 Rain to snow. 24–29 Rain, then snow showers, cold. 30–31 Snowstorm.

FEB. 2019: Temp. –5.5°C (1° above avg.); precip. 140mm (40mm above avg.). 1–6 Snow showers, cold. 7–10 Rain and snow, then sunny, cold. 11–13 Snowstorm. 14–17 Stormy, snow to rain. 18–22 Snow showers, cold. 23–24 Rainy, mild. 25–28 Snow to rain, then sunny, mild.

MAR. 2019: Temp. –4°C (1° below avg.); precip. 160mm (40mm above avg.). 1–3 Flurries, cold. 4–9 Snowstorm, then flurries, cold. 10–14 Rain, then showers, mild. 15–17 Rain to snow. 18–25 Rain to snow, then flurries, cool. 26–31 Rain, then flurries, cool.

APR. 2019: Temp. 3°C (1° below avg.); precip. 100mm (10mm below avg.). 1–7 Rain to snow, cool. 8–13 Rain, then sunny, cool. 14–17 Showers, cool. 18–22 Snow, then sunny, cool. 23–30 Periods of rain and wet snow, chilly.

MAY 2019: Temp. 7.5°C (2° below avg.); precip. 110mm (avg.). 1–6 Showers, then sunny, cool. 7–15 Showers, cool. 16–22 Periods of rain and wet snow, chilly. 23–31 A few showers, cool.

JUNE 2019: Temp. 14.5°C (avg.); precip. 90mm (10mm below avg.). 1–5 Rainy periods, cool. 6–10 Sunny, warmer. 11–17 Rainy periods, warm. 18–22 Showers, cool. 23–30 Rainy periods, cool.

JULY 2019: Temp. 17°C (1° below avg.); precip. 125mm (20mm below avg.). 1–5 Rainy periods, cool. 6–10 Scattered t-storms, hot. 11–25 A few showers, cool. 26–31 Scattered t-storms, warm.

AUG. 2019: Temp. 18°C (avg.); precip. 110mm (20mm below avg.). 1–6 A few showers, cool north; sunny, warm south. 7–13 Showers, cool. 14–17 Sunny, hot. 18–24 A few t-storms, cool. 25–28 Sunny, warm. 29–31 Tropical storm threat.

SEPT. 2019: Temp. 14°C (avg.); precip. 165mm (60mm above avg.). 1–6 A few showers, cool. 7–11 Showers, warm. 12–18 Rainy periods, mild. 19–22 Showers, cool. 23–30 Rainy periods, mild.

OCT. 2019: Temp. 7.5°C (1° below avg.); precip. 130mm (10mm above avg.). 1–8 A few showers, chilly. 9–13 Rainy periods, cool. 14–17 Rain and snow showers, chilly. 18–22 Rainy, cool. 23–31 Showers, mild.

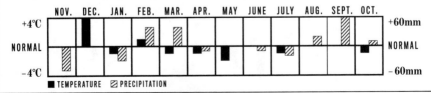

	NOV.	DEC.	JAN.	FEB.	MAR.	APR.	MAY	JUNE	JULY	AUG.	SEPT.	OCT.	

■ TEMPERATURE ▨ PRECIPITATION

SOUTHERN QUEBEC

SUMMARY: Winter will be snowier than normal in most locations, with above-normal precipitation and slightly below-normal temperatures. The coldest periods will be from late December into the first half of January and in late January and early and mid-February, with the snowiest periods in early December, late February, and mid-March. **April** and **May** will be rainier and slightly cooler than normal. **Summer** will be slightly drier than normal, with near-normal temperatures. The hottest periods will be in late June and mid-August. **September** and **October** will be cooler than normal, with precipitation above normal east and below normal west.

NOV. 2018: Temp. 1.5°C (0.5° above avg.); precip. 60mm (20mm below avg.). 1–5 Snow showers, cold. 6–14 Rain to snow, then sunny, cold. 15–24 Rainy periods, mild. 25–30 Snowy periods, cold.

DEC. 2018: Temp. –5.5°C (0.5° above avg.); precip. 130mm (50mm above avg.). 1–5 Heavy snow to rain, then sunny, mild. 6–10 Snow showers, cold. 11–16 Rain and snow east, snowy periods west. 17–21 Snow showers, cold east; showers, mild west. 22–24 Showers, mild. 25–31 Snow showers, cold.

JAN. 2019: Temp. –11.5°C (1° below avg.); precip. 65mm (10mm below avg.). 1–13 Snow showers, cold. 14–18 Snow east, snow to rain west; turning mild. 19–25 Rain and snow showers, mild. 26–31 Sunny, very cold.

FEB. 2019: Temp. –8°C (1° above avg.); precip. 90mm (30mm above avg.). 1–4 Sunny, cold. 5–12 Snow to rain, then sunny, cold. 13–17 Snowy periods, cold. 18–23 Showers, mild. 24–28 Snowstorm east, rain west; mild.

MAR. 2019: Temp. –6.5°C (2° below avg.); precip. 115mm (40mm above avg.). 1–9 Flurries, cold. 10–14 Snowstorm, then flurries, cold. 15–20 Snowy periods, cold. 21–23 Sunny, cold. 24–31 Periods of rain and snow, chilly.

APR. 2019: Temp. 3°C (2° below avg.); precip. 55mm (10mm below avg.). 1–7 Snow showers, cold. 8–14 Rain, then sunny, cool. 15–21 Rain, then sunny, warm. 22–30 Rain and snow, then showers, cool.

MAY 2019: Temp. 12°C (1° below avg.); precip. 105mm (40mm above avg.). 1–11 Rainy periods, cool. 12–15 Sunny, nice. 16–24 A few showers, cool. 25–31 Showers, warm.

JUNE 2019: Temp. 19°C (avg.); precip. 90mm (avg.). 1–4 Showers, warm. 5–9 Sunny, cool. 10–14 T-storms, warm. 15–24 Isolated t-storms, cool. 25–30 A couple of t-storms, hot.

JULY 2019: Temp. 20°C (avg.); precip. 120mm (20mm above avg.). 1–13 Scattered t-storms, warm. 14–16 Sunny, cool. 17–31 Scattered t-storms, cool.

AUG. 2019: Temp. 19°C (avg.); precip. 70mm (30mm below avg.). 1–10 Sunny, warm. 11–17 Scattered t-storms, hot. 18–31 A few showers, cool.

SEPT. 2019: Temp. 13°C (1° below avg.); precip. 105mm (50mm above avg. east, 20mm below west). 1–7 Scattered t-storms, warm. 8–20 A few showers, cool. 21–23 Showers, warm. 24–30 Periods of rain and wet snow, cold.

OCT. 2019: Temp. 7°C (1° below avg.); precip. 60mm (20mm below avg.). 1–12 A few showers, mild. 13–18 Sunny, cool. 19–22 Snow showers, cold. 23–31 Showers, mild.

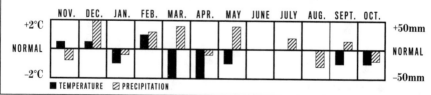

QUÉBEC DU SUD

RÉSUMÉ: **L'hiver** sera plus neigeux que la normale dans la majeure partie de la région, avec des précipitations supérieures à la normale et des températures légèrement inférieures à la normale. Les périodes les plus froides seront de fin décembre à début janvier, à la fin du mois, et à début février et la mi-février, avec les périodes les plus neigeuses au début du mois de décembre, à la fin du mois de février et à la mi-mars. **Avril** et **mai** seront plus pluvieux et légèrement plus frais que la normale. **L'été** sera légèrement plus sec que la normale, avec des températures proches de la normale. Les périodes les plus chaudes seront à la fin juin et à la mi-août. **Septembre** et **octobre** seront plus frais que la normale, avec des précipitations supérieures à la normale à l'est et inférieures à la normale à l'ouest.

NOV. 2018: Temp. 1,5°C (0,5° au-dessus de la moy.); précip. 60mm (20mm en dessous de la moy.). 1–5 Chutes de neige, froid. 6–14 Pluie voire neige, puis ensoleillé, froid. 15–24 Périodes pluvieuses, doux. 25–30 Périodes de neige, froid.

DÉC. 2018: Temp. −5,5°C (0,5° au-dessus de la moy.); précip. 130mm (50mm au-dessus de la moy.). 1–5 Fortes neiges à pluie, puis ensoleillé, doux. 6–10 Chutes de neige, froid. 11–16 Pluie et neige à l'est, périodes de neige à l'ouest. 17–21 Chutes de neige, froid à l'est; averses, doux à l'ouest. 22–24 Averses, doux. 25–31 Chutes de neige, froid.

JAN. 2019: Temp. −11,5°C (1° en dessous de la moy.); précip. 65mm (10mm en dessous de la moy.). 1–13 Chutes de neige, froid. 14–18 Neige à l'est, neige voire pluie à l'ouest; devenant doux. 19–25 Averses et chutes de neige, doux. 26–31 Ensoleillé, très froid.

FÉV. 2019: Temp. −8°C (1° au-dessus de la moy.); précip. 90mm (30mm au-dessus de la moy.). 1–4 Ensoleillé, froid. 5–12 Neige voire pluie, puis ensoleillé, froid. 13–17 Périodes de neige, froid. 18–23 Averses, doux. 24–28 Tempête de neige à l'est, pluie à l'ouest; doux.

MARS 2019: Temp. −6,5°C (2° en dessous de la moy.); précip. 115mm (40mm au-dessus de la moy.). 1–9 Rafales, froid. 10–14 Tempête de neige, puis rafales, froid. 15–20 Périodes de neige, froid. 21–23 Ensoleillé, froid. 24–31 Périodes pluvieuses et neigeuses, très frais.

AVR. 2019: Temp. 3°C (2° en dessous de la moy.); précip. 55mm (10mm en dessous de la moy.). 1–7 Chutes de neige, froid. 8–14 Pluie, puis ensoleillé, frais. 15–21 Pluie, puis ensoleillé, chaud. 22–30 Pluie et neige, puis averses, frais.

MAI 2019: Temp. 12°C (1° en dessous de la moy.); précip. 105mm (40mm au-dessus de la moy.). 1–11 Périodes pluvieuses, frais. 12–15 Ensoleillé, beau. 16–24 Quelques averses, frais. 25–31 Averses, chaud.

JUIN 2019: Temp. 19°C (moy.); précip. 90mm (moy.). 1–4 Averses, chaud. 5–9 Ensoleillé, frais. 10–14 Orages, chaud. 15–24 Orages isolés, frais. 25–30 Quelques orages, très chaud.

JUIL. 2019: Temp. 20°C (moy.); précip. 120mm (20mm au-dessus de la moy.). 1–13 Orages épars, chaud. 14–16 Ensoleillé, frais. 17–31 Orages épars, frais.

AOÛT 2019: Temp. 19°C (moy.); précip. 70mm (30mm en dessous de la moy.). 1–10 Ensoleillé, chaud. 11–17 Orages épars, très chaud. 18–31 Quelques averses, frais.

SEPT. 2019: Temp. 13°C (1° en dessous de la moy.); précip. 105mm (50mm au-dessus de la moy. à l'est, 20mm en dessous de la moy. à l'ouest). 1–7 Orages épars, chaud. 8–20 Quelques averses, frais. 21–23 Averses, chaud. 24–30 Périodes de pluie et de neige mouillée, froid.

OCT. 2019: Temp. 7°C (1° en dessous de la moy.); précip. 60mm (20mm en dessous de la moy.). 1–12 Quelques averses, doux. 13–18 Ensoleillé, frais. 19–22 Chutes de neige, froid. 23–31 Averses, doux.

SOUTHERN ONTARIO

Thunder Bay
Sudbury
Toronto

SUMMARY: Winter temperatures will be close to normal, on average, with above-normal precipitation and snowfall. The coldest periods will be in mid- and late December, early and late January, and early February. The snowiest periods will be in early December, mid-February, and early to mid-March. **April** and **May** will be cooler than normal, with above-normal precipitation. **Summer** will be cooler and rainier than normal. The hottest periods will be from late June into early July and in early to mid-July and mid-August. **September** and **October** will be cooler and rainier than normal.

NOV. 2018: Temp. 5°C (3° above avg.); precip. 105mm (30mm above avg.). 1–5 Snow showers, cold. 6–11 Rain to snow, then flurries, cold. 12–23 Rainy periods, mild. 24–27 Sunny, mild. 28–30 Rain to snow.

DEC. 2018: Temp. –6°C (2° below avg.); precip. 60mm (20mm above avg. east, 20mm below west). 1–4 Snow showers, mild. 5–12 Snow, then flurries, cold. 13–17 Snowy periods east, flurries west; cold. 18–22 Rainy periods east, snow showers west; mild. 23–31 Snow showers, cold.

JAN. 2019: Temp. –8°C (1° below avg.); precip. 80mm (20mm above avg.). 1–6 Sunny west, snow showers east; cold. 7–10 Rainy periods east, snow showers west. 11–13 Sunny; cold east, mild west. 14–24 Rainy periods east, snowy periods west; mild. 25–31 Snow showers, very cold.

FEB. 2019: Temp. –4°C (1° above avg.); precip. 90mm (30mm above avg.). 1–5 Snow showers, cold. 6–11 Flurries; mild, then cold. 12–15 Snow, then flurries, mild. 16–20 Snowstorm, then flurries east; sunny west; cold. 21–23 Showers east, snowy periods west. 24–28 Rainy, mild.

MAR. 2019: Temp. –1°C (1° below avg.); precip. 65mm (10mm above avg.). 1–8 Rain, then sunny, cold. 9–16 Snow, then flurries, cold. 17–22 Snow showers east, sunny west; cold. 23–25 Showers, mild. 26–31 Rain east, snow west, then flurries, cold.

APR. 2019: Temp. 6°C (1° below avg.); precip. 80mm (10mm below avg. east, 40mm above west). 1–4 Sunny, cool. 5–11 Rain, then sunny, mild. 12–14 Sunny, cool. 15–19 Rain, then sunny, cool. 20–24 Showers, warm. 25–30 Rainy periods, cool.

MAY 2019: Temp. 10.5°C (2° below avg.); precip. 95mm (20mm above avg.). 1–4 Rainy east, sunny west; cool. 5–11 Rainy periods, cool. 12–14 Sunny, cool. 15–23 A few showers; warm, then cool. 24–28 Sunny, cool. 29–31 Showers, warm.

JUNE 2019: Temp. 16.5°C (1° below avg.); precip. 140mm (60mm above avg.). 1–4 Showers; hot east, cool west. 5–12 A few showers, cool. 13–22 Scattered t-storms, cool east; sunny, warm west. 23–30 Scattered t-storms, turning hot.

JULY 2019: Temp. 21°C (avg.); precip. 110mm (30mm above avg.). 1–4 Showers, hot. 5–6 Sunny, cool. 7–13 Scattered t-storms, hot. 14–20 Sunny, warm. 21–31 A few showers, cooler.

AUG. 2019: Temp. 19°C (1° below avg.); precip. 100mm (20mm above avg.). 1–8 Scattered showers, warm. 9–12 T-storms, cool. 13–17 Scattered t-storms, hot. 18–26 A few showers, cool. 27–31 Sunny, cool.

SEPT. 2019: Temp. 13°C (2° below avg.); precip. 110mm (20mm above avg.). 1–3 Showers, cool. 4–6 T-storms, warm. 7–20 A few showers, cool. 21–28 Rain, then sunny, cool. 29–30 Rain east, snow west.

OCT. 2019: Temp. 10°C (avg.); precip. 75mm (avg.). 1–7 Showers, cool. 8–12 Rain, then flurries, cold. 13–21 Sunny, turning mild. 22–25 Showers, mild. 26–31 Showers, cool.

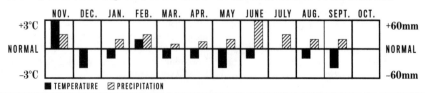

SUMMARY: Winter temperatures will be colder than normal, with above-normal precipitation and snowfall. The coldest periods will occur in mid- to late December, early January, and mid- to late January, with the snowiest periods in early to mid-December, mid- and late January, late February, and mid- to late April. **April** and

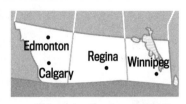

May will be cooler and rainier than normal. **Summer** will be drier than normal in the east and rainier in the west. Temperatures will be near normal, on average, with the hottest periods in early to mid-June, early and mid-July, and early August. **September** and **October** will be warmer and drier than normal.

NOV. 2018: Temp. –6°C (3° below avg.); precip. 15mm (avg.). 1–6 Snow showers, cold. 7–17 Rain to snow, then snow showers, very cold. 18–22 Flurries; mild, then cold. 23–30 Flurries; mild east, cold west.

DEC. 2018: Temp. –10°C (1° below avg.); precip. 35mm (20mm above avg.). 1–2 Rain east, snow west. 3–5 Snow showers, mild. 6–10 Snow, then flurries, cold. 11–16 Sunny, turning mild. 17–21 Snow showers, mild. 22–25 Flurries, very cold. 26–31 Sunny, very cold east; snowy periods west.

JAN. 2019: Temp. –18°C (5° below avg.); precip. 40mm (20mm above avg.). 1–6 Flurries, frigid. 7–10 Snowy periods, cold. 11–15 Sunny, mild. 16–20 Snowy periods, mild. 21–27 Snow showers, turning bitterly cold. 28–31 Snowy, cold.

FEB. 2019: Temp. –9°C (2° above avg.); precip. 25mm (10mm above avg.). 1–5 Sunny, mild. 6–8 Snow showers, cold. 9–15 Sunny, mild. 16–20 Sunny, cold, then mild east; snow, then sunny, cold west. 21–26 Snow showers, turning mild. 27–28 Snow, then cold.

MAR. 2019: Temp. –8°C (4° below avg.); precip. 40mm (20mm above avg.). 1–6 Sunny; cold, then mild. 7–12 Flurries, cold. 13–20 Snow showers, cold. 21–24 Sunny, cool. 25–31 Flurries, cool.

APR. 2019: Temp. 5°C (avg.); precip. 40mm (10mm above avg.). 1–6 Sunny, then showers, cool. 7–12 Sunny, cool. 13–19 Rain and snow showers, then sunny, warm. 20–26

Snowstorm, then showers, cool. 27–30 Sunny, warm.

MAY 2019: Temp. 9°C (2° below avg.); precip. 80mm (30mm above avg.). 1–6 Rainy periods, cool. 7–18 Showers, cool. 19–24 Sunny, cool. 25–31 Scattered showers, warm.

JUNE 2019: Temp. 16.5°C (1° above avg.); precip. 80mm (50mm below avg. east, 50mm above west). 1–13 Showers, then sunny, turning hot. 14–21 Scattered t-storms; hot east, turning cool west. 22–30 A few showers; hot east, cool west.

JULY 2019: Temp. 19.5°C (1° above avg.); precip. 85mm (10mm above avg.). 1–5 Scattered t-storms, hot. 6–10 Sunny; cool, then hot. 11–21 Isolated t-storms; hot, then cool. 22–25 Scattered t-storms, cool. 26–31 Isolated t-storms, warm.

AUG. 2019: Temp. 15°C (2° below avg.); precip. 70mm (10mm above avg.). 1–3 Sunny, hot east; showers, cool west. 4–10 Scattered t-storms, cool. 11–20 Isolated t-storms, cool. 21–27 T-storms, then sunny, cool. 28–31 Showers, cool.

SEPT. 2019: Temp. 9°C (2° below avg.); precip. 35mm (10mm below avg.). 1–5 Rainy periods, cool. 6–11 Sunny, warm. 12–16 Showers, then sunny, cool. 17–19 Sunny, warm. 20–22 Showers, cool. 23–30 Snow showers, chilly.

OCT. 2019: Temp. 10°C (4° above avg.); precip. 15mm (10mm below avg.). 1–4 Sunny, mild. 5–15 A few showers, mild. 16–21 Sunny, mild. 22–26 Showers, mild. 27–31 Sunny, mild.

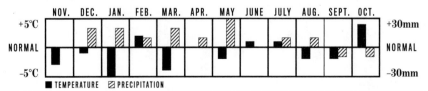

SOUTHERN BRITISH COLUMBIA

Prince
George

Vancouver

Cranbrook

SUMMARY: Winter will have near-normal temperatures, on average, with above-normal precipitation and snowfall. The coldest periods will be in late December, early January, and late February, with the snowiest periods in early to mid-January and late February. **April** and **May** will have below-normal temperatures with above-normal precipitation. **Summer** will be slightly cooler and drier than normal, with the hottest periods in mid- to late July and early to mid-August. **September** and **October** will be warmer and drier than normal.

NOV. 2018: Temp. 4°C (1° below avg.); precip. 190mm (40mm above avg.). 1–3 Rainy, cool. 4–10 Snowy periods north; showers, mild south. 11–20 Rain and snow showers coast, snowy periods inland; cold. 21–30 Snow showers north; rainy periods, mild south.

DEC. 2018: Temp. 3°C (1° above avg.); precip. 160mm (10mm above avg.). 1–3 Sunny, mild. 4–9 Rain, some heavy, coast; showers inland; mild. 10–13 Showers, mild. 14–18 Rainy periods coast, snow showers inland; mild. 19–31 Snow showers, then sunny, cold.

JAN. 2019: Temp. 0°C (1° below avg.); precip. 250mm (50mm above avg.). 1–5 Snow showers, cold. 6–10 Heavy snow north, snow to rain south; turning mild. 11–16 Showers and flurries, mild. 17–22 Snowy periods north, rain south; mild. 23–26 Snow north, rain and snow south; cold. 27–31 Snowy north, showers south; mild.

FEB. 2019: Temp. 1°C (1° above avg.); precip. 130mm (10mm below avg.). 1–5 Sunny, cold coast; showers, mild inland. 6–15 Rainy periods coast, snow showers inland; mild. 16–23 Showers coast, snow showers inland. 24–28 Snow, then sunny, cold.

MAR. 2019: Temp. 4°C (avg.); precip. 160mm (40mm above avg.). 1–11 Periods of snow north, rain south; mild. 12–18 Sunny, cool. 19–31 Rain and snow showers north, rainy periods south; cool.

APR. 2019: Temp. 8°C (avg.); precip. 110mm (10mm above avg.). 1–5 Showers, mild. 6–8 Sunny, cool. 9–18 A few showers, cool. 19–30 Scattered showers, turning warm.

MAY 2019: Temp. 10°C (2° below avg.); precip. 120mm (30mm above avg.). 1–9 Showers, cool. 10–16 Sunny coast, showers inland; cool. 17–23 Rain, then sunny, cool. 24–31 Rainy periods, cool.

JUNE 2019: Temp. 15°C (avg.); precip. 50mm (30mm below avg.). 1–15 Isolated showers north, sunny south; warm. 16–22 Showers, cool. 23–30 Scattered showers, cool.

JULY 2019: Temp. 16°C (1° below avg.); precip. 55mm (avg.). 1–5 Showers, cool. 6–9 Sunny, cool. 10–16 Scattered showers, cool. 17–27 Sunny, warm. 28–31 Scattered showers, cool.

AUG. 2019: Temp. 17.5°C (0.5° above avg.); precip. 70mm (20mm above avg.). 1–6 Scattered showers, warm. 7–14 Sunny; warm coast, hot inland. 15–17 Showers. 18–28 Sunny, warm. 29–31 Showers, cool.

SEPT. 2019: Temp. 14.5°C (0.5° above avg.); precip. 40mm (20mm below avg.). 1–4 Showers, cool. 5–18 Sunny, warm. 19–24 Showers, then sunny, cool. 25–30 Showers, cool.

OCT. 2019: Temp. 10°C (1° above avg.); precip. 70mm (30mm below avg.). 1–6 A few showers, cool. 7–12 Showers north, sunny south; mild. 13–20 Showers, then sunny, cool. 21–31 A few showers; mild, then cool.

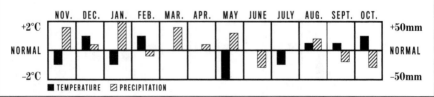

	NOV.	DEC.	JAN.	FEB.	MAR.	APR.	MAY	JUNE	JULY	AUG.	SEPT.	OCT.	
+2°C													+50mm
NORMAL													NORMAL
-2°C													-50mm

■ TEMPERATURE   ▨ PRECIPITATION

FROSTS AND GROWING SEASONS

Dates given are normal averages for a light freeze; local weather and topography may cause considerable variations. The possibility of frost occurring after the spring dates and before the fall dates is 33 percent. The classification of freeze temperatures is usually based on their effect on plants. **Light freeze:** –2° to 0°C (29° to 32°F)—tender plants killed. **Moderate freeze:** –4° to –2°C (25° to 28°F)—widely destructive to most plants. **Severe freeze:** –4°C (24°F and colder)—heavy damage to most plants.   –dates courtesy Environment Canada

PROV.	CITY	GROWING SEASON (DAYS)	LAST SPRING FROST	FIRST FALL FROST	PROV.	CITY	GROWING SEASON (DAYS)	LAST SPRING FROST	FIRST FALL FROST
AB	Athabasca	103	May 28	Sept. 9	NT	Fort Simpson	81	May 31	Aug. 21
AB	Calgary	99	May 29	Sept. 6	NT	Norman Wells	91	May 29	Aug. 29
AB	Edmonton	123	May 15	Sept. 16	NT	Yellowknife	102	May 31	Sept. 11
AB	Grande Prairie	106	May 22	Sept. 6	ON	Barrie	147	May 12	Oct. 7
AB	Lethbridge	113	May 22	Sept. 13	ON	Brantford	151	May 5	Oct. 4
AB	Medicine Hat	118	May 18	Sept. 14	ON	Hamilton	156	May 5	Oct. 9
AB	Peace River	96	May 28	Sept. 2	ON	Kapuskasing	75	June 18	Sept. 2
AB	Red Deer	108	May 24	Sept. 10	ON	Kingston	150	May 4	Oct. 2
BC	Abbotsford	168	Apr. 30	Oct. 16	ON	London	141	May 15	Oct. 4
BC	Castlegar	141	May 8	Sept. 27	ON	Ottawa	135	May 13	Sept. 26
BC	Chilliwack	191	Apr. 19	Oct. 28	ON	Owen Sound	147	May 14	Oct. 9
BC	Coombs	139	May 13	Sept. 30	ON	Peterborough	125	May 17	Sept. 20
BC	Dawson Creek	76	June 8	Aug. 24	ON	Sudbury	124	May 21	Sept. 23
BC	Kamloops	152	May 3	Oct. 3	ON	Timmins	85	June 9	Sept. 3
BC	Kelowna	122	May 19	Sept. 19	ON	Toronto	161	May 4	Oct. 13
BC	Nanaimo	163	May 4	Oct. 15	ON	Wawa	97	June 6	Sept. 12
BC	Prince George	77	June 8	Aug. 25	ON	Windsor	172	Apr. 28	Oct. 18
BC	Prince Rupert	145	May 14	Oct. 7	PE	Alberton	122	May 31	Oct. 1
BC	Vancouver	236	Mar. 19	Nov. 11	PE	Charlottetown	142	May 22	Oct. 12
BC	Victoria	217	Apr. 5	Nov. 9	PE	Summerside	154	May 13	Oct. 15
MB	Brandon	106	May 27	Sept. 11	QC	Baie Comeau	103	June 2	Sept. 14
MB	Lynn Lake	87	June 10	Sept. 6	QC	La Tuque	101	June 5	Sept. 15
MB	The Pas	106	May 31	Sept. 15	QC	Magog	129	May 19	Sept. 26
MB	Thompson	58	June 18	Aug. 16	QC	Montréal	152	May 6	Oct. 6
MB	Winnipeg	116	May 21	Sept. 15	QC	Québec	129	May 17	Sept. 24
NB	Bathurst	101	June 4	Sept. 14	QC	Rimouski	140	May 18	Oct. 6
NB	Fredericton	116	May 23	Sept. 17	QC	Roberval	117	May 25	Sept. 20
NB	Miramichi	115	May 27	Sept. 20	QC	Thetford Mines	128	May 20	Sept. 26
NB	Moncton	103	June 3	Sept. 15	QC	Trois-Rivières	128	May 19	Sept. 25
NB	Saint John	128	May 22	Sept. 28	SK	Moose Jaw	110	May 24	Sept. 12
NL	Corner Brook	129	May 27	Oct. 4	SK	North Battleford	108	May 26	Sept. 12
NL	Gander	115	June 6	Sept. 30	SK	Prince Albert	88	June 7	Sept. 4
NL	Grand Falls	105	June 8	Sept. 22	SK	Regina	91	June 1	Sept. 1
NL	St. John's	117	June 11	Oct. 7	SK	Saskatoon	102	May 26	Sept. 6
NS	Halifax	164	May 8	Oct. 20	SK	Weyburn	107	May 26	Sept. 11
NS	Kentville	122	May 26	Sept. 26	SK	Yorkton	106	May 26	Sept. 10
NS	Sydney	135	May 27	Oct. 10	YT	Dawson	62	June 9	Aug. 11
NS	Truro	103	June 7	Sept. 19	YT	Watson Lake	83	June 6	Aug. 29
NS	Yarmouth	162	May 4	Oct. 14	YT	Whitehorse	72	June 12	Aug. 24

U.S. WEATHER REGIONS

Local 7-day weather forecasts for postal codes in the United States and Canada, as well as long-range weather predictions and weather history, are available at Almanac.ca/Weather.

WEATHER

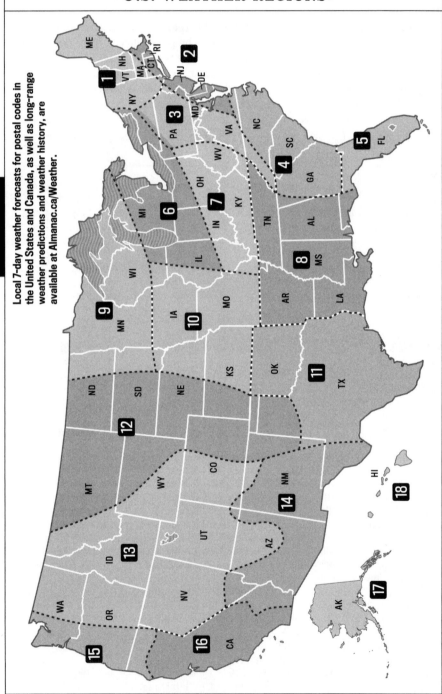

U.S. REGIONAL WEATHER FORECASTS, 2018–19

1. NORTHEAST

SUMMARY: Winter will be milder than normal, on average, with above-normal precipitation and near-normal snowfall. The coldest periods will occur from late December into mid-January and late January into early February and in mid- to late February. The snowiest periods will be in early January, early to mid-February, mid-March, and early April. **April** and **May** will be rainier than normal, with below-normal temperatures. **Summer** temperatures and rainfall will be near normal, with the hottest periods in late July and early to mid-August. **September** and **October** will be slightly cooler and drier than normal.

2. ATLANTIC CORRIDOR

SUMMARY: Winter temperatures will be much above normal, on average, with the coldest periods in early to mid-December, early and late January, and early February. Precipitation will be slightly above normal, with below-normal snowfall. The snowiest periods will occur in early December, late January, and mid-February. **April** and **May** will be slightly warmer and drier than normal. **Summer** will be rainier and cooler than normal, with the hottest periods in late June, early July, and early to mid-August. **September** and **October** will be warmer and drier than normal.

3. APPALACHIANS

SUMMARY: Winter will be warmer than normal, with above-normal precipitation and near- to below-normal snowfall. The coldest periods will be in mid- and late December, early and late January, and early and mid-February. The snowiest periods will be in mid-December, early January, and early February. **April** and **May** will be cooler and drier than normal. **Summer** will be cooler than normal, with the hottest periods in early and late June, early July, and early August. Rainfall will be below normal in the north and above normal in the south. **September** and **October** will be drier than normal, with near-normal temperatures.

4. SOUTHEAST

SUMMARY: Winter will be much warmer and slightly drier than normal, with below-normal snowfall. The coldest periods will be in mid-December, mid- and late January and mid- to late February. The best chances for snow will be in early to mid-December and mid-March. **April** and **May** will be warmer and rainier than normal. **Summer** will be cooler and rainier than normal, with the hottest periods in mid- to late May, early and late July, and mid-August. **September** and **October** will be drier than normal, with near-normal temperatures.

5. FLORIDA

SUMMARY: Winter will be milder and drier than normal, with the coldest temperatures in early and mid-December and early and mid-February. **April** and **May** will be a bit hotter and rainier than normal. **Summer** will be slightly cooler as well as rainier than normal, with the hottest periods in mid-June, mid-July, and mid- to late August. Watch for tropical storm threats in mid- to late June, early to mid- and mid- to late September, and early October. Overall,

WEATHER

September and October will be warmer and drier than normal.

6. LOWER LAKES

SUMMARY: Winter will be warmer and rainier than normal, with near-normal snowfall. The coldest periods will be in mid- and late December, early and late January, and early February. The snowiest periods will be in early December, early and late January, early February, and mid-March. **April** and **May** will be slightly warmer than normal, with near-normal precipitation. **Summer** will be cooler and slightly drier than normal. The hottest periods will be in late May, late June, early July, and mid-August. **September** and **October** will be drier than normal, with near-normal temperatures.

7. OHIO VALLEY

SUMMARY: Winter will be warmer than normal, with above-normal precipitation and below-normal snowfall. The coldest periods will be in mid- and late December, late January, and early February. The snowiest periods will be in early and mid-December and early February. **April** and **May** will be warmer than normal, with near-normal rainfall. **Summer** will be cooler and rainier than normal, with the hottest periods in late June, early and mid-July, and mid-August. **September** and **October** will be slightly drier than normal, with near-normal temperatures.

8. DEEP SOUTH

SUMMARY: Winter will be warmer than normal, on average, with the coldest periods in late November, the first half of December, early January, and early February. Rainfall will be above normal in the north and near normal in the south, with the best chance for snowfall in mid- and late December across the north. **April** and **May** will be warmer and rainier than normal. **Summer** will be cooler and rainier than normal, with the hottest periods in mid-June, mid-July, and early August. Watch for a hurricane threat in early September. Overall, **September** and **October** will be slightly cooler and drier than normal.

9. UPPER MIDWEST

SUMMARY: Winter will be slightly milder and drier than normal, with snowfall near to below normal. The coldest periods will be in early to mid-December, from late December into January, and from late January into February. The snowiest periods will be in mid- and late November, early and mid-December, and early and late March. **April** and **May** will be slightly cooler and rainier than normal. **Summer** will be slightly cooler than normal, with the hottest periods in late June, late July, and early to mid-August. Rainfall will be above normal in the east and below normal in the west. **September** and **October** will be slightly rainier than normal, with near-normal temperatures.

10. HEARTLAND

SUMMARY: Winter will be milder than normal, with above-normal precipitation. The coldest periods will be in mid- and late December and early January. Snowfall will be below normal in the north and above normal in central and southern areas, with the snowiest periods in late November, mid-December, early January, and mid-March. **April** and **May** will be warmer and rainier than normal. **Summer** will be cooler than normal, with the hottest periods in late June and the first half of July. Rainfall will be below normal in the north and above normal in the south. **September** and **October** will bring near-normal temperatures and precipitation.

11. TEXAS-OKLAHOMA

SUMMARY: Winter will be milder and drier than normal, with below-normal snowfall. The coldest periods will be in late December, late January, and mid-February, with the best chances for snow in mid- and late December, early January, and mid-February. **April** and **May** will be warmer and slightly rainier than normal. **Summer** will be cooler and rainier than normal, with the hottest periods in mid-June and early and mid-July. Watch for a tropical storm threat in mid- to late August and a hurricane threat in early September. Otherwise, **September** and **October** will be slightly cooler and rainier than normal.

12. HIGH PLAINS

SUMMARY: Winter will be warmer than normal, with slightly below-normal precipitation. The coldest periods will be in late November, mid- and late December, early and late January, and mid-February. Snowfall will be below normal in the east and above normal in the west, with the snowiest periods in mid- and late December, late January, and late March. **April** and **May** will be warmer and slightly rainier than nor-

mal. **Summer** will be hotter and drier than normal, with the hottest periods in mid- and late June, mid-July, and early to mid-August. **September** and **October** will have near-normal temperatures and precipitation.

13. INTERMOUNTAIN

SUMMARY: Winter temperatures and precipitation will be above normal, on average, with the coldest periods in late December, early January, and early February. Snowfall will be above normal in the north and below normal in the south, with the snowiest periods in late November, late December, early and late January, mid- to late February, and early March. **April** and **May** will have temperatures below normal in the north and above normal in the south and will be slightly drier than normal. **Summer** will be hotter and slightly drier than normal, with the hottest periods in mid- and late June and mid- to late July. **September** and **October** will be warmer than normal, with near-normal precipitation.

14. DESERT SOUTHWEST

SUMMARY: Winter will be colder than normal, with above-normal precipitation. The coldest periods will be in mid- and late December, early and late January, and mid-February. Snowfall will be below normal in the east and above normal in other places that receive snow, with the snowiest periods in late December, early January, and mid-February. **April** and **May** will be warmer and slightly drier than normal. **Summer** will be slightly hotter than normal in most of the region, with

WEATHER

slightly below-normal rainfall. The hottest periods will occur in much of June, mid-July, and early to mid-August. **September** and **October** will be rainier than normal, with near- or below-normal temperatures.

15. PACIFIC NORTHWEST

SUMMARY: Winter will be warmer and much rainier than normal, with below-normal snowfall. The coldest periods will occur in early and late December, early January, and mid- and late February, with the snowiest periods in early January and mid-February. **April** and **May** will be warmer and drier than normal. **Summer** will be warmer and drier than normal, with the hottest temperatures in mid- to late July and early and mid-August. **September** and **October** will be warmer and slightly drier than normal.

16. PACIFIC SOUTHWEST

SUMMARY: Winter temperatures will be near or cooler than normal, with rainfall above normal in the north and slightly below normal in the south. The coldest periods will occur in late December, mid-January, and early February. Mountain snows will be near normal, with the stormiest periods in late November, late December, and early January. **April** and **May** will be cooler and drier than normal. **Summer** will be warmer than normal, with near-normal rainfall. The hottest periods will be in mid- to late June, mid-July, and late August. **September** and **October** will see temperatures above normal in the northeast and below normal in the southwest. Rainfall will be slightly above normal.

17. ALASKA

SUMMARY: Winter temperatures will be milder than normal, with the coldest periods in mid-January and early February. Precipitation will be above normal north and below normal south, while snowfall will be near to below normal. The snowiest periods will be in early to mid-November and mid- to late December. **April** and **May** will be warmer than normal, with slightly above-normal precipitation. **Summer** will be slightly warmer and drier than normal, with the hottest periods in mid- to late July and early August. **September** and **October** temperatures will be colder than normal north and milder central and south. There will be near-normal precipitation and snowfall, with the snowiest periods in early to mid-October central and early October east and west.

18. HAWAII

SUMMARY: Winter temperatures will be above normal, on average, with the coolest periods in early to mid-December, mid-February, and early March. Rainfall will be above normal east and below normal west, with the stormiest periods in mid- to late November and early February. **April** and **May** will be warmer than normal, with rainfall above normal east and below normal west. **Summer** temperatures will be slightly cooler than normal, on average, with above-normal rainfall. The warmest periods will be in late June, late July, and early August. **September** and **October** will see temperatures above normal east and below normal west and be slightly rainier than normal. ∎

TABLE OF MEASURES

LINEAR

1 hand = 4 inches
1 link = 7.92 inches
1 span = 9 inches
1 foot = 12 inches
1 yard = 3 feet
1 rod = 5½ yards
1 mile = 320 rods = 1,760 yards = 5,280 feet
1 international nautical mile = 6,076.1155 feet
1 knot = 1 nautical mile per hour
1 fathom = 2 yards = 6 feet
1 furlong = ⅛ mile = 660 feet = 220 yards
1 league = 3 miles = 24 furlongs
1 chain = 100 links = 22 yards

SQUARE

1 square foot = 144 square inches
1 square yard = 9 square feet
1 square rod = 30½ square yards = 272½ square feet = 625 square links

1 square chain = 16 square rods
1 acre = 10 square chains = 160 square rods = 43,560 square feet
1 square mile = 640 acres = 102,400 square rods

CUBIC

1 cubic foot = 1,728 cubic inches
1 cubic yard = 27 cubic feet
1 cord = 128 cubic feet
1 U.S. liquid gallon = 4 quarts = 231 cubic inches
1 imperial gallon = 1.20 U.S. gallons = 0.16 cubic foot
1 board foot = 144 cubic inches

DRY

2 pints = 1 quart
4 quarts = 1 gallon
2 gallons = 1 peck
4 pecks = 1 bushel

LIQUID

4 gills = 1 pint
63 gallons = 1 hogshead
2 hogsheads = 1 pipe or butt
2 pipes = 1 tun

KITCHEN

3 teaspoons = 1 tablespoon
16 tablespoons = 1 cup
1 cup = 8 ounces
2 cups = 1 pint
2 pints = 1 quart
4 quarts = 1 gallon

AVOIRDUPOIS

(for general use)
1 ounce = 16 drams
1 pound = 16 ounces
1 short hundredweight = 100 pounds
1 ton = 2,000 pounds
1 long ton = 2,240 pounds

APOTHECARIES'

(for pharmaceutical use)
1 scruple = 20 grains
1 dram = 3 scruples
1 ounce = 8 drams
1 pound = 12 ounces

METRIC CONVERSIONS

LINEAR

1 inch = 2.54 centimeters
1 centimeter = 0.39 inch
1 meter = 39.37 inches
1 yard = 0.914 meter
1 mile = 1.61 kilometers
1 kilometer = 0.62 mile

SQUARE

1 square inch = 6.45 square centimeters
1 square yard = 0.84 square meter
1 square mile = 2.59 square kilometers

1 square kilometer = 0.386 square mile
1 acre = 0.40 hectare
1 hectare = 2.47 acres

CUBIC

1 cubic yard = 0.76 cubic meter
1 cubic meter = 1.31 cubic yards

HOUSEHOLD

½ teaspoon = 2 mL
1 teaspoon = 5 mL
1 tablespoon = 15 mL
¼ cup = 60 mL

⅓ cup = 75 mL
½ cup = 125 mL
⅔ cup = 150 mL
¾ cup = 175 mL
1 cup = 250 mL
1 liter = 1.057 U.S. liquid quarts
1 U.S. liquid quart = 0.946 liter
1 U.S. liquid gallon = 3.78 liters
1 gram = 0.035 ounce
1 ounce = 28.349 grams
1 kilogram = 2.2 pounds
1 pound = 0.45 kilogram

TO CONVERT CELSIUS AND FAHRENHEIT: $°C = (°F - 32)/1.8$; $°F = (°C × 1.8) + 32$

SECRETS OF THE ZODIAC

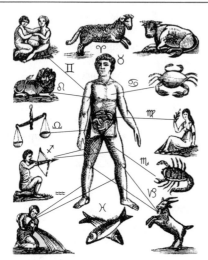

The Man of the Signs

Ancient astrologers believed that each astrological sign influenced a specific part of the body. The first sign of the zodiac—Aries—was attributed to the head, with the rest of the signs moving down the body, ending with Pisces at the feet.

♈	Aries, head	**ARI**	*Mar. 21–Apr. 20*
♉	Taurus, neck	**TAU**	*Apr. 21–May 20*
♊	Gemini, arms	**GEM**	*May 21–June 20*
♋	Cancer, breast	**CAN**	*June 21–July 22*
♌	Leo, heart	**LEO**	*July 23–Aug. 22*
♍	Virgo, belly	**VIR**	*Aug. 23–Sept. 22*
♎	Libra, reins	**LIB**	*Sept. 23–Oct. 22*
♏	Scorpio, secrets	**SCO**	*Oct. 23–Nov. 22*
♐	Sagittarius, thighs	**SAG**	*Nov. 23–Dec. 21*
♑	Capricorn, knees	**CAP**	*Dec. 22–Jan. 19*
♒	Aquarius, legs	**AQU**	*Jan. 20–Feb. 19*
♓	Pisces, feet	**PSC**	*Feb. 20–Mar. 20*

ASTROLOGY VS. ASTRONOMY

Astrology is a tool we use to plan events according to the placements of the Sun, the Moon, and the planets in the 12 signs of the zodiac. In astrology, the planetary movements do not cause events; rather, they explain the path, or "flow," that events tend to follow. *The Moon's astrological place is given on the next page.* **Astronomy** is the study of the actual placement of the known planets and constellations. The Moon's astronomical place is given in the **Left-Hand Calendar Pages, 120–146.** *(The placement of the planets in the signs of the zodiac is not the same astrologically and astronomically. See page 85.)*

The dates in the **Best Days** table, **pages 230–231,** are based on the astrological passage of the Moon.

WHEN MERCURY IS RETROGRADE

Sometimes the other planets appear to be traveling backward through the zodiac; this is an illusion. We call this illusion *retrograde motion.*

Mercury's retrograde periods can cause our plans to go awry. However, intuition is high during these periods and coincidences can be extraordinary.

When Mercury is retrograde, remain flexible, allow extra time for travel, and avoid signing contracts. Review projects and plans but wait until Mercury is direct again to make final decisions.

In 2019, Mercury will be retrograde during **March 5–28, July 7–August 2,** and **October 31–November 20.**

—Celeste Longacre

GARDENING BY THE MOON'S SIGN

USE CHART ON NEXT PAGE TO FIND THE BEST DATES FOR THE FOLLOWING GARDEN TASKS . . .

PLANT, TRANSPLANT, AND GRAFT: Cancer, Scorpio, Pisces, or Taurus
HARVEST: Aries, Leo, Sagittarius, Gemini, or Aquarius
BUILD/FIX FENCES OR GARDEN BEDS: Capricorn

CONTROL INSECT PESTS, PLOW, AND WEED: Aries, Gemini, Leo, Sagittarius, or Aquarius
PRUNE: Aries, Leo, or Sagittarius. During a waxing Moon, pruning encourages growth; during a waning Moon, it discourages it.

SETTING EGGS BY THE MOON'S SIGN

Chicks take about 21 days to hatch. Those born under a waxing Moon in Cancer, Scorpio, or Pisces are healthier and mature faster. To ensure that chicks are born during these times, "set eggs" (place eggs in an incubator or under a hen) 21 days before the desired hatching dates.

EXAMPLE:
The Moon is new on April 5 and full on April 19. Between these dates, the Moon is in the sign of Cancer on April 11 and 12, and in Scorpio on April 19. To have chicks born on April 11, count back 21 days; set eggs on March 21.

Below are the best days to set eggs in 2019, using only the fruitful dates
between the new and full Moons, and counting back 21 days:

JAN.: 16, 17, 25, 26	**APR.:** 17, 18, 26, 27	**JULY:** 16–18	**OCT.:** 7, 8, 16, 17
FEB.: 13, 14, 22, 23	**MAY:** 14–16, 23, 24	**AUG.:** 13, 14, 22–24	**NOV.:** 12, 13
MAR.: 21, 22, 29	**JUNE:** 11, 12, 19, 20	**SEPT.:** 9, 10, 18-20	**DEC.:** 9–11, 19, 20

The Moon's Astrological Place, 2018–19

	NOV.	DEC.	JAN.	FEB.	MAR.	APR.	MAY	JUNE	JULY	AUG.	SEPT.	OCT.	NOV.	DEC.
1	LEO	LIB	SCO	CAP	CAP	PSC	ARI	TAU	GEM	LEO	LIB	SCO	CAP	AQU
2	VIR	LIB	SAG	CAP	CAP	PSC	ARI	GEM	CAN	VIR	LIB	SAG	CAP	AQU
3	VIR	LIB	SAG	AQU	AQU	PSC	ARI	GEM	CAN	VIR	SCO	SAG	AQU	PSC
4	LIB	SCO	SAG	AQU	AQU	ARI	TAU	CAN	LEO	LIB	SCO	CAP	AQU	PSC
5	LIB	SCO	CAP	AQU	PSC	ARI	TAU	CAN	LEO	LIB	SAG	CAP	AQU	ARI
6	SCO	SAG	CAP	PSC	PSC	TAU	GEM	CAN	VIR	SCO	SAG	CAP	PSC	ARI
7	SCO	SAG	AQU	PSC	PSC	TAU	GEM	LEO	VIR	SCO	CAP	AQU	PSC	ARI
8	SCO	CAP	AQU	ARI	ARI	TAU	CAN	LEO	LIB	SCO	CAP	AQU	ARI	TAU
9	SAG	CAP	AQU	ARI	ARI	GEM	CAN	VIR	LIB	SAG	CAP	PSC	ARI	TAU
10	SAG	CAP	PSC	ARI	TAU	GEM	LEO	VIR	SCO	SAG	AQU	PSC	ARI	GEM
11	CAP	AQU	PSC	TAU	TAU	CAN	LEO	LIB	SCO	CAP	AQU	PSC	TAU	GEM
12	CAP	AQU	ARI	TAU	GEM	CAN	VIR	LIB	SAG	CAP	PSC	ARI	TAU	GEM
13	AQU	PSC	ARI	GEM	GEM	LEO	VIR	SCO	SAG	AQU	PSC	ARI	GEM	CAN
14	AQU	PSC	ARI	GEM	GEM	LEO	VIR	SCO	SAG	AQU	PSC	TAU	GEM	CAN
15	AQU	PSC	TAU	CAN	CAN	VIR	LIB	SAG	CAP	AQU	ARI	TAU	CAN	LEO
16	PSC	ARI	TAU	CAN	CAN	VIR	LIB	SAG	CAP	PSC	ARI	TAU	CAN	LEO
17	PSC	ARI	GEM	LEO	LEO	LIB	SCO	CAP	AQU	PSC	TAU	GEM	CAN	VIR
18	ARI	TAU	GEM	LEO	LEO	LIB	SCO	CAP	AQU	ARI	TAU	GEM	LEO	VIR
19	ARI	TAU	CAN	VIR	VIR	SCO	SAG	CAP	AQU	ARI	TAU	CAN	LEO	LIB
20	ARI	GEM	CAN	VIR	VIR	SCO	SAG	AQU	PSC	ARI	GEM	CAN	VIR	LIB
21	TAU	GEM	LEO	LIB	LIB	SAG	CAP	AQU	PSC	TAU	GEM	LEO	VIR	SCO
22	TAU	CAN	LEO	LIB	LIB	SAG	CAP	PSC	ARI	TAU	CAN	LEO	LIB	SCO
23	GEM	CAN	VIR	SCO	SCO	SAG	AQU	PSC	ARI	GEM	CAN	LEO	LIB	SAG
24	GEM	CAN	VIR	SCO	SCO	CAP	AQU	PSC	ARI	GEM	LEO	VIR	SCO	SAG
25	CAN	LEO	LIB	SCO	SAG	CAP	AQU	ARI	TAU	GEM	LEO	VIR	SCO	SAG
26	CAN	LEO	LIB	SAG	SAG	AQU	PSC	ARI	TAU	CAN	VIR	LIB	SAG	CAP
27	LEO	VIR	SCO	SAG	CAP	AQU	PSC	TAU	GEM	CAN	VIR	LIB	SAG	CAP
28	LEO	VIR	SCO	CAP	CAP	AQU	PSC	TAU	GEM	LEO	LIB	SCO	CAP	AQU
29	VIR	LIB	SAG	—	CAP	PSC	ARI	TAU	CAN	LEO	LIB	SCO	CAP	AQU
30	VIR	LIB	SAG	—	AQU	PSC	ARI	GEM	CAN	VIR	SCO	SAG	CAP	PSC
31	—	SCO	SAG	—	AQU	—	TAU	—	LEO	VIR	—	SAG	—	PSC

BEST DAYS FOR 2019

This chart is based on the Moon's sign and shows the best days each month for certain activities. –*Celeste Longacre*

	JAN.	FEB.	MAR.	APR.	MAY	JUNE	JULY	AUG.	SEPT.	OCT.	NOV.	DEC.
Quit smoking	24	20, 25	24, 29	20, 24	27, 31	1, 24, 29	21, 26	17, 22	18, 27	16, 25	21, 25	18, 22
Bake	19, 20	15, 16	15, 16	11, 12	8, 9	4–6	2, 3, 29, 30	26, 27	22, 23	19, 20	15–17	13, 14
Brew	1, 27, 28	23–25	23, 24	19, 20	17, 18	13, 14	10, 11	6–8	3, 4, 30	1, 28, 29	24, 25	21, 22
Dry fruit/vegetables/meat	3, 4, 29–31	26, 27	25, 26	21–23	1–3, 29, 30	25, 26	22–24	18–20	24, 25	22, 23	18, 19	15, 16
Make jams/jellies	10, 11	6, 7	5–7	1–3, 29, 30	26–28	22–24	20, 21	16, 17	12–14	9–11	6, 7	3, 4, 30, 31
Can, pickle, or make sauerkraut	1, 27, 28	23–25	5, 23, 24	1–3, 29, 30	26–28	22–24	20, 21	16, 17	22, 23	19, 20	15–17	21, 22
Begin diet to lose weight	24	20, 25	24, 29	20, 24	27, 31	1, 24, 29	21, 26	17, 22	18, 27	16, 25	21, 25	18, 22
Begin diet to gain weight	11, 16	7, 12	7, 11, 20	7, 11	5, 18	10, 14	7, 11	3, 8	4, 8	1, 11	7, 30	9, 31
Cut hair to encourage growth	10, 11, 15, 16	11, 12	10, 11	17, 18	5, 15, 16	11, 12	8, 9	4, 5	1, 2, 29	9–11	6, 7	3, 4
Cut hair to discourage growth	25, 26	21, 22	5, 22	1–3, 29, 30	26–28	22–24	20, 21	21, 22	17–19	26	22, 23	19, 20
Perm hair	7–9	3–5	3, 4, 30, 31	26–28	23–25	20, 21	17–19	13–15	10, 11	7, 8	3–5	1, 2, 28, 29
Color hair	15, 16	11, 12	10, 11	6–8	4, 5	1, 27–29	25, 26	21, 22	17–19	14–16	11, 12	8, 9
Straighten hair	2–4, 29–31	26, 27	25, 26	21–23	19, 20	15, 16	12–14	9, 10	5, 6	2, 3, 30, 31	26, 27	23–25
Have dental care	23, 24	19, 20	19, 20	15, 16	12–14	9, 10	6, 7	2, 3, 30, 31	26, 27	24, 25	20, 21	17, 18
Start projects	7	5	7	6	5	4	3	2	29	29	27	27
End projects	4	3	5	4	3	2	1	29	27	26	25	25
Demolish	1, 27, 28	23–25	23, 24	19, 20	17, 18	13, 14	10, 11	6–8	3, 4, 30	1, 28, 29	24, 25	21, 22
Lay shingles	21, 22	17, 18	17, 18	13, 14	10, 11	7, 8	4, 5	1, 28, 29	24, 25	21–23	18, 19	15, 16
Paint	15, 16, 25, 26	11, 12	21, 22	6–8	4, 5	11, 12	25, 26	21, 22	17–19	14–16	11, 12	8, 9
Wash windows	12–14	8–10	8, 9	4, 5	2, 3, 29, 30	25, 26	22–24	18–20	15, 16	12, 13	8–10	5–7
Wash floors	10, 11	6, 7	5–7	1–3, 29, 30	26–28	22–24	20, 21	16, 17	12–14	9–11	6, 7	3, 4, 30, 31
Go camping	2–4, 29–31	26, 27	25, 26	21–23	19, 20	15, 16	12–14	9, 10	5, 6	2, 3	26, 27	23–25

	JAN.	FEB.	MAR.	APR.	MAY	JUNE	JULY	AUG.	SEPT.	OCT.	NOV.	DEC.
Travel for pleasure	21, 22	17, 18	17, 18	13, 14	10, 11	7, 8	4, 5	1, 28, 29	24, 25	22, 23	18, 19	15, 16
Get married	25, 26	21, 22	21, 22	17, 18	15, 16	11, 12	8, 9	4, 5	1, 2, 28, 29	26, 27	22, 23	19, 20
Ask for a loan	24, 28	24, 28	23, 24	20, 29, 30	23–25	20, 21	23–25	21, 22	17, 18	14–16	24, 25	21, 22
Buy a home	16, 20	12, 16	10, 11	6–8	5, 17	13, 14	10, 11	6–8	3, 4	1, 29	11, 29, 30	8, 9
Move (house/household)	17, 18	13, 14	12–14	9, 10	6, 7	2, 3	1, 27, 28	23–25	20, 21	17, 18	13, 14	10–12
Advertise to sell	15, 16	11, 12	10, 11	6–8	5, 17	13, 14	10, 11	6–8	3, 4	1, 28, 29	11	8, 9
Mow to promote growth	12–14	8–10	8, 9	5	17	13, 14	10, 11	6–8	3, 4	12	8–10	6, 7
Mow to slow growth	27, 28	23–25	23, 24	4	29, 30	25, 26	22, 23	19, 20	15, 16	19, 20	24, 25	21, 22
Plant aboveground crops	10, 11, 19, 20	15, 16	15, 16	11, 12	8, 9	5, 6, 13, 14	10, 11	7, 8	3, 4, 30	1, 9, 10	6, 7	3, 4
Plant belowground crops	1, 27, 28	23–25	5, 23, 24	1–3, 29, 30	26–28	22, 23	20, 21	17, 26, 27	22, 23	19, 20	15–17	21, 22
Destroy pests and weeds	12–14	8–10	8, 9	4, 5	1–3, 29, 30	25, 26	22–24	18–20	15, 16	12, 13	8–10	5–7
Graft or pollinate	19, 20	15, 16	15, 16	11, 12	8, 9	4–6	2, 3, 29, 30	26, 27	22, 23	19, 20	15–17	13, 14
Prune to encourage growth	12–14	8–10	8, 9	13, 14	10, 11	7, 8	4, 5	9, 10	5, 6	2, 3	8–10	5–7
Prune to discourage growth	2–4, 29–31	26, 27	25, 26	22, 23	1–3, 29, 30	25, 26	22–24	18–20	15, 16	21, 22	18, 19	15, 16
Pick fruit	23, 24	19, 20	19, 20	15, 16	12–14	9, 10	6, 7	2, 3, 30, 31	26, 27	24, 25	20, 21	17, 18
Harvest above-ground crops	15, 16	11, 12	10, 11	6–8	4, 5, 12–14	9, 10	6, 7	2, 3	7–9	4–6	1, 2, 29, 30	8, 9
Harvest below-ground crops	23, 24	1, 2, 28	27, 28	24, 25	21, 22, 31	1, 27–29	25, 26	21, 22	17, 18	14–16	20, 21	17, 18
Cut hay	12–14	8–10	8, 9	4, 5	1–3, 29, 30	25, 26	22–24	18–20	15, 16	12, 13	8–10	5–7
Begin logging	5, 6	1, 2, 28	1, 2, 27–29	24, 25	21, 22	17–19	15, 16	11, 12	7–9	4–6	1, 2, 28–30	26, 27
Set posts or pour concrete	5, 6	1, 2, 28	1, 2, 27–29	24, 25	21, 22	17–19	15, 16	11, 12	7–9	4–6	1, 2, 28–30	26, 27
Purchase animals	19, 20	15, 16	15, 16	11, 12	8, 9	4–6	2, 3, 29, 30	26, 27	22, 23	19, 20	15–17	13, 14
Breed animals	1, 27, 28	23–25	23, 24	19, 20	17, 18	13, 14	10, 11	6–8	3, 4, 30	1, 28, 29	24, 25	21, 22
Wean animals or children	24	20, 25	24, 29	20, 24	27, 31	1, 24, 29	21, 26	17, 22	18, 27	16, 25	21, 25	18, 22
Castrate animals	7–9	3–5	3, 4, 30, 31	26, 27	23–25	20, 21	17–19	13–15	10, 11	7, 8	3–5	28, 29
Slaughter livestock	1, 27, 28	23–25	23, 24	19, 20	17, 18	13, 14	10, 11	6–8	3, 4, 30	1, 28, 29	24, 25	21, 22

BEST FISHING DAYS AND TIMES

The best times to fish are when the fish are naturally most active. The Sun, Moon, tides, and weather all influence fish activity. For example, fish tend to feed more at sunrise and sunset, and also during a full Moon (when tides are higher than average). However, most of us go fishing simply when we can get the time off. But there are best times, according to fishing lore:

■ One hour before and one hour after high tides, and one hour before and one hour after low tides. The times of high tides for Halifax are given on **pages 120–146**; also see **pages 236–237**. (Inland, the times for high tides correspond with the times when the Moon is due south. Low tides are halfway between high tides.)

GET HIGH AND LOW TIDE TIMES NEAREST TO YOUR LOCATION AT ALMANAC.CA/TIDES.

■ During the "morning rise" (after sunup for a spell) and the "evening rise" (just before sundown and the hour or so after).

■ During the rise and set of the Moon.

■ When the barometer is steady or on the rise. (But even during stormy periods, the fish aren't going to give up feeding. The clever angler will find just the right bait.)

■ When there is a hatch of flies—caddis flies or mayflies, commonly.

■ When the breeze is from a westerly quarter, rather than from the north or east.

■ When the water is still or slightly rippled, rather than during a wind.

THE BEST FISHING DAYS FOR 2019, WHEN THE MOON IS BETWEEN NEW AND FULL

January 5–21
February 4–19
March 6–20
April 5–19
May 4–18
June 3–17
July 2–16, 31
August 1–15, 30, 31
September 1–14, 28–30
October 1–13, 27–31
November 1–12, 26–30
December 1–12, 26–31

Dates based on Eastern Time.

HOW TO ESTIMATE THE WEIGHT OF A FISH

Measure the fish from the tip of its nose to the tip of its tail. Then measure its girth at the thickest portion of its midsection.

The weight of a fat-bodied fish (bass, salmon) = (length x girth x girth)/800

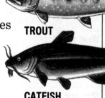

SALMON

The weight of a slender fish (trout, northern pike) = (length x girth x girth)/900

TROUT

EXAMPLE: If a trout is 20 inches long and has a 12-inch girth, its estimated weight is (20 x 12 x 12)/900 = 2,880/900 = 3.2 pounds

CATFISH

GESTATION AND MATING TABLES

	PROPER AGE OR WEIGHT FOR FIRST MATING	PERIOD OF FERTILITY (YRS.)	NUMBER OF FEMALES FOR ONE MALE	PERIOD OF GESTATION (DAYS) AVERAGE	RANGE
CATTLE: Cow	15–18 mos.[1]	10–14		283	279–290[2] 262–300[3]
Bull	1 yr., well matured	10–12	50[4] / thousands[5]		
GOAT: Doe	10 mos. or 85–90 lbs.	6		150	145–155
Buck	well matured	5	30		
HORSE: Mare	3 yrs.	10–12		336	310–370
Stallion	3 yrs.	12–15	40–45[4] / record 252[5]		
PIG: Sow	5–6 mos. or 250 lbs.	6		115	110–120
Boar	250–300 lbs.	6	50[6] / 35–40[7]		
RABBIT: Doe	6 mos.	5–6		31	30–32
Buck	6 mos.	5–6	30		
SHEEP: Ewe	1 yr. or 90 lbs.	6		147 / 151[8]	142–154
Ram	12–14 mos., well matured	7	50–75[6] / 35–40[7]		
CAT: Queen	12 mos.	6		63	60–68
Tom	12 mos.	6	6–8		
DOG: Bitch	16–18 mos.	8		63	58–67
Male	12–16 mos.	8	8–10		

[1]Holstein and beef: 750 lbs.; Jersey: 500 lbs. [2]Beef; 8–10 days shorter for Angus. [3]Dairy. [4]Natural. [5]Artificial. [6]Hand-mated. [7]Pasture. [8]For fine wool breeds.

INCUBATION PERIOD OF POULTRY (DAYS)

Chicken	21
Duck	26–32
Goose	30–34
Guinea	26–28
Turkey	28

AVERAGE LIFE SPAN OF ANIMALS IN CAPTIVITY (YEARS)

Cat (domestic)	14	Goose (domestic)	20
Chicken (domestic)	8	Horse	22
Dog (domestic)	13	Pig	12
Duck (domestic)	10	Rabbit	6
Goat (domestic)	14	Turkey (domestic)	10

	ESTRAL/ESTROUS CYCLE (INCLUDING HEAT PERIOD) AVERAGE	RANGE	LENGTH OF ESTRUS (HEAT) AVERAGE	RANGE	USUAL TIME OF OVULATION	WHEN CYCLE RECURS IF NOT BRED
Cow	21 days	18–24 days	18 hours	10–24 hours	10–12 hours after end of estrus	21 days
Doe goat	21 days	18–24 days	2–3 days	1–4 days	Near end of estrus	21 days
Mare	21 days	10–37 days	5–6 days	2–11 days	24–48 hours before end of estrus	21 days
Sow	21 days	18–24 days	2–3 days	1–5 days	30–36 hours after start of estrus	21 days
Ewe	16½ days	14–19 days	30 hours	24–32 hours	12–24 hours before end of estrus	16½ days
Queen cat		15–21 days	3–4 days, if mated	9–10 days, in absence of male	24–56 hours after coitus	Pseudo-pregnancy
Bitch	24 days	16–30 days	7 days	5–9 days	1–3 days after first acceptance	Pseudo-pregnancy

PLANTING BY THE MOON'S PHASE

ACCORDING TO THIS AGE-OLD PRACTICE, CYCLES OF THE MOON AFFECT PLANT GROWTH.

Plant annual flowers and vegetables that bear crops above ground during the light, or waxing, of the Moon: from the day the Moon is new to the day it is full.

Plant flowering bulbs, biennial and perennial flowers, and vegetables that bear crops below ground during the dark, or waning, of the Moon: from the day after it is full to the day before it is new again.

The Planting Dates columns give the safe periods for planting in areas that receive frost. (See **page 221** for frost dates in your area.) The Moon Favorable columns give the best planting days within the Planting Dates based on the Moon's phases for 2019. (See **pages 120–146** for the exact days of the new and full Moons.)

The dates listed in this table are meant as general guidelines only. For seed-sowing dates based on frost dates in your local area, go to **Almanac.ca/PlantingTable.**

Aboveground crops are marked *.
(E) means early; (L) means late.

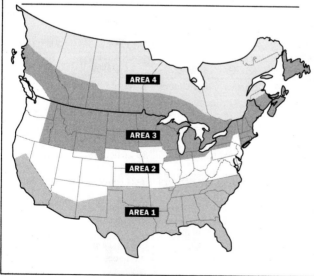

* Barley	
* Beans	(E)
	(L)
Beets	(E)
	(L)
* Broccoli plants	(E)
	(L)
* Brussels sprouts	
* Cabbage plants	
Carrots	(E)
	(L)
* Cauliflower plants	(E)
	(L)
* Celery plants	(E)
	(L)
* Collards	(E)
	(L)
* Corn, sweet	(E)
	(L)
* Cucumbers	
* Eggplant plants	
* Endive	(E)
	(L)
* Kale	(E)
	(L)
Leek plants	
* Lettuce	
* Muskmelons	
* Okra	
Onion sets	
* Parsley	
Parsnips	
* Peas	(E)
	(L)
* Pepper plants	
Potatoes	
* Pumpkins	
Radishes	(E)
	(L)
* Spinach	(E)
	(L)
* Squashes	
Sweet potatoes	
* Swiss chard	
* Tomato plants	
Turnips	(E)
	(L)
* Watermelons	
* Wheat, spring	
* Wheat, winter	

AREA 1		AREA 2		AREA 3		AREA 4	
PLANTING DATES	MOON FAVORABLE	PLANTING DATES	MOON FAVORABLE	PLANTING DATES	MOON FAVORABLE	PLANTING DATES	MOON FAVORABLE
2/15-3/7	2/15-19, 3/6-7	3/15-4/7	3/15-20, 4/5-7	5/15-6/21	5/15-18, 6/3-17	6/1-30	6/3-17
3/15-4/7	3/15-20, 4/5-7	4/15-30	4/15-19	5/7-6/21	5/7-18, 6/3-17	5/30-6/15	6/3-15
8/7-31	8/7-15, 8/30-31	7/1-21	7/2-16	6/15-7/15	6/15-17, 7/2-15	—	—
2/7-28	2/20-28	3/15-4/3	3/21-4/3	5/1-15	5/1-3	5/25-6/10	5/25-6/2
9/1-30	9/15-27	8/15-31	8/16-29	7/15-8/15	7/17-30	6/15-7/8	6/18-7/1
2/15-3/15	2/15-19, 3/6-15	3/7-31	3/7-20	5/15-31	5/15-18	6/1-25	6/3-17
9/7-30	9/7-14, 9/28-30	8/1-20	8/1-15	6/15-7/7	6/15-17, 7/2-7	—	—
2/11-3/20	2/11-19, 3/6-20	3/7-4/15	3/7-20, 4/5-15	5/15-31	5/15-18	6/1-25	6/3-17
2/11-3/20	2/11-19, 3/6-20	3/7-4/15	3/7-20, 4/5-15	5/15-31	5/15-18	6/1-25	6/3-17
2/15-3/7	2/20-3/5	3/7-31	3/21-31	5/15-31	5/19-31	5/25-6/10	5/25-6/2
8/1-9/7	8/16-29	7/7-31	7/17-30	6/15-7/21	6/18-7/1, 7/17-21	6/15-7/8	6/18-7/1
2/15-3/7	2/15-19, 3/6-7	3/15-4/7	3/15-20, 4/5-7	5/15-31	5/15-18	6/1-25	6/3-17
8/7-31	8/7-15, 8/30-31	7/1-8/7	7/2-16, 7/31-8/7	6/15-7/21	6/15-17, 7/2-16	—	—
2/15-28	2/15-19	3/7-31	3/7-20	5/15-6/30	5/15-18, 6/3-17	6/1-30	6/3-17
9/15-30	9/28-30	8/15-9/7	8/15, 8/30-9/7	7/15-8/15	7/15-16, 7/31-8/15	—	—
2/11-3/20	2/11-19, 3/6-20	3/7-4/7	3/7-20, 4/5-7	5/15-31	5/15-18	6/1-25	6/3-17
9/7-30	9/7-14, 9/28-30	8/15-31	8/15, 8/30-31	7/1-8/7	7/2-16, 7/31-8/7	—	—
3/15-31	3/15-20	4/1-17	4/5-17	5/10-6/15	5/10-18, 6/3-15	5/30-6/20	6/3-17
8/7-31	8/7-15, 8/30-31	7/7-21	7/7-16	6/15-30	6/15-17	—	—
3/7-4/15	3/7-20, 4/5-15	4/7-5/15	4/7-19, 5/4-15	5/7-6/20	5/7-18, 6/3-17	5/30-6/15	6/3-15
3/7-4/15	3/7-20, 4/5-15	4/7-5/15	4/7-19, 5/4-15	6/1-30	6/3-17	6/15-30	6/15-17
2/15-3/20	2/15-19, 3/6-20	4/7-5/15	4/7-19, 5/4-15	5/15-31	5/15-18	6/1-25	6/3-17
8/15-9/7	8/15, 8/30-9/7	7/15-8/15	7/15-16, 7/31-8/15	6/7-30	6/7-17	—	—
2/11-3/20	2/11-19, 3/6-20	3/7-4/7	3/7-20, 4/5-7	5/15-31	5/15-18	6/1-15	6/3-15
9/7-30	9/7-14, 9/28-30	8/15-31	8/15, 8/30-31	7/1-8/7	7/2-16, 7/31-8/7	6/25-7/15	7/2-15
2/15-4/15	2/20-3/5, 3/21-4/4	3/7-4/7	3/21-4/4	5/15-31	5/19-31	6/1-25	6/1-2, 6/18-25
2/15-3/7	2/15-19, 3/6-7	3/1-31	3/6-20	5/15-6/30	5/15-18, 6/3-17	6/1-30	6/3-17
3/15-4/7	3/15-20, 4/5-7	4/15-5/7	4/15-19, 5/4-7	5/15-6/30	5/15-18, 6/3-17	6/1-30	6/3-17
4/15-6/1	4/15-19, 5/4-18	5/25-6/15	6/3-15	6/15-7/10	6/15-17, 7/2-10	6/25-7/7	7/2-7
2/1-28	2/1-3, 2/20-28	3/1-31	3/1-5, 3/21-31	5/15-6/7	5/19-6/2	6/1-25	6/1-2, 6/18-25
2/20-3/15	3/6-15	3/1-31	3/6-20	5/15-31	5/15-18	6/1-15	6/3-15
1/15-2/4	1/22-2/3	3/7-31	3/21-31	4/1-30	4/1-4, 4/20-30	5/10-31	5/19-31
1/15-2/7	1/15-21, 2/4-7	3/7-31	3/7-20	4/15-5/7	4/15-19, 5/4-7	5/15-31	5/15-18
9/15-30	9/28-30	8/7-31	8/7-15, 8/30-31	7/15-31	7/15-16, 7/31	7/10-25	7/10-16
3/1-20	3/6-20	4/1-30	4/5-19	5/15-6/30	5/15-18, 6/3-17	6/1-25	6/1-2, 6/18-25
2/10-28	2/20-28	4/1-30	4/1-4, 4/20-30	5/1-31	5/1-3, 5/19-31	6/1-30	6/3-17
3/7-20	3/7-20	4/23-5/15	5/4-15	5/15-31	5/15-18	5/15-6/5	5/19-6/2
1/21-3/1	1/22-2/3, 2/20-3/1	3/7-31	3/21-31	4/15-30	4/20-30	7/10-31	7/17-30
10/1-21	10/14-21	9/7-30	9/15-27	8/15-31	8/16-29	6/1-25	6/3-17
2/7-3/15	2/7-19, 3/6-15	3/15-4/20	3/15-20, 4/5-19	5/15-31	5/15-18	7/20-8/5	7/31-8/5
10/1-21	10/1-13	8/1-9/15	8/1-15, 8/30-9/14	7/17-9/7	7/31-8/15, 8/30-9/7	6/1-30	6/3-17
3/15-4/15	3/15-20, 4/5-15	4/15-30	4/15-19	5/15-6/15	5/15-18, 6/3-15	6/1-30	6/3-17
3/23-4/6	3/23-4/4	4/21-5/9	4/21-5/3	5/15-6/15	5/19-6/2	5/15-31	5/15-18
2/7-3/15	2/7-19, 3/6-15	3/15-4/15	3/15-20, 4/5-15	5/1-31	5/4-18	5/15-31	5/15-18
3/7-20	3/7-20	4/7-30	4/7-19	5/15-31	5/15-18	6/1-15	6/3-15
1/20-2/15	1/22-2/3	3/15-31	3/21-31	4/7-30	4/20-30	5/10-31	5/19-31
9/1-10/15	9/15-27, 10/14-15	8/1-20	8/16-20	7/1-8/15	7/1, 7/17-30	—	—
3/15-4/7	3/15-20, 4/5-7	4/15-5/7	4/15-19, 5/4-7	5/15-6/30	5/15-18, 6/3-17	6/1-30	6/3-17
2/15-28	2/15-19	3/1-20	3/6-20	4/7-30	4/7-19	5/15-6/10	5/15-18, 6/3-10
10/15-12/7	10/27-11/12, 11/26-12/7	9/15-10/20	9/28-10/13	8/11-9/15	8/11-15, 8/30-9/14	8/5-30	8/5-15, 8/30

HIGH TIDE TIMES AND HEIGHTS

This table lists the biweekly times and heights of high tide at Churchill, Manitoba, and Vancouver, British Columbia. (A dash indicates that high tide occurs on or after midnight and is recorded on the next day.) Tide times for other days can be interpolated; low tides occur about 6 hours before and after high tides. In addition, the **Calendar Pages, 120–147,** list times and some heights of high tides at Halifax, Nova Scotia. This table is *not* meant to be used for navigation. To get accurate tide times and heights by postal code, go to **Almanac.ca/Tides.**

Standard time shown, except for Daylight Saving Time between 2:00 A.M., Mar. 10, and 2:00 A.M., Nov. 3.

CHURCHILL					VANCOUVER				
DATE	CST/CDT	HEIGHT (FT.)	CST/CDT	HEIGHT (FT.)	DATE	PST/PDT	HEIGHT (FT.)	PST/PDT	HEIGHT (FT.)
TUES., JAN. 1	3:40	12.7	**4:07**	13.2	TUES., JAN. 1	3:08	12.8	**1:28**	14.9
SAT., JAN. 5	7:34	13.5	**7:38**	13.6	SAT., JAN. 5	6:25	15.7	**4:01**	13.9
TUES., JAN. 8	9:24	13.9	**9:26**	13.8	TUES., JAN. 8	8:08	15.8	**5:57**	13.0
SAT., JAN. 12	11:42	13.3	**11:49**	12.7	SAT., JAN. 12	10:07	15.4	**9:34**	10.7
TUES., JAN. 15	1:25	11.9	**1:57**	12.3	TUES., JAN. 15	12:57	10.9	11:44	14.8
SAT., JAN. 19	5:51	12.8	**6:06**	13.3	SAT., JAN. 19	5:19	15.2	**2:49**	15.1
TUES., JAN. 22	8:32	14.7	**8:42**	14.9	TUES., JAN. 22	7:24	16.4	**5:39**	14.8
SAT., JAN. 26	11:45	14.8	—	—	SAT., JAN. 26	9:56	16.2	**10:12**	11.8
TUES., JAN. 29	1:53	12.7	**2:19**	12.9	TUES., JAN. 29	1:36	12.3	11:53	14.5
SAT., FEB. 2	6:28	12.4	**6:37**	12.4	SAT., FEB. 2	5:26	15.2	**3:11**	13.3
TUES., FEB. 5	8:32	13.3	**8:33**	13.3	TUES., FEB. 5	7:02	15.4	**5:22**	13.3
SAT., FEB. 9	10:36	13.6	**10:43**	13.3	SAT., FEB. 9	8:44	15.1	**8:27**	12.0
TUES., FEB. 12	**12:19**	12.8	—	—	TUES., FEB. 12	10:06	14.5	—	—
SAT., FEB. 16	4:01	11.8	**4:27**	12.1	SAT., FEB. 16	4:06	14.5	**1:34**	14.2
TUES., FEB. 19	7:22	13.9	**7:35**	14.2	TUES., FEB. 19	6:10	15.8	**4:48**	14.8
SAT., FEB. 23	10:33	15.2	**10:51**	14.8	SAT., FEB. 23	8:29	15.8	**8:55**	13.1
TUES., FEB. 26	12:23	13.4	**12:43**	13.3	TUES., FEB. 26	10:14	13.9	—	—
SAT., MAR. 2	4:47	11.2	**5:07**	11.3	SAT., MAR. 2	4:13	14.5	**2:15**	12.3
TUES., MAR. 5	7:33	12.6	**7:39**	12.6	TUES., MAR. 5	5:50	14.7	**4:45**	13.0
SAT., MAR. 9	9:35	13.7	**9:45**	13.6	SAT., MAR. 9	7:25	14.5	**7:41**	13.0
TUES., MAR. 12	**12:07**	13.4	—	—	TUES., MAR. 12	9:37	14.0	**11:40**	12.9
SAT., MAR. 16	3:10	11.7	**3:37**	11.7	SAT., MAR. 16	3:32	14.2	**1:10**	12.9
TUES., MAR. 19	7:06	13.0	**7:25**	13.3	TUES., MAR. 19	5:52	15.3	**4:57**	13.9
SAT., MAR. 23	10:23	15.1	**10:43**	15.0	SAT., MAR. 23	8:04	15.3	**8:55**	14.1
TUES., MAR. 26	12:09	14.1	**12:24**	13.9	TUES., MAR. 26	9:39	13.4	—	—
SAT., MAR. 30	3:36	11.2	**4:02**	10.9	SAT., MAR. 30	3:38	14.1	**1:56**	11.0
TUES., APR. 2	7:15	12.0	**7:30**	11.9	TUES., APR. 2	5:28	14.2	**5:02**	12.2
SAT., APR. 6	9:34	13.6	**9:49**	13.6	SAT., APR. 6	7:06	14.1	**7:58**	13.6
TUES., APR. 9	11:08	13.8	**11:32**	13.6	TUES., APR. 9	8:14	13.7	**10:33**	14.0
SAT., APR. 13	1:47	12.5	**2:06**	12.2	SAT., APR. 13	1:49	14.5	11:36	11.9
TUES., APR. 16	5:39	12.5	**6:07**	12.6	TUES., APR. 16	4:27	15.0	**4:04**	12.7
SAT., APR. 20	9:14	14.8	**9:37**	14.8	SAT., APR. 20	6:43	14.9	**8:04**	14.6
TUES., APR. 23	11:15	14.4	**11:45**	14.1	TUES., APR. 23	8:13	13.3	**10:49**	14.7
SAT., APR. 27	1:58	12.1	**2:12**	11.5	SAT., APR. 27	1:43	14.3	11:49	10.2
TUES., APR. 30	5:23	11.5	**5:52**	11.3	TUES., APR. 30	3:55	14.0	**4:10**	11.1
SAT., MAY 4	8:29	13.3	**8:50**	13.3	SAT., MAY 4	5:43	13.9	**7:14**	13.7
TUES., MAY 7	10:11	14.1	**10:40**	14.1	TUES., MAY 7	6:57	13.9	**9:38**	14.8
SAT., MAY 11	12:50	13.4	**1:02**	13.1	SAT., MAY 11	12:21	15.1	**10:12**	11.7
TUES., MAY 14	4:08	12.7	**4:39**	12.4	TUES., MAY 14	2:58	15.1	**3:02**	11.5
SAT., MAY 18	8:06	14.4	**8:35**	14.3	SAT., MAY 18	5:22	14.7	**7:17**	14.7
TUES., MAY 21	10:12	14.5	**10:45**	14.4	TUES., MAY 21	6:56	13.5	**9:43**	15.3
SAT., MAY 25	12:49	13.2	**12:56**	12.6	SAT., MAY 25	9:44	10.5	—	—
TUES., MAY 28	3:26	11.9	**3:53**	11.3	TUES., MAY 28	2:06	14.2	**2:45**	10.1
SAT., JUNE 1	7:13	13.0	**7:42**	12.9	SAT., JUNE 1	4:15	14.0	**6:27**	13.5
TUES., JUNE 4	9:13	14.1	**9:46**	14.2	TUES., JUNE 4	5:45	14.3	**8:44**	15.1
SAT., JUNE 8	12:00	14.3	**12:11**	14.0	SAT., JUNE 8	9:05	12.3	**11:54**	15.6

Bold = P.M. Light = A.M.

CHURCHILL					VANCOUVER				
DATE	CST/CDT	HEIGHT (FT.)	CST/CDT	HEIGHT (FT.)	DATE	PST/PDT	HEIGHT (FT.)	PST/PDT	HEIGHT (FT.)
TUES., JUNE 11	2:47	13.6	3:13	13.0	TUES., JUNE 11	1:27	15.3	1:42	10.9
SAT., JUNE 15	6:55	13.9	7:32	13.8	SAT., JUNE 15	4:01	14.5	6:28	14.4
TUES., JUNE 18	9:15	14.2	9:52	14.3	TUES., JUNE 18	5:48	13.7	8:44	15.3
SAT., JUNE 22	11:57	13.5	—	—	SAT., JUNE 22	8:32	11.5	11:11	15.0
TUES., JUNE 25	1:54	12.9	2:09	12.2	TUES., JUNE 25	12:21	14.6	12:15	9.9
SAT., JUNE 29	5:34	12.5	6:13	12.4	SAT., JUNE 29	2:39	14.0	5:33	13.0
TUES., JULY 2	8:08	13.8	8:46	14.0	TUES., JULY 2	4:35	14.6	7:46	15.0
SAT., JULY 6	11:18	14.9	11:55	15.1	SAT., JULY 6	8:09	13.3	10:35	15.8
TUES., JULY 9	1:35	14.7	1:57	14.0	TUES., JULY 9	12:06	11.1	—	—
SAT., JULY 13	5:33	13.4	6:18	13.2	SAT., JULY 13	2:41	14.1	5:35	14.1
TUES., JULY 16	8:22	13.8	9:01	14.1	TUES., JULY 16	4:49	13.5	7:45	15.0
SAT., JULY 20	11:02	14.1	11:31	14.3	SAT., JULY 20	7:40	12.4	9:53	14.9
TUES., JULY 23	12:42	13.8	12:53	13.2	TUES., JULY 23	10:23	10.7	11:19	14.4
SAT., JULY 27	3:40	12.5	4:18	12.1	SAT., JULY 27	12:58	13.9	4:22	12.4
TUES., JULY 30	6:50	13.2	7:34	13.5	TUES., JULY 30	3:23	14.4	6:41	14.7
SAT., AUG. 3	10:17	15.4	10:52	15.7	SAT., AUG. 3	7:15	14.1	9:16	15.6
TUES., AUG. 6	12:27	15.7	12:47	15.1	TUES., AUG. 6	10:39	12.0	11:06	15.2
SAT., AUG. 10	3:58	13.3	4:44	12.9	SAT., AUG. 10	1:16	13.6	4:29	13.7
TUES., AUG. 13	7:21	13.2	8:04	13.7	TUES., AUG. 13	3:57	13.0	6:42	14.7
SAT., AUG. 17	10:08	14.2	10:34	14.5	SAT., AUG. 17	6:57	12.9	8:37	14.6
TUES., AUG. 20	11:49	13.9	—	—	TUES., AUG. 20	9:17	11.9	9:50	14.1
SAT., AUG. 24	1:59	13.0	2:30	12.4	SAT., AUG. 24	2:27	12.2	—	—
TUES., AUG. 27	5:11	12.4	6:05	12.7	TUES., AUG. 27	2:06	13.6	5:26	14.4
SAT., AUG. 31	9:12	15.3	9:46	15.8	SAT., AUG. 31	6:23	14.4	7:55	15.4
TUES., SEPT. 3	11:38	15.8	—	—	TUES., SEPT. 3	9:31	13.2	9:36	15.0
SAT., SEPT. 7	2:24	13.8	3:03	13.2	SAT., SEPT. 7	2:56	13.5	—	—
TUES., SEPT. 10	5:57	12.5	6:47	13.0	TUES., SEPT. 10	3:03	12.1	5:29	14.4
SAT., SEPT. 14	9:14	14.1	9:36	14.5	SAT., SEPT. 14	6:18	13.0	7:19	14.2
TUES., SEPT. 17	10:50	14.4	11:06	14.6	TUES., SEPT. 17	8:29	13.0	8:26	13.8
SAT., SEPT. 21	12:40	13.6	1:09	13.2	SAT., SEPT. 21	12:32	13.0	10:23	12.9
TUES., SEPT. 24	3:22	12.3	4:18	12.4	TUES., SEPT. 24	12:39	12.5	3:58	14.3
SAT., SEPT. 28	8:05	14.8	8:37	15.5	SAT., SEPT. 28	5:33	14.1	6:33	15.2
TUES., OCT. 1	10:30	16.1	10:51	16.3	TUES., OCT. 1	8:33	14.4	8:08	14.8
SAT., OCT. 5	1:01	14.5	1:35	14.0	SAT., OCT. 5	1:03	14.1	10:52	11.7
TUES., OCT. 8	4:04	12.1	4:56	12.5	TUES., OCT. 8	1:50	11.0	4:00	14.4
SAT., OCT. 12	8:10	13.6	8:30	14.2	SAT., OCT. 12	5:41	12.8	5:58	14.1
TUES., OCT. 15	9:50	14.4	10:03	14.7	TUES., OCT. 15	7:47	13.8	7:03	13.8
SAT., OCT. 19	12:05	14.0	—	—	SAT., OCT. 19	11:11	14.3	8:49	12.8
TUES., OCT. 22	1:49	12.8	2:40	12.8	TUES., OCT. 22	2:18	14.8	—	—
SAT., OCT. 26	6:51	14.8	7:21	14.8	SAT., OCT. 26	4:47	13.3	5:10	15.3
TUES., OCT. 29	9:23	15.8	9:39	16.0	TUES., OCT. 29	7:44	15.1	6:44	14.9
SAT., NOV. 2	12:22	14.7	—	—	SAT., NOV. 2	11:26	15.2	9:05	11.8
TUES., NOV. 5	1:14	12.5	1:59	12.7	TUES., NOV. 5	1:12	14.7	—	—
SAT., NOV. 9	5:48	12.7	6:09	13.4	SAT., NOV. 9	4:02	12.2	3:31	14.2
TUES., NOV. 12	7:49	14.0	7:58	14.1	TUES., NOV. 12	6:08	14.2	4:41	14.0
SAT., NOV. 16	10:09	14.5	10:13	14.3	SAT., NOV. 16	9:08	15.5	6:37	13.3
TUES., NOV. 19	12:25	13.5	—	—	TUES., NOV. 19	11:44	15.6	10:00	11.1
SAT., NOV. 23	4:24	13.2	4:56	14.0	SAT., NOV. 23	2:57	12.5	2:43	15.4
TUES., NOV. 26	7:16	14.9	7:30	15.3	TUES., NOV. 26	5:58	15.3	4:23	15.0
SAT., NOV. 30	10:16	15.0	10:22	14.6	SAT., NOV. 30	9:11	16.1	6:48	12.6
TUES., DEC. 3	12:28	13.4	—	—	TUES., DEC. 3	11:21	15.4	10:03	10.0
SAT., DEC. 7	3:51	11.7	4:19	12.4	SAT., DEC. 7	3:07	11.3	1:52	14.5
TUES., DEC. 10	6:36	13.0	6:46	13.5	TUES., DEC. 10	5:27	14.1	3:18	14.4
SAT., DEC. 14	9:13	14.5	9:17	14.5	SAT., DEC. 14	8:11	16.0	5:41	14.1
TUES., DEC. 17	11:23	14.3	11:33	13.9	TUES., DEC. 17	10:21	16.3	8:41	11.8
SAT., DEC. 21	2:43	12.8	3:19	13.1	SAT., DEC. 21	1:49	11.7	1:12	15.6
TUES., DEC. 24	6:05	13.7	6:20	14.1	TUES., DEC. 24	5:10	15.1	3:08	14.9
SAT., DEC. 28	9:16	14.6	9:21	14.5	SAT., DEC. 28	8:05	16.3	5:51	13.4
TUES., DEC. 31	11:14	13.9	11:18	13.2	TUES., DEC. 31	9:50	15.9	8:13	11.1

TIME CORRECTIONS

Astronomical data for Ottawa are given on **pages 104, 108–109,** and **120–146.** Use the Key Letters shown on those pages with this table to find the number of minutes that you must add to or subtract from Ottawa time to get the approximate time for your locale. Time zone codes represent standard time. Newfoundland is –1½, Atlantic is –1, Eastern is 0, Central is 1, Mountain is 2, Pacific is 3. For more information on the use of Key Letters, see **How to Use This Almanac, page 116.**

GET EXACT TIMES EASILY: Download astronomical times calculated for your postal code and presented as Left-Hand Calendar Pages at **Almanac.ca/Access.**

PROVINCE	CITY	NORTH LATITUDE °	NORTH LATITUDE '	WEST LONGITUDE °	WEST LONGITUDE '	TIME ZONE CODE	KEY LETTERS (MINUTES) A	B	C	D	E
AB	Athabasca	54	43	113	17	2	–18	+9	+28	+51	+71
AB	Banff	51	10	115	34	2	+12	+27	+38	+51	+62
AB	Calgary	51	5	114	5	2	+6	+21	+32	+45	+56
AB	Edmonton	53	33	113	28	2	–10	+13	+29	+48	+65
AB	Fort McMurray	56	45	111	27	2	–41	–3	+21	+49	+75
AB	Fort Vermilion	58	24	116	0	2	–38	+9	+38	+73	+105
AB	Grande-Prairie	55	10	118	48	2	0	+30	+50	+74	+95
AB	Lethbridge	49	42	112	50	2	+8	+19	+27	+37	+45
AB	Medicine Hat	50	3	110	40	2	–1	+10	+19	+29	+38
AB	Peace River	56	14	117	17	2	–14	+21	+44	+71	+96
AB	Red Deer	52	16	113	48	2	–1	+17	+31	+46	+60
BC	Dawson Creek	55	46	120	14	2	+1	+34	+56	+81	+105
BC	Fort Nelson	58	49	122	39	3	–75	–26	+5	+41	+75
BC	Kamloops	50	40	120	20	3	–26	–12	–2	+9	+19
BC	Nelson	49	30	117	17	3	–32	–21	–14	–5	+2
BC	Port Alice	50	23	127	27	3	+3	+16	+26	+37	+46
BC	Prince George	53	55	122	45	3	–35	–10	+6	+26	+44
BC	Prince Rupert	54	19	130	19	3	–8	+18	+36	+58	+77
BC	Telegraph Creek	57	55	131	10	3	–32	+11	+39	+72	+102
BC	Trail	49	6	117	42	3	–28	–19	–12	–4	+2
BC	Vancouver	49	16	123	7	3	–7	+1	+9	+17	+24
BC	Victoria	48	25	123	21	3	–2	+4	+10	+16	+22
MB	Brandon	49	50	99	57	1	+16	+28	+36	+46	+54
MB	Churchill	58	46	94	10	1	–68	–19	+11	+47	+80
MB	Flin Flon	54	46	101	53	1	–4	+23	+43	+65	+85
MB	Gillam	56	21	94	43	1	–45	–9	+14	+41	+66
MB	Gimli	50	38	96	59	1	0	+14	+24	+35	+45
MB	Gypsumville	51	47	98	38	1	0	+18	+30	+45	+57
MB	Norway House	53	59	97	50	1	–15	+9	+27	+47	+65
MB	Portage-la-Prairie	49	59	98	18	1	+9	+21	+29	+39	+48
MB	The Pas	53	50	101	15	1	–1	+23	+40	+60	+78
MB	Winnipeg	49	53	97	9	1	+5	+16	+25	+34	+43
NB	Bathurst	47	36	65	39	–1	+10	+15	+19	+24	+28
NB	Chatham	47	2	65	28	–1	+11	+16	+19	+22	+25
NB	Fredericton	45	58	66	39	–1	+21	+22	+23	+25	+26
NB	Moncton	46	6	64	47	–1	+13	+15	+16	+17	+19
NB	Saint John	45	16	66	3	–1	+21	+21	+21	+21	+21
NL	Corner Brook	48	57	57	57	–1½	+3	+12	+18	+26	+32
NL	Gander	48	57	54	37	–1½	–10	–1	+5	+13	+19
NL	Goose Bay	53	20	60	25	–1	–11	+12	+27	+46	+62
NL	Grand Falls	48	56	55	40	–1½	–6	+3	+9	+17	+23

PROVINCE/STATE	CITY	NORTH LATITUDE °	′	WEST LONGITUDE °	′	TIME ZONE CODE	KEY LETTERS (MINUTES) A	B	C	D	E
NL	St. John's	47	34	52	43	−1½	−11	−5	−1	+2	+6
NL	Stephenville	48	33	58	35	−1½	+7	+15	+21	+28	+33
NS	Halifax	44	39	63	36	−1	+14	+12	+11	+10	+9
NS	Sydney	46	9	60	11	−1	−5	−3	−1	0	0
NS	Yarmouth	43	50	66	7	−1	+27	+24	+21	+19	+16
ON	Fort Severn	56	0	87	38	0	−10	+23	+46	+72	+96
ON	Hamilton	43	15	79	51	0	+24	+20	+16	+13	+9
ON	Kapuskasing	49	25	82	26	0	+8	+19	+26	+35	+42
ON	Kingston	44	15	76	30	0	+7	+5	+3	+1	0
ON	London	42	59	81	14	0	+31	+26	+22	+18	+14
ON	Pembroke	45	49	77	7	0	+3	+4	+5	+6	+7
ON	Peterborough	44	18	78	19	0	+14	+12	+10	+8	+7
ON	Port Arthur	48	30	89	17	0	+40	+48	+53	+60	+66
ON	Sault Sainte Marie	46	31	84	20	0	+29	+32	+34	+36	+38
ON	Sioux Lookout	50	6	91	55	1	−16	−4	+4	+14	+23
ON	Sudbury	46	30	81	0	0	+16	+19	+21	+23	+25
ON	Thunder Bay	48	23	89	15	0	+40	+48	+53	+60	+65
ON	Timmins	48	28	81	20	0	+8	+16	+22	+28	+34
ON	Toronto	43	39	79	23	0	+21	+17	+15	+11	+9
ON	Waterloo	43	28	80	31	0	+26	+22	+19	+16	+13
ON	Windsor	42	18	83	1	0	+40	+34	+29	+24	+19
PE	Charlottetown	46	14	63	8	−1	+6	+8	+9	+11	+13
QC	Chicoutimi	48	26	71	4	0	−32	−24	−18	−12	−6
QC	Fort George	53	50	79	0	0	−30	−4	+12	+31	+49
QC	Gaspé	48	50	64	29	0	−60	−51	−45	−37	−31
QC	Montréal	45	31	73	34	0	−9	−8	−8	−8	−7
QC	Québec	46	49	71	11	0	−24	−20	−18	−15	−12
QC	Schefferville	54	48	66	50	0	−85	−56	−36	−14	+5
QC	Sept-Îles	50	12	66	23	0	−59	−46	−37	−27	−18
QC	Sherbrooke	45	25	71	54	0	−15	−15	−15	−14	−14
QC	Trois-Rivières	46	21	72	33	0	−16	−14	−12	−10	−8
QC	Val-d'Or	48	7	77	47	0	−3	+3	+8	+13	+18
SK	Estevan	49	7	103	5	1	+32	+42	+49	+57	+63
SK	Moose Jaw	50	37	105	32	1	+34	+48	+58	+70	+79
SK	North Battleford	52	47	108	17	2	−26	−5	+9	+26	+41
SK	Prince Albert	53	12	105	46	1	+21	+43	+59	+77	+93
SK	Regina	50	25	104	39	1	+32	+45	+55	+66	+75
SK	Saskatoon	52	7	106	38	1	+31	+49	+62	+77	+91
SK	Swift Current	50	17	107	50	1	+45	+58	+67	+78	+87
SK	Uranium City	59	34	108	36	2	−79	−24	+9	+47	+84
SK	Yorkton	51	13	102	28	1	+19	+35	+46	+59	+70

SELECTED U.S. CITIES

PROVINCE/STATE	CITY	NORTH LATITUDE °	′	WEST LONGITUDE °	′	TIME ZONE CODE	KEY LETTERS (MINUTES) A	B	C	D	E
AL	Decatur	34	36	86	59	1	+20	+1	−13	−31	−45
AL	Mobile	30	42	88	3	1	+35	+10	−9	−32	−50
AR	Little Rock	34	45	92	17	1	+41	+22	+7	−10	−23
CA	Palm Springs	33	49	116	32	3	+21	0	−16	−35	−50
CA	Redding	40	35	122	24	3	+24	+14	+7	−1	−7
CO	Grand Junction	39	4	108	33	2	+33	+21	+11	+1	−7
CT	New Haven	41	18	72	56	0	+4	−4	−10	−17	−23
DE	Wilmington	39	45	75	33	0	+19	+8	0	−9	−17
GA	Macon	32	50	83	38	0	+72	+49	+32	+12	−2
IA	Dubuque	42	30	90	41	1	+10	+4	0	−4	−9
ID	Boise	43	37	116	12	2	+48	+44	+42	+38	+36
ID	Pocatello	42	52	112	27	2	+36	+31	+27	+22	+19
IL	Chicago–Oak Park	41	52	87	38	1	0	−6	−11	−18	−23

(continued)

STATE	CITY	NORTH LATITUDE °	'	WEST LONGITUDE °	'	TIME ZONE CODE	A	B	C	D	E
IL	Springfield	39	48	89	39	1	+15	+4	–3	–13	–21
IN	Fort Wayne	41	4	85	9	0	+53	+44	+38	+30	+24
IN	South Bend	41	41	86	15	0	+55	+48	+42	+36	+30
IN	Terre Haute	39	28	87	24	0	+67	+56	+47	+37	+28
KS	Oakley	39	8	100	51	1	+62	+50	+41	+30	+21
KS	Topeka	39	3	95	40	1	+42	+29	+20	+9	0
LA	Lake Charles	30	14	93	13	1	+57	+31	+11	–12	–30
LA	Shreveport	32	31	93	45	1	+53	+30	+13	–7	–23
MA	Boston	42	22	71	3	0	–6	–13	–17	–23	–27
MD	Hagerstown	39	39	77	43	0	+28	+17	+8	–1	–9
MD	Salisbury	38	22	75	36	0	+24	+10	0	–11	–21
MI	Cheboygan	45	39	84	29	0	+33	+34	+35	+35	+36
MI	Ironwood	46	27	90	9	1	–6	–4	–2	0	+1
MI	Jackson	42	15	84	24	0	+46	+40	+35	+29	+24
MN	Bemidji	47	28	94	53	1	+7	+12	+16	+20	+24
MO	St. Joseph	39	46	94	50	1	+36	+25	+17	+7	0
MO	Springfield	37	13	93	18	1	+38	+22	+11	–2	–13
MS	Biloxi	30	24	88	53	1	+39	+13	–5	–29	–47
MS	Tupelo	34	16	88	34	1	+28	+7	–7	–25	–39
MT	Glasgow	48	12	106	38	2	–8	–1	+3	+9	+14
MT	Miles City	46	25	105	51	2	–3	–1	0	+2	+4
NC	Raleigh	35	47	78	38	0	+44	+26	+12	–3	–15
NC	Wilmington	34	14	77	55	0	+45	+25	+9	–8	–22
ND	Minot	48	14	101	18	1	+29	+36	+42	+48	+53
ND	Williston	48	9	103	37	1	+39	+46	+51	+57	+62
NE	Lincoln	40	49	96	41	1	+40	+31	+24	+16	+9
NE	North Platte	41	8	100	46	1	+55	+47	+40	+33	+27
NJ	Trenton	40	13	74	46	0	+14	+4	–3	–12	–19
NM	Las Cruces	32	19	106	47	2	+46	+23	+5	–15	–31
NV	Elko	40	50	115	46	3	–3	–12	–19	–27	–33
NY	Binghamton	42	6	75	55	0	+13	+6	+1	–4	–9
NY	Ogdensburg	44	42	75	30	0	+1	0	0	–1	–2
OH	Columbus	39	57	83	1	0	+48	+38	+29	+20	+12
OH	Toledo	41	39	83	33	0	+45	+37	+31	+25	+19
OK	Tulsa	36	9	95	60	1	+52	+35	+22	+6	–5
OR	Pendleton	45	40	118	47	3	–8	–8	–7	–7	–6
OR	Salem	44	57	123	1	3	+10	+9	+9	+8	+8
PA	Reading	40	20	75	56	0	+19	+9	+1	–7	–14
PA	Scranton–Wilkes-Barre	41	25	75	40	0	+14	+6	0	–6	–12
SC	Columbia	34	0	81	2	0	+58	+38	+22	+4	–10
SC	Spartanburg	34	56	81	57	0	+59	+40	+26	+8	–4
SD	Sioux Falls	43	33	96	44	1	+31	+27	+24	+21	+18
TN	Knoxville	35	58	83	55	0	+64	+47	+33	+18	+5
TX	Amarillo	35	12	101	50	1	+78	+59	+45	+28	+15
TX	El Paso	31	45	106	29	2	+46	+22	+4	–17	–33
TX	San Antonio	29	25	98	30	1	+80	+53	+32	+8	–11
UT	Moab	38	35	109	33	2	+39	+26	+16	+4	–4
UT	Ogden	41	13	111	58	2	+40	+31	+25	+18	+12
VA	Norfolk	36	51	76	17	0	+31	+15	+3	–11	–22
VA	Roanoke	37	16	79	57	0	+44	+29	+17	+4	–6
VA	Winchester	39	11	78	10	0	+31	+19	+10	0	–8
WA	Bellingham	48	45	122	29	3	–7	0	+6	+13	+19
WI	Oshkosh	44	1	88	33	1	–3	–6	–8	–10	–12
WI	Wausau	44	58	89	38	1	–2	–3	–4	–4	–5
WV	Charleston	38	21	81	38	0	+48	+34	+24	+12	+2
WY	Sheridan	44	48	106	58	2	+7	+5	+5	+4	+3

Get local rise, set, and tide times at Almanac.ca/Astronomy.

TIDAL GLOSSARY

APOGEAN TIDE: A monthly tide of decreased range that occurs when the Moon is at apogee (farthest from Earth).

CURRENT: Generally, a horizontal movement of water. Currents may be classified as tidal and nontidal. Tidal currents are caused by gravitational interactions between the Sun, Moon, and Earth and are part of the same general movement of the sea that is manifested in the vertical rise and fall, called tide. Nontidal currents include the permanent currents in the general circulatory systems of the sea as well as temporary currents arising from more pronounced meteorological variability.

DIURNAL TIDE: A tide with one high water and one low water in a tidal day of approximately 24 hours.

MEAN LOWER LOW WATER: The arithmetic mean of the lesser of a daily pair of low waters, observed over a specific 19-year cycle called the National Tidal Datum Epoch.

NEAP TIDE: A tide of decreased range that occurs twice a month, when the Moon is in quadrature (during its first and last quarters, when the Sun and the Moon are at right angles to each other relative to Earth).

PERIGEAN TIDE: A monthly tide of increased range that occurs when the Moon is at perigee (closest to Earth).

RED TIDE: Toxic algal blooms caused by several genera of dinoflagellates that usually turn the sea red or brown. These pose a serious threat to marine life and may be harmful to humans.

RIP CURRENT: A potentially dangerous, narrow, intense, surf-zone current flowing outward from shore.

SEMIDIURNAL TIDE: A tide with one high water and one low water every half-day. East Coast tides, for example, are semidiurnal, with two highs and two lows during a tidal day of approximately 24 hours.

SLACK WATER (SLACK): The state of a tidal current when its speed is near zero, especially the moment when a reversing current changes direction and its speed is zero.

SPRING TIDE: A tide of increased range that occurs at times of syzygy each month. Named not for the season of spring but from the German *springen* ("to leap up"), a spring tide also brings a lower low water.

STORM SURGE: The local change in the elevation of the ocean along a shore due to a storm, measured by subtracting the astronomic tidal elevation from the total elevation. It typically has a duration of a few hours and is potentially catastrophic, especially on low-lying coasts with gently sloping offshore topography.

SYZYGY: The nearly straight-line configuration that occurs twice a month, when the Sun and the Moon are in conjunction (on the same side of Earth, at the new Moon) and when they are in opposition (on opposite sides of Earth, at the full Moon). In both cases, the gravitational effects of the Sun and the Moon reinforce each other, and tidal range is increased.

TIDAL BORE: A tide-induced wave that propagates up a relatively shallow and sloping estuary or river with a steep wave front.

TSUNAMI: Commonly called a tidal wave, a tsunami is a series of long-period waves caused by an underwater earthquake or volcano. In open ocean, the waves are small and travel at high speed; as they near shore, some may build to more than 30 feet high, becoming a threat to life and property.

VANISHING TIDE: A mixed tide of considerable inequality in the two highs and two lows, so that the lower high (or higher low) may appear to vanish. ■

- The *bight* is any part of a rope between the ends or the curved section of a rope in a knot.

- A bight becomes a *loop* when two parts of a rope cross.

- The place at which two parts of a rope meet in a loop is the *crossing point.*

- The place at which two or more loops bend is the *elbow.*

- The *working end* of a rope is the end being used to make a knot.

- The *standing end* (or standing part) of a rope is the end not involved in making a knot.

overhand knot

figure-eight knot

granny knot

square knot

common whipping

fisherman's knot

cow hitch

clove hitch

heaving line knot

sheet bend

double sheet bend

sheepshank

bowline

running bowline

bowline on a bight

GENERAL STORE CLASSIFIEDS

CLASSIFIEDS

CLASSIFIEDS

Advertisements and statements contained herein are the sole responsibility of the persons or entities that post the advertisement, and *The Old Farmer's Almanac* does not make any warranty as to the accuracy, completeness, truthfulness, or reliability of such advertisements. *The Old Farmer's Almanac* has no liability whatsoever for any third-party claims arising in connection with such advertisements or any products or services mentioned therein.

Index to Advertisers

THE OLD FARMER'S GENERAL STORE

A SPECIAL SECTION FEATURING
UNIQUE MAIL-ORDER PRODUCTS FOR OUR
READERS WHO SHOP BY MAIL

2018 ESSAY CONTEST WINNERS

"How Weather Changed My Life"

First Prize: $300

I met my husband 10 years ago, when I went hiking near Mount Orford. The weather had already been gray when I left, and I was well into the trail when it began to drizzle. The few raindrops dripping down soon became a downpour. I carried on, sliding on the mud with my heavy backpack, soaked clothes, and wet hair. I was getting cold and cursing the weather when I saw another hiker standing still and smiling at the sky. The picture seemed so absurd to me that I started laughing, and the man—Chris, I later learned—joined in. We laughed like kids playing in the rain, and it was one of the best moments of my life. We finished the trail together and got coffee. Long story short, the rain had taken him by surprise, but he loved it. Over the years, Chris taught me to embrace the unpredictable, quirky, capricious nature of weather. Every time it rains, I think of weather's chaotic beauty and I smile, because, even if I had a runny nose for days, it is thanks to the rain that I met Chris.

–Eugénie Adlhoch-Mathé,
Montreal, Quebec

Second Prize: $200

It is not remarkable for Orangeville, Ontario, to get plenty of snow during the winter, but on January 26, 1971, a sudden and heavy snowstorm overwhelmed and paralyzed the entire road system for miles around. The principal called an emergency assembly for the whole high school. He appealed to town students to take country students home, even if they didn't know them well. The alternative would be that country students would spend the night in the cafeteria. In an outpouring of charity, everyone—staff and students alike—had a home in which to stay. There were 100 extra billet offers that were not needed. Conditions were so severe that it took me 3 days to finally reach my farm.

As a country girl, I learned that town folk and country folk share the same love for humanity. Whether surrounded by fields or other houses, the warmth of a home comes from the hearts within. As a high school English student, I learned firsthand that, more than 300 years after he wrote them, the words of William Shakespeare still rang true: "One touch of nature makes the whole world kin."

–Eleanor Stringer, Duncan, British Columbia

Third Prize: $100

Since going "back to the land" 10 years ago (although I had never worked the land before), I have found that weather, in all its eternal motion, has come to the forefront of my life. To me as a child, weather always seemed perfect; there were sun-filled summer days at the pool and snowy winter evenings at the outdoor rink. Until now, I had never given thought to lungwort's need for shade or its tendency to give up on flowering if it's too wet, or that lettuce will bolt to seed in the heat of summer. I didn't agonize in advance about the wind that will accompany the arrival of a cold front. I never expected to be one of those who rush outdoors in October, lengths of cloth flowing behind me—like a confused bride making a run for it with "cold feet"—to cover tomato plants before nightfall. No, I can't say that I ever knew about mare's tails and mackerel skies, either. But now, I am obsessed with climate changes so that I can tend to all that comprises the garden. Did gardening change me or did the weather become my nemesis? No matter: One must weather the weather, whither the weather.

–Jane Webster, Bon Accord, Alberta

Honorable Mention

This story is about lessons learned when caught in a nasty blizzard near Goose Bay, Labrador, in the fall of 1970. My friend Jim and I had hiked back in the bush to his isolated camp. All went well until the oil stove fuel control failed. The result was a cold night, with the smell of stove oil and a lack of sleep. The next day started with a fine snow falling with increasing intensity. It was clear to us that it was time to leave. As the day progressed, the snow turned into a full-on blizzard, with the trail hard to follow and hiking difficult in snow up to our thighs. We made our way out just at dark and were very wet and cold. It was a relief to see my dad's truck. From that day to the present, I have never gone into the bush without a compass, waterproof matches, energy food, proper clothing—and a check of the weather. Over the years, Jim and I have always laughed when we recall that, at the time, he worked for the Canadian weather service.

–William Duggan, Musquodoboit Harbour, Nova Scotia

ANNOUNCING THE 2019 ESSAY CONTEST TOPIC: KIDS SAY THE FUNNIEST THINGS

SEE CONTEST RULES ON PAGE 251.

MADDENING MIND-MANGLERS

An Apple Romance

How many names of heirloom apple varieties can you find hidden in the following romantic tale? Use your imagination!

The duchess and Ben Davis went on a date. They met at the Blue Pearmain, a tea room on the bank of the Wolf River. Many people called it "Courtland" because so many people met there. There was snow in the air, so the duchess wore her yellow transparent raincoat, her stout russet boots, and her red astrakhan fur toque. Ben wore his macintosh. The duchess was very beautiful, so everyone was looking at her. One brash young fellow was heard to say that she sure was a pippin, a remark that made more than one maiden blush. One girl was heard to ask, "How can one so bald win such a Rome beauty?" Her companion replied that Ben was very wealthy.

They found a table, and Ben hung up their coats. Before he sat down, he presented the duchess with a corsage of bellflowers from his greenhouse. As he gave them to her, he told her that she was every pound sweet.

They studied the menu, and the duchess said that she would like some creamed crabmeat on toast and a peach melba. Ben said that he would have the crab and a strawberry shortcake. He asked the duchess if she would like a little porter. She declined with thanks, saying that she thought that wine saps the mind. The waitress took their order and soon returned with their food. When they had finished, the waitress came back. The duchess thanked her for her kind service and said that the food had been delicious.

The duchess's uncle, the king, disapproved of his niece's keeping company with a commoner, so he had his spies watching all the time. Just as they had finished their meal, Ben's brother Jonathan dashed in and announced that Red William, the king's northern spy, was coming at great speed astride the king's fastest steed, Pewaukee.

They left hastily by a back door. Red William entered the tea room and sighed with relief when he found that they had gone, because he had sympathy for them. He sat down at a table and ordered a piece of apple pie and a cup of coffee.

–courtesy of Bessie DesRosiers,
The Old Farmer's Almanac, *1977*

Mental Math

*Using only your brain, answer
the following:*

1. What is the sum of 1, 2, 3, 4, 5,
6, all the way through 100?

2. Assuming that pi = 3, what is the
difference between the area of a
square with sides of 10 and the area
of a circle with a diameter of 10?

3. 0, 1, 1, 2, 3, 5, 8, __.
What number comes next?

4. 1, 1, 2, 8, 3, 27, 4, __.
What number comes next?

5. 2, 3, 4, 5, 6, 7, 12, 9, __.
What number comes next?

6. 1, 0, 1, 2, 2, 3, 5, 7, 10, __.
What number comes next?

*–courtesy of Morris Bowles,
Cane Ridge, Tennessee*

ANSWERS:

Apple Romance (in order of
appearance): Duchess, Ben Davis,
Blue Pearmain, Wolf River, Cortland
("Courtland"), Snow, Yellow
Transparent, Russet, Red Astrachan
(astrakhan), McIntosh (macintosh),
Pippin, Maiden Blush, Baldwin, Rome
Beauty, Wealthy, Bellflower, Pound
Sweet, Crab, Peach, Strawberry, Porter,
Winesap, Delicious, King, Jonathan, Red
William, Northern Spy, Pewaukee.

Mental Math: **1.** 5,050. **2.** 25. **3.** 13
(add number plus previous number).
4. 64 (cube every other number).
5. 24 (keep totalling the preceding even
numbers). **6.** 15 (to get the next number,
add the present number to the second
number back). ∎

ESSAY AND RECIPE CONTEST RULES

Cash prizes (first, $300; second, $200; third, $100) will be awarded for the best essays in 200 words or less on the subject "Kids Say the Funniest Things" and the best recipes in the category "Pasta." Entries must be yours, original, and unpublished. Amateur cooks only, please. One recipe per person. All entries become the property of Yankee Publishing, which reserves all rights to the material. The deadline for entries is Friday, January 25, 2019. Enter at Almanac.ca/EssayContest or Almanac.ca/RecipeContest or label "Essay Contest" or "Recipe Contest" and mail to The Old Farmer's Almanac, P.O. Box 520, Dublin, NH 03444. Include your name, mailing address, and email address. Winners will appear in *The 2020 Old Farmer's Almanac Canadian Edition* and on Almanac.ca. ∎

ANECDOTES & PLEASANTRIES

*A sampling from the thousands of letters, clippings,
articles, and emails sent to us by Almanac readers from all over
the United States and Canada during the past year.*

ILLUSTRATIONS BY TIM ROBINSON

The Underwear Soil Test

....

*A "brief" explanation of how
healthy soil devours drawers.*

....

STEP #1: Dig a hole 6 to 8 inches deep in your garden or field bed. Bury a pair of clean, 100 percent cotton, white or undyed men's underwear. (Of course, the waistband will not be 100 percent cotton.) Repeat, as desired.

STEP #2: Leave them for 2 months.

STEP #3: Remove the briefs from the soil. The amount of remaining cotton fabric indicates, roughly, the amount of earthworms, fungi, bacteria, and other microscopic organisms in the soil, or its organic quality.

If only the waistband remains, the organic quality is very high. If most of the drawers remain, the soil is lacking in biological life because it has been overused.

*–courtesy of the Soil Conservation
Council of Canada*

IN THE NEWS

....

• Jason and the Cornstalks: After growing a world-record 35-foot-tall cornstalk in 2011, upstate New York's Jason Karl moved to the milder winters of Costa Rica, where his tassels now reach 45 feet above ground.

• Nashoba Brook Bakery in West Concord, Massachusetts, tried to list "Love" as an ingredient in its granola. Not so fast, said the FDA: "'Love' is not a common or usual name of an ingredient and is considered to be intervening material because it is not part of the common or usual name of the ingredient."

• In Berlin, Germany, a 16-inch, 11-pound zucchini was mistaken for an unexploded World War II bomb.

–courtesy of The Scientist,
Associated Press, Bloomberg

The Kid's in the Mail

....

*The early days of parcel post gave new meaning
to the term "special delivery."*

....

Need a way to get your kids to Grandma's house? Just slap on a few stamps, and off they go! Or at least that was the practice back at the beginning of the last century, when U.S. postal patrons figured out that new parcel post regulations allowed just that.

The first parcel poster child was shipped off in 1913 in Batavia, Ohio, when a young boy was sent to his grandmother's, about a mile away, for 15 cents.

As word spread about this easy and economical way to get the kids out of the house, so too did the number of children entrusted to the Post Office. Fifteen cents was the going rate if the "parcel" weighed less than 50 pounds; a 6-year-old was once sent 73 miles for just 53 cents. In reality, mailed kids were accompanied by trusted postal workers, but photographs of toddlers in mailbags and sweet-faced children who supposedly had been treated like freight eventually called into question the whole idea.

By 1914, Postmaster General Albert Burleson had heard enough to issue an edict barring humans from the post—for all the good it did him, as 1915 then turned out to be the biggest kid-shipping year yet, with several more trips being made. Six-year-old Edna Neff, for example, set the distance record by being posted from Pensacola, Florida, to Christiansburg, Virginia. Fortunately for her, she rode the mail train for most of the 700-plus miles.

But enough was enough, and eventually the rules were enforced and the practice ended. There is no record of any kid ever having been "lost in the mail," but just in case, postal insurance was always available. In fact, Mr. and Mrs. Jesse Beauge of Glen Este, Ohio, senders of that first child back in 1913, had covered all of their bases by insuring their son for a whopping $50.

*–courtesy of O. P., Ames, Iowa, from http://
postalmuseumblog.si.edu*

(continued)

The Almanac

Cold it was, clear and fair.
Frost was hanging in midair.
A halo held the Sun at bay.
No warmth would be reaching here
today.

Snow was due sometime tonight,
Time to bundle up real tight.
Can't escape this winter's chill.
Guess I'll head back up the hill . . .

Close up the barn and throw some
hay
To feed the mare and the old bay.
Then go into the house to have
some tea
And a piece of apple pie for me.

Nothin' more that I can do
'Cept hunker down and wait for you.

I'll put more wood upon the fire,
Read a book and then retire
To our cozy little featherbed
With a woolly cap upon my head.

Spring is still so far away.
Nothin' I do, nothin' I say
Will make it come before it's due,
If what I read in the Almanac's true.

–R. V. Bartles, Meriden, New Hampshire

THREE SISTERS

Three sisters, ages 92, 94, and 96, live in a house together. One night, the 96-year-old draws a bath. She puts her foot in, pauses, and yells to the other sisters, "Was I getting into or out of the bath?"

The 94-year-old yells back, "I don't know—I'll come and see!" She starts up the stairs, pauses, and calls out, "Was I going up the stairs or down?"

The 92-year-old is sitting in the kitchen having tea and listening to her sisters. She shakes her head, raps on the table, and says, "Knock on wood, I sure hope I never get that forgetful."

Then she yells, "I'll come up and help you both as soon as I see who's at the door!"

–courtesy of L. M., Little Rock, Arkansas

You Never Know What You'll Find in Canada

- Stuart Thompson, of Charlottetown, Prince Edward Island, found a 15-inch-long piece of string in a can of crushed tomatoes in 2017.

- Also in that year, an anonymous Manitoban uncovered the 44,000-year-old fossilized jawbone of a giant beaver that would have weighed as much as a black bear.

- 1-carrot ring: In 2017, a woman near Armena, Alberta, pulled up a carrot growing through an engagement ring—which had been lost by her mother-in-law in 2004.

–courtesy of CBC.ca, gearsofbiz.com, CBC.ca

ARE YOU LOSING YOUR GRIP?

Take this simple test to find out.

QUESTION #1: What do you put in a toaster?

QUESTION #2: Say "silk" 10 times. Now spell "silk." What do cows drink?

QUESTION #3: If a red house is made from red bricks and a blue house is made from blue bricks and a pink house is made from pink bricks and a black house is made from black bricks, what is a green house made from?

QUESTION #4: *(Use of calculator not permitted, but pencil and paper are OK.)* You are driving a bus from New York City to Philadelphia. On Staten Island, 17 people get on the bus. In New Brunswick, six people get off the bus and nine people get on. In Windsor, two people get off and four get on. In Trenton, 11 people get off and 16 people get on. In Bristol, three people get off and five people get on. And in Camden, six people get off and three get on. The bus then arrives at Philadelphia Station. Without going back to review, how old is the bus driver?

–courtesy of A. B., Wilmington, Vermont, from the Internet

ANSWERS: 1. Bread. 2. Water. 3. Glass. 4. Your own age.

SCORING: 4 correct—You're holding on tight. 3 correct—Slippage! 2 correct—Uh-oh. Only 1 correct—Hanging on by your fingertips, like most people who take this quiz. None correct—Yup, you've officially lost it!

Send your contribution for *The 2020 Old Farmer's Almanac* by January 25, 2019, to "A & P," The Old Farmer's Almanac, P.O. Box 520, Dublin, NH 03444, or email it to almanac@ypi.com (subject: A & P).

Vinegar, Better than Prescription Drugs?

by **James Victor**

Thousands of years ago ancient healers trusted apple cider vinegar, and modern research shows - *vinegar truly is a wonder cure!*

From the Bible to Cleopatra to the fierce Samurai warriors of Japan, vinegar has been documented as a powerful tonic to ensure strength, power and long life.

You'll get easy recipes that mix vinegar with other common household items to help:

- Calm an upset stomach
- Ease leg cramps
- Soothe sprained muscles
- Control appetite to lose weight
- Relieve coughs
- Banish nausea
- Arthritis pain
- Make hiccups disappear
- Cool a sunburn
- Boost memory
- Reduce sore throat pain
- Relieve itchy skin
- Lower blood pressure & cholesterol
- Eliminate bladder infections
- Chase away a cold
- Treat burns
- Reduce infection
- Aid digestion
- Improve memory
- Soothe sore feet
- Treat blemishes & age spots
- Remove corns & calluses
- Replace many household cleaners

And that's just the beginning of the over 1000 new and improved hints and tips that you'll get.

Strep and Staph infections? Vinegar is a powerful antiseptic and kills even these dangerous bacteria on contact.

Headaches will fade away with this simple vinegar concoction.

Feel good and look good with these hair and skin-friendly vinegar remedies.

You'll learn when you should *and should not* use vinegar.

Yes that's over 1000 tried-and-true remedies and recipes in this handsome collector's edition and it's yours to enjoy for 90-risk free days. That's right, you can read and benefit from all 168-pages without obligation to keep it.

Simply write "Vinegar Anniversary" on a piece of paper and send it with your check or money order of only $12.95 plus $3.98 shipping and handling (total of $16.93, OH residents please add 6.5% sales tax, Canada residents add an additional $8 to your order) to: James Direct Inc., Dept. VA3152, 500 S. Prospect Ave., Box 980, Hartville, Ohio 44632.

You can charge to your VISA, MasterCard, Discover or American Express by mail. Be sure to include your card number, expiration date and signature.

Remember: You're protected by the publisher's 90-Day Money Back Guarantee if you are not delighted.

WANT TO SAVE MORE? Do a favor for a relative or friend and get 2 books for the low introductory price of $20 postpaid. You save $13.86.

Special Bonus - Act promptly to also receive "The Very Best Old-Time Remedies" booklet absolutely FREE. Supplies are limited so order now.

©2018 JDI VA226S02

http://www.jamesdirect.com